C000136175

BRITISH RAILWAYS Locomotives 1962

BRITISH RAILWAYS Locomotives 1962

Chris Banks

An imprint of
Ian Allan Publishing

Half title page: **Class 108 Derby built two-car unit with No M56257 leading M50974, and also attached to a Class 115 four-car unit, is seen leaving Cowburn Tunnel on the Hope Valley line on the 7.10pm Sheffield Midland to Liverpool Lime Street on Whit Sunday, 17 May 1964. No M56257 dated from July 1959 and was withdrawn, numbered 54257, in April 1993.** *M. Mensing*

Title page: **Looking in superb condition is LMS 4F 0-6-0 No 44575, approaching Wigston North Junction with the 5.20pm Leicester to Wellingborough local on Saturday 20 May 1961. No 44575 was built at Crewe Works and entered traffic at Leicester Midland shed in September 1937. Wellingborough was its base at nationalisation, where it remained until January 1963, when transfer to Toton was actioned. Then it was back to its first shed, Leicester Midland, in August 1964 for only a month before moving to Coalville. By this time the engine must have been in poor condition for it was withdrawn during the week ended 14 November 1964. It was cut up at Cohen's at Kettering in February 1965.** *B. O. Hilton*

This page: **Class 33 Bo-Bo No D6560 is at Hither Green shed in April 1962 with No D6532 behind. New to Hither Green on 15 July 1961, it remained on allocation until November 1985, when it was based at Stewarts Lane for maintenance, then to Eastleigh two months later, and finally back to 'the Lane' in March 1988. Withdrawn as No 33042 on 8 October 1996 after storage at Stewarts Lane, it was cut up on site by contractors.** *R. H. G. Simpson*

Contents page: **'57xx' class 0-6-0PT No 7780 is photographed in the streets near Weymouth Quay on a van train in June 1960. No 7780 was one of only three from this batch to survive the 1962 withdrawals. Dating from November 1930, it had come to Weymouth shed in April 1957 from Bristol St Philips Marsh and remained until withdrawn on 7 July 1963. After around 11 months in storage No 7780 was dispatched to Ward's at Briton Ferry for scrapping.** *P. H. Groom*

First published 2005

ISBN (10) 0 86093 591 4
ISBN (13) 978 0 86093 591 9

Published by Oxford Publishing Co

an imprint of Ian Allan Publishing Ltd, Hersham, Surrey KT12 4RG.
Printed in England by Ian Allan Printing Ltd, Hersham, Surrey KT12 4RG.

Visit the Ian Allan Publishing website at www.ianallanpublishing.com

Code 0511/3

Contents

The northbound 'Midland Pullman' is at Wigston North Junction, Leicester, on Monday 24 July 1961. In 1966 the LMR sets were transferred to the Western Region and all had been withdrawn by the end of May 1973. *M. Mitchell*

Andrew Barclay Class 06 0-4-0 diesel shunter No D2428 is at Glasgow Polmadie shed in August 1960. Entering traffic on 21 December 1959 at Motherwell shed, it moved to Polmadie in April 1960, to Greenock in March 1961, to Hamilton in May 1964 and back to Polmadie in May 1968, withdrawal following the next month on the 15th. Sold to G. H. Campbell at Airdrie, it was cut up in February 1969. *P. H. Groom*

Introduction

To many observers, 1962 was a year that for the first time really marked the impending end of steam traction on British Railways (BR), with a staggering 2,924 steam locomotives withdrawn. Few classes escaped unscathed, with many having locomotives withdrawn for the first time. Fifty-nine different classes were extinguished from the railway scene including:

GWR 'King' class 4-6-0s; SR '700' class 0-6-0s; SR 'N15' 'King Arthur' class 4-6-0s; SR 'Lord Nelson' class 4-6-0s; SR 'Schools' class 4-4-0s; SR 'K' class 2-6-0s; LMS Stanier and Fowler 3MT 2-6-2Ts; both MR and LMS 2P 4-4-0s; LMS Stanier three-cylinder 2-6-4Ts; LMS unrebuilt 'Patriot' class 4-6-0s; LMS Aspinall 3F 0-6-0s; LMS Pickersgill 3P 4-4-0s; LMS McIntosh '439' class 0-4-4Ts; LMS McIntosh 3F 0-6-0Ts; LNER 'K2' class 2-6-0s; LNER 'K3' class 2-6-0s; LNER 'J6' class 0-6-0s; LNER 'J11' class 0-6-0s; LNER 'J15' class 0-6-0s; LNER 'J17' class 0-6-0s; LNER 'J19' class 0-6-0s; LNER 'J20' class 0-6-0s; LNER 'J25' class 0-6-0s; LNER 'J26' class 0-6-0s; LNER 'J35' class 0-6-0s; LNER 'J39' class 0-6-0s; LNER 'L1' class 2-6-4Ts; LNER 'N2' class 0-6-2Ts; LNER 'N7' class 0-6-2Ts; LNER 'N15' class 0-6-2Ts; LNER 'V1' class 2-6-2Ts.

The BR Standard classes were also not spared with 2-6-4T No 80103 being the first to go, followed by the unique Class 8P 4-6-2 No 71000 *Duke of Gloucester* and five Scottish 'Clan' class 4-6-2s. Of the ex-WD locomotives, all 22 2-10-0s were withdrawn along with 80 2-8-0s. Ex-LMS engines also fared badly with Fowler, Fairburn and Stanier 2-6-4Ts all being targeted, along with 0-6-0 classes and the Hughes/Fowler 2-6-0s. Of the larger types, 41 'Jubilees', 30 'Royal Scots' and three 'Princess Coronation' 4-6-2s all went, as well as the remaining 'Princess Royal' class. Perhaps less surprising were the 79 ex-LNWR 0-8-0s that went to the breakers, as well as the last Fowler 0-8-0.

British Railways' first complete major dieselisation programme reached fruition on 9 September when steam working was eliminated in East Anglia. One week later all the remaining locomotives of GER origin in capital stock were condemned. Only March shed continued with steam locomotive operation alongside its growing fleet of diesels. Other LNER classes suffered severe losses during the year with withdrawals of 'A1', 'A2', 'A3', 'V2' and 'B1' classes in significant numbers. Even the 'A4' class was not immune, with five going to the scrap merchants.

During the latter part of 1962 the rate of Southern Region withdrawals increased rapidly, as it did elsewhere on British Railways, with the ex-LSWR 'H16' 4-6-2Ts and 'G16' 4-8-0Ts both losing their entire complement virtually overnight. Another ex-LSWR class to be withdrawn was the Beattie '0298' class 2-4-0WT, of which the three survivors, dating from 1874/5, had outlived the remainder of the class by 63 years.

Ex-GWR steam locomotives did not escape with 603 going, including 55 'Castle' class and 73 'Hall' class 4-6-0s and, as mentioned earlier, the complete class of 30 'King' 4-6-0s.

Dieselisation continued with diesel multiple-units taking over more services and electrification also extending. On 18 June the full service of electric trains between Liverpool and Crewe was introduced, marking the second stage of the London Midland Region (LMR) main-line 25kV electrification. Introduction of summer services and full electrification added 82 trains each week to the densely trafficked Liverpool to Crewe line, with all local trains being electric multiple-units. Also on 18 June the full electrified service on the London, Tilbury & Southend line commenced with the mass withdrawal of the steam tank engines previously used, seeing the demise of the Stanier three-cylinder 2-6-4Ts which had provided the backbone of the services for nearly 30 years. With the new traction came a dramatic improvement in timings, the 39 daily services managing a start-to-stop speed of over 60mph for the first time.

On the East Coast main line the greatly accelerated services with 'Deltic' diesel power were further improved when the Summer Timetable was introduced, which included the nonstop King's Cross to Edinburgh 'Elizabethan' and vastly improved timings on the 'Heart of Midlothian', 'Northumbrian', 'Queen of Scots' and 'Tees-Tyne Pullman' trains.

When the new Summer Timetable was introduced in Scotland on 18 June the Northern Division was all but clear of steam traction. On the Highland lines, for example, the only steam to be seen was a shunter at Dingwall and an ex-Caledonian 0-4-4T No 55269 serving as a stationary boiler at Inverness. On the West Highland line, the workings were covered by the BRCW Type 2 diesels based at Glasgow Eastfield, as steam locomotives no longer worked from Fort William shed.

When the second phase of the Kent Coast electrification was completed in mid-June, the end of the '73' group of motive power depots, as far as steam traction was concerned, was complete; Stewarts Lane became a Central Division depot, recoded 75D, and Bricklayers Arms closed.

The speed at which diesel and electric traction was replacing steam was revealed in the British Transport Commission aggregate statistics for the 24 weeks to 17 June, the half-year ending immediately before the introduction of the Summer Timetable. Steam traction miles were 19.9% down on the first half of 1961, all-line. On the London Midland Region (LMR) they were down 13.9%, Western Region (WR) 18.1%, Eastern Region (ER) 25% and in Scotland 32.3%. Diesel-hauled train mileages went up all round, except for the Southern Region (SR) which showed a drop of 38%, explained by the Kent electrification.

The introduction of new types of modern traction during the year was also a factor in steam's decline. The first Brush Type 4 Class 47 diesels appeared as did the Clayton Type 1 Bo-Bo Class 17s and the electro-diesels for the Southern, the Class 73s. The first, No E6001, emerged from Eastleigh for trials on 5 February and should have run light from Eastleigh to Fareham, but on the morning trip got no further than Botley and had to return to base. Further trials with empty stock took place from Eastleigh to Basingstoke the next day. No E6001 left Eastleigh later the same week for Stewarts Lane, running via Brighton, where it was retained for a day for inspection by the drawing office staff. A new class of diesel shunter was also introduced to the Southern, the Class 07 from Ruston & Hornsby, and took over shunting duties from the 'USA' tank engines at Southampton Docks, with No D2986 arriving for work in the New Docks on 21 June and No D2988 the next day for duties in the Old Docks. On the Western Region the first of the 'Western' class diesel-hydraulics, No D1000 *Western Enterprise*, reached Plymouth Laira depot on Sunday 28 January piloting the 4.15pm Paddington to Plymouth from Bristol. Soon after it was put on a crew training diagram in readiness for many more of the class to arrive. By the end of March the line west from Plymouth was virtually completely dieselised with both St Blazey and Truro sheds ending steam operation.

There was still plenty to interest the steam and diesel enthusiasts, with many unprecedented workings and transfers. Just a sample of some of the noteworthy events are related below.

At the end of January the six remaining 'Princess Royal' class 4-6-2s were taken out of store and put into traffic as a result of a motive power shortage and put up some fine performances. However, on 10 September all were returned to store, with the exception of No 46200. Nos 46201 and 46203 were held at Carlisle Kingmoor, Nos 46206 and 46209 at Camden and No 46208 at Liverpool Edge Hill. No 46200 was still entrusted to express passenger work and on Wednesday 26 September was recorded in charge of the 9.25am Crewe to Perth, which it worked from Carlisle. However, the reprieve was short-lived for by 6 November No 46200 had joined its sisters in store at Kingmoor.

A number of ex-LNER Pacifics worked into Derby during January deputising for failed diesels on the Newcastle to Bristol through trains.

On Thursday 11 January 'A3' 4-6-2 No 60088 *Book Law* appeared on the 12.43pm from Newcastle and in the evening worked the 7.43pm from Derby to Sheffield. It was back at Derby the next morning to take over the 8.30am Cardiff to Newcastle. On Tuesday 16 January another 'A3', No 60058 *Blair Athol* arrived on the 7.05pm Newcastle to Bristol and returned from Derby the next morning with the 8.05am to Tyneside from Birmingham. On Wednesday 17 January an 'A2' visited Derby when No 60526 *Sugar Palm* brought in the 3.30pm Newcastle to Birmingham. It returned north the same evening with the 11.05pm Birmingham to York parcels.

A most unusual sight on the southbound 'Yorkshire Pullman' on Monday 22 January was Finsbury Park-based 'Deltic' No D9009 *Alycidon* piloting King's Cross 'A3' 4-6-2 No 60109 *Hermit*. The 'A3' had run short of steam and the 'Deltic', which was returning home light engine, was attached north of Hitchin. On the same day another unusual sighting was that of 'B16/3' 4-6-0 No 61418, York-based, working north at Hitchin on a loose-coupled freight. It had worked from Neasden to Temple Mills earlier in the day on a special freight and then run light from Stratford to King's Cross. Even more unusual at Hitchin in February was the use of King's Cross 'A4' 4-6-2 No 60017 *Silver Fox* on the 6.25pm Hitchin to Huntingdon on the 12th, 13th and 16th, with the normal load of two coaches.

The Bromford Bridge, Birmingham, to Fawley oil traffic was renowned for bringing unusual engines to Eastleigh and on Saturday 6 January on Eastleigh shed were 'foreigners' — 'Manor' class 4-6-0 No 7813 *Freshford Manor* (84E), Stanier 5MT 4-6-0s Nos 44664 (17A), 44966 (21A) and Standard '9F' 2-10-0s Nos 92157 (21A) and 92221 (82E). All had arrived in connection with the oil traffic. Later in the year Saltley-allocated 'Royal Scot' 4-6-0s were used on the oil trains, bringing these engines to Eastleigh for the first time. On Saturday 3 March No 46141 *The North Staffordshire Regiment* arrived and the next day entered Southampton Docks to haul a banana train back to the West Midlands, via Salisbury. On Wednesday 7 March No 46122 *Royal Ulster Rifleman* was used and duly appeared at Eastleigh shed. On Saturday 3 February the last two 'Vulcans', the 'C2X' class 0-6-0s, made their farewell run when No 32535, running light from Three Bridges, and No 32523 from Brighton coupled up at Lewes and proceeded to St Leonards where they resurrected 'Schools' class 4-4-0 No 30900 *Eton* from the depths of the shed. All three locomotives then made their final run to Ashford Works for scrapping.

On the same day, memories of the 1939 era were recalled when 'Lord Nelson' class 4-6-0 No 30863 *Lord Rodney* was at Stewarts Lane shed in steam being prepared to work a Hither Green to Tonbridge freight. It then ran light engine to Ashford Works for withdrawal and cutting up.

In Scotland the last 'D11' 4-4-0, No 62685 *Malcolm Graeme*, ended its days as a stationary boiler for the Caledonian Hotel in Edinburgh. It finished this job on 16 January and was then towed back to Haymarket shed. It had been withdrawn from the 'active' list the previous day. On a more positive note, the Scottish Region planned to introduce in the Summer Timetable the long-awaited three-hour timings between Glasgow and Aberdeen using 'A4' Pacifics. On Thursday 22 February a test run was made behind No 60027 *Merlin* supplied by Haymarket depot. It was intended to use No 60031 *Golden Plover* which had been transferred from Haymarket to Glasgow St Rollox on 3 February, but it had been declared a failure a few days before. The test run involved a departure from Glasgow at 7.05am with an arrival at Aberdeen at 10.05am. The return test run left Aberdeen at 12.20pm with arrival at Glasgow Buchanan Street at 3.20pm. The test proved to be highly successful, paving the way for the introduction of these legendary steam-hauled expresses. No 60031 was despatched to Doncaster Works and, when fresh from overhaul, worked the 'West Riding' into King's Cross, bringing what was possibly the unprecedented sight of a 65B-allocated locomotive to the station on Friday 30 March. It had replaced failed 'Deltic' D9015 at Doncaster. Next day No 60031 worked the 10.20am King's Cross to Leeds and returned again on 1 April with the 6.45pm Doncaster to King's Cross, finally returning north on 2 April with the 11.35pm King's Cross to Edinburgh.

Other interesting 'A4' activity was the arrival at Leeds Holbeck shed of Haymarket's No 60024 *Kingfisher* in the early morning hours of Friday 2 February, joining St Margarets-allocated 'A3' No 60057 *Ormonde* which had arrived earlier. The 'A4' had worked in on the overnight 10.05pm Edinburgh Waverley to St Pancras sleeper and it returned north the same day on the Fridays-only 5.38pm Manchester to Newcastle from Leeds. No 60057 worked out on the 3.03am Leeds to Glasgow and returned to work several more trips over the Settle & Carlisle to Glasgow before returning home light engine on Monday 5 February.

Another unusual 'A3' working was on Monday 19 March when Gateshead-allocated No 60078 *Night Hawk* arrived at Banbury. It had come south to Woodford Halse earlier in the day and was appropriated for the 6.45pm stopping train from Woodford to Banbury. It returned to the Great Central line at 9.16pm on the Swindon to Sheffield through train.

A sign of the rapidly expanding dieselisation in the Scottish Region was the creation of stored locomotive dumps. On 31 March at Bo'ness were:

Nos 40154, 40158, 40177, 40200, 57245, 57285, 57287, 57314, 57338, 57366, 57470, 57576, 62031, 62052, 62496, 62691, 62693, 64461, 64472, 64477, 64514, 64515, 64518, 64532, 64535, 65230, 65280, 67601, 67611, 67614, 67619, 67622, 67625, 67626, 67632, 67650, 67655, 68119, 68448, 68454, 68472, 68479, 69014, 69126, 69131, 69137, 69163, 69181, 69183, 69191 and 90436.

At Bathgate on the same day were:

Nos 60813, 60818, 60819, 60824, 60892, 60920, 60927, 60931, 60937, 60953, 60958, 62685, 64497, 64500, 65235, 65258, 65268, 65305, 67615, 67620, 68335, 68342, 68481, 69156, 69159, 69211 and 69216.

The availability and failure of diesel locomotives was a cause for concern, due to a number of reasons. In particular the 'Baby Deltics' suffered badly with only two available for traffic in late April. On Saturday 28 April 'Peak' class No D41 failed on the 10.30am Bristol to Newcastle with a burst fuel pipe at Ryhope Colliery and 'J39' class 0-6-0 No 64846 was attached, running tender first. On reaching Sunderland, 'V3' class 2-6-2T No 67687 was added, bunker first, and the trio proceeded to Newcastle in fine style, arriving only 48 minutes late. Availability of 'Deltic' diesels was also causing problems, there being only sufficient units to cover the diagrams timed for 'Deltic' traction, with the majority of other diagrams being worked by other diesel types or steam traction. One example of a 'Deltic' failure occurred on Thursday 24 May when Haymarket-based No D9010 succeeded in almost paralysing King's Cross at the height of the rush hour when it expired in Copenhagen Tunnel with the northbound 'Tees-Tyne Pullman'. An army of fitters descended on the diesel, but it was almost an hour before the luckless passengers saw daylight again. The down slow line could not be used because of the fitters working in the tunnel and northbound trains had to use the goods road through the tunnel. Empty stock was unable to leave the terminus and southbound trains were queuing up to enter King's Cross. The North Eastern Region Type 4s were also reported to be experiencing problems. On Monday 14 May No D243 had to be assisted from Huntingdon by 'V2' 2-6-2 No 60903 whilst working a southbound Edinburgh sleeper and on the same day No D357 had to be replaced by 'A1' 4-6-2 No 60153 *Flamboyant* at Grantham on the 2.00pm King's Cross to Newcastle. Two days later No D243 was again in trouble, this time at Tempsford between St Neots and Sandy. 'K3' class 2-6-0 No 61864 had to drag the diesel and the 9.55am Newcastle to King's Cross as far as Hitchin where Brush A1A-A1A No D5677 was substituted. The 'K3' completed the Brush diesel's diagram by working the 4.33pm Hitchin to King's Cross.

Saturday 26 May marked the departure of the last 'N2' class 0-6-2T from the London area with No 69568 being transferred from King's Cross to Peterborough New England. Earlier in the week the other three survivors, Nos 69523, 69535 and 69538, had moved to Peterborough. All had been withdrawn by 16 September.

On the Great Central, after working the RCTS (Railway

A Stanier 8F 2-8-0 at work. The date is Saturday 9 November 1963 and Heaton Mersey-based No 48501 is starting off with a train of empties for the Sheffield line at Chinley. This was one of the batch built at Darlington Works by the LNER in June 1944, passing to the LMS in 1946. The first allocation was March shed. No 48501 spent many years at Heaton Mersey, going there in June 1955 from Manchester Longsight and remaining until withdrawn during the week ended 15 July 1967. It was then one of the 1,233 steam locomotives scrapped at Cashmore's, Great Bridge. *Author's collection*

In August 1962 'M7' class 0-4-4T No 30241 is near London Waterloo on an empty stock working. Dating from May 1899, No 30241 spent virtually the whole of its British Railways days allocated to Nine Elms, moving in October 1962 to Salisbury and then to Eastleigh in March 1963, from where it was withdrawn a few months later on 7 July and cut up at the works. *P. H. Groom*

Class 81 electric locomotives Nos E3016 and E3022 are at Crewe station in September 1961. No E3016 became 81014 in October 1973 and No E3022 81019 in May 1973. E3016 was withdrawn on 30 March 1988 and stored at Crewe electric depot until November 1991 and scrapped at Coopers Metals, Attercliffe, Sheffield. E3022 was withdrawn on 3 January 1989 and was also stored at Crewe until November 1991 and scrapped alongside E3016. *G. W. Sharpe*

Correspondence and Travel Society) East Midlands Branch excursion to Darlington on Sunday 13 May, 'Schools' class 4-4-0 No 30925 *Cheltenham* returned to Neasden and was used to work the 6.10pm Marylebone to Woodford Halse on 17, 18, 21 and 22 May before returning to the Southern Region. The diagram involved light running to Banbury and return on the Banbury to Marylebone milk train.

During the week ended 12 May 'Royal Scot' 4-6-0s Nos 46106, without nameplates, and 46118 *Royal Welch Fusilier* were transferred to Leicester Central from Saltley. They were employed on two diagrams. The first involved working from Leicester to Banbury on the 8.30am Newcastle to Bournemouth, then the 4.20pm Woodford Halse to Rugby local, the 5.35pm Rugby to Woodford, usually tender first, then the 6.50pm Woodford to Banbury and back home on the 7.40pm Swindon to Sheffield. The second diagram was to take over the 1.30pm Nottingham to Marylebone Class C freight at Leicester and return on either the 8.45pm Marylebone to Wavertree Class C or the 9.00pm Marylebone to York Class C. Their time at Leicester was short as both were sent back to Saltley and then to Carlisle Upperby, both moves taking place during the week ended 30 June. They were replaced at Leicester by Standard 5MT 4-6-0s Nos 73066, 73069, 73156 and 73159. 'Royal Scots' returned to the Great Central later in the year during the week ended 29 September when Nos 46112, 46143, 46153 and 46158 were transferred to Annesley replacing 'Britannia' Pacifics Nos 70014, 70015, 70048 and 70049, which were sent to Willesden.

Nuneaton shed was in a unique position by mid-June in having 18 Stanier 2-6-0s on its allocation, which was over half the class. They had replaced the Hughes/Fowler and Ivatt Moguls. At the same time the Fridays-only Coventry to Glasgow, which was routed via Stoke, Manchester, Hellifield and Carlisle and worked nonstop from Stoke, was transferred from an Aston shed working to that of Nuneaton. Diagrammed for one of Nuneaton's 'Jubilee' 4-6-0s, the regular engine was No 45599 *Bechuanaland*, which was kept specially clean and adorned with red-backed nameplates.

On Friday 22 June 'Castle' class 4-6-0 No *5043 Earl of Mount Edgcumbe*, a Cardiff Canton engine, penetrated the Southern Region from Salisbury as far as Eastleigh, working an Educational Excursion from Abertridwr to Portsmouth Harbour. As 'Castles' were not permitted to work on the Southern except on former GWR routes, No 5043 was removed from the train at Eastleigh and later in the day allowed to run light to Salisbury, subject to speed restrictions, and took up the return working.

On the Midland Division the diesels were taking over in strength and, as an example, observations at Luton on Wednesday 11 July found every passenger train diesel-powered from 10.00am until 4.34pm when Longsight-based 'Britannia' Pacific No 70019 *Lightning* appeared on a Manchester to St Pancras express. Freight working continued with steam power, with Standard '9F' 2-10-0s being the most frequent performers.

The place to still see steam in abundance was the North Wales coast main line. During a period of eight hours between Crewe and Bangor on Saturday 14 July, the only two diesels seen were Nos D305 (8A) on the down 'Irish Mail' and D380 (1B) on a Llandudno train, later returning on the 2.50pm Llandudno to Birmingham. 'Royal Scots', rebuilt 'Patriots' and 'Britannias' were to be seen, supplemented by 2-6-0s, 'Jubilees' and passenger tank engines.

On the London, Tilbury & Southend lines, following the complete closure of Plaistow shed on 18 June, the train crews were transferred to the electric depot at East Ham. The shed building was then used for storage of redundant steam locomotives awaiting disposal. On Monday 30 July it contained Nos 41981, 42218, 42219, 42223, 42254, 42257, 42505, 42513, 47328, 47351, 47555, 80070, 80103, 90023, 90093, 90196, 90244, 90256, 90296 and 90653. Of these, No 42505 was in steam as it was booked to travel light engine to Doncaster the next day for cutting up. Tilbury shed also closed on 18 June and was then regarded as a sub-shed to Stratford as it still had servicing facilities for steam locomotives working in for the Thames Haven traffic. On 30 July the shed contained Nos 42255, 42527 and 90034 in store and 48431 (81A) in steam. Shoeburyness shed presented a sorry sight on Monday 13 August with 24 locomotives in store, all in a deplorably filthy state. Present were Nos 42501, 42502, 42503, 42504, 42508, 42509, 42516, 42517, 42518, 42522, 42523, 42525, 42526, 42529, 42530, 42532, 42533, 42535, 42536, 42679, 42687, 69461, 80104 and 80133. The 'N1', No 69461, had survived as a stationary boiler at the carriage siding and was the last of its class in existence for several years, still carrying a 37A shedplate.

Stored locomotives awaiting scrapping were increasing in numbers around Scotland, with engine sheds also becoming dumping grounds for unwanted stock. At Carnbroe dump, near Coatbridge, on Tuesday 17 July were Nos 55201, 55267, 56298, 56318, 56356, 57268, 57271, 57288, 57303, 57319, 57325, 57363, 57369, 57389, 57417, 57418, 57436, 57461, 57463, 57563, 57564 and 57593. In early August stored at the following sheds were:

Glasgow Kipps — Nos 56029, 64470, 64507, 64574, 65210, 65216, 65241, 65260, 68104, 68117, 68345, 68350, 68442 and 68445.

Hurlford — Nos 40151, 40640, 40642, 40665, 55240, 57249, 57295, 57300, 57341, 57353, 57359, 57650, 57651, 67607, 67633 and 67679.

Ardrossan — Nos 40578, 40625, 40668, 40669, 42191, 45167, 56232, 57254, 57263, 57274, 57357, 57579, 57669, 57673 and 90505.

Ayr — Nos 42927, 44329, 55262, 55264, 57262, 57364, 57392, 57569,

57580, 57596, 57611, 57614, 57615, 57633, 57640, 57644, 64541, 64626 and 90198.

Glasgow Eastfield — Nos 40566, 40624, 64540, 64581, 64622, 64639, 64711, 64816, 64863, 64867, 64947, 64971, 65218, 65228, 65239, 65315, 65320, 67602, 67603 and 67644.

In the Welsh Valleys there was still plenty of steam to be seen, as on Sunday 5 August the following were recorded at sub-sheds in the area:

Rhymney — Nos 5603, 5605, 5618, 5645, 5650, 5652, 5655, 5672, 5681 and 5696.

Dowlais Cae Harris — Nos 5622, 5660, 5662, 5666 and 5671.

Glyn Neath — Nos 4255, 4282, 5239, 9625 and 9734.

Neath N&B — Nos 3621, 3652, 3741, 3757, 3768, 3790, 5773, 8732 and 9786.

Upper Bank— Nos 6714, 6741, 6749, 6755, 6757, 6762, 6764, 6765, 6767, 6768, 6770 and 6777.

By August only two unrebuilt 'Patriot' class 4-6-0s were still on the active list, Nos 45543 and 45550, both based at Carnforth. They were regularly employed on the 7.00am Barrow to Manchester Victoria, returning with the 5.10pm Manchester Exchange to Windermere, and the 8.45am Barrow to Preston, returning with the 2.45pm Preston to Barrow. The last regular express working of this class was on Saturday 8 September when No 45550 powered the 10.53am Workington to Euston as far as Preston. On 10 September both 45543 and 45550 were placed in store at the closed Preston shed. On 8 October No 45543 was steamed again and worked the 7.15am freight to Southport as part of its preparation for working the LCGB 'The Midland Limited Railtour' from St Pancras to Derby on Sunday 14 October. After this it worked its way back to Preston where, by 21 October, it was back in store, not going to Crewe Works until September 1963 for scrapping.

On Saturday 25 August the 10.05am Paddington to Kingswear, with 'Warship' diesel No D833 *Panther* in charge, had difficulty in climbing the grade out from Torquay station with 15 coaches in tow, finally stalling on the stretch of 1 in 56 gradient. After about three minutes the guard proceeded to carry out Rule 55, walking back to Torquay signalbox. As he did so, the following train, the 7.45am Paddington to Kingswear via Bristol, with 'Hall' class No 4932 *Hatherton Hall* heading the train, came blasting up the grade, exploded two detonators and hit the rear of the 10.05am, the last coach of which was lifted onto No 4932's buffer beam. Seventeen passengers were injured.

Another accident, this time involving freight trains, occurred on Friday 7 September. 'A1' class 4-6-2 No 60123 *H. A. Ivatt* heading the 8.50pm King's Cross to Leeds freight ran into the rear of the 8.25pm King's Cross to Aberdeen freight at Offord between St Neots and Huntingdon. The wreckage blocked the East Coast main line for two days and No 60123 was so extensively damaged that it was withdrawn.

On Monday 10 September, the day of the introduction of the Winter Timetable, the full diesel-worked service from Paddington to Birmingham Snow Hill and Wolverhampton was inaugurated, using 'Western' class locomotives, ensuring the end for the Old Oak Common and Stafford Road 'Kings'. A sign of the times was the large number of stored locomotives at Old Oak Common on Saturday 15 September, all without cab numberplates and nameplates: Nos 3750, 5008, 5011, 5034, 5036, 5066, 5082, 5084, 5931, 6009, 6010, 6019, 6020, 6021, 6026, 6029, 8761, 8763, 9407, 9410, 9709 and 9758.

On the East Coast main line, the introduction of the Winter Timetable required a total of 20 'Deltic' diagrams on a weekday basis with, ironically, more steam diagrams for King's Cross shed than in the Summer Timetable. With the exception of Nos 60003, 60006 and 60007, which were in Doncaster Works at the time, all the 'Top Shed' 'A4s' were at work during the first week of the new timetable.

On the Southern, by the end of September only two 'Lord Nelson' 4-6-0s, Nos 30861 and 30862, were active, with only two 'N15' 'King Arthur' 4-6-0s, Nos 30765 and 30770, serviceable. No 30861 had a 'last fling' duty on 8 September when it powered the nonstop 10.00am Bournemouth to Waterloo and 5.30pm return.

Further storage points for steam locomotives were appearing and in early September Scarborough shed was put to such use. Present in store on Sunday 9 September were Nos 40117, 46409, 60515, 60516, 60518, 60522, 60526, 60831, 60837, 60847, 60864, 60877, 61421, 61434, 61448, 61454, 61475, 68046, 68061, 90030, 90045 and 90078.

Blaydon Goods Yard, opposite the shed, was another gathering point for stored steam and to be found there on Saturday 6 October were Nos 60511, 60521, 60538, 60539, 60801, 60843, 60860, 60926, 60929, 60932, 60947, 60978, 64852, 64856, 64860, 64865, 64871, 64921, 64923, 64936, 64938, 64942 and 64978. At Tyne Dock shed there was also a sizeable dump and on Saturday 3 November in store were Nos 60805, 60807, 60886, 60923, 60942, 60945, 60952, 60964, 60979, 63464, 63465, 63466, 64842, 64939, 65693, 67639, 67645, 67654, 67673, 67685, 68016, 68048, 68704 and 69027.

At Sunderland shed, by 3 November all its 'J39' class 0-6-0s were in store as a prelude for all members of this class to be withdrawn. In contrast, 19 of the 20 allocated 'J27s' were in use, the missing one, No 65854, being under repair at Darlington.

With the ever increasing numbers of diesel locomotives in use, stabling points were being used at weekends at a variety of locations. One example was the officially closed steam shed at Sheffield Grimesthorpe which was being used as a diesel depot pending the completion of the construction of the purpose-built depot at Tinsley. On Sunday 14 October the following were present at Grimesthorpe: Nos D18, D58, D90, D3056, D3127, D3254, D3574, D3698, D3727, D4036, D4039, D4043, D4048, D5688, D5807, D5826, D5831, D5836, D8021, D8022, D8024, D8052, D8054, D8055, D8056, D8058, D8059, D8061, D8063, D8064, D8065, D8066, D8068 and D8069.

As the end of 1962 approached, railway operations were dominated at the beginning of December by extremely severe weather conditions with snow, ice and freezing fog creating late-running trains, locomotive and unit failures, and cancellations. During the last days of the year there began a period of continuous and severe frost with frequent snowstorms. These conditions lasted throughout much of Great Britain until early in March 1963. Diesel motive power had a difficult time and as a result many steam locomotives withdrawn during the last months of 1962 were brought back into service for a time, some for only a few days and others for longer periods.

For the railway enthusiast and historian, 1962 was the beginning of the end for steam traction, with the introduction of diesel locomotives in such haste that some of the types lasted in service only a fraction of the time that their steam companions had achieved. This volume lists all the locomotives and diesel multiple-units in service on 1 January 1962 and represents a moment in time that was a turning point in British Railways' history, with the elimination of steam traction gathering pace at unprecedented levels during the year. For those who remember it, it was a period of tremendous interest, tinged with sadness at the sight of so many familiar steam classes going to the breakers, and yet with a sense of purpose and excitement at the prospect of modern power and what was to come in the area of performance and service standards.

Chris Banks
Hinckley
July 2005

British Railways Locomotive Sheds and Shed Codes at 1 January 1962

London Midland Region

1A **London Willesden**
1B London Camden
1C Watford
1D London Devons Road
1E Bletchley
Leighton Buzzard

2A **Rugby**
2B Nuneaton
2E Northampton
2F Woodford Halse

5A **Crewe North**
Crewe Gresty Lane
5B Crewe South
5C Stafford
5D Stoke-on-Trent
5E Alsager
5F Uttoxeter

6A **Chester**
6B Mold Junction
6C Birkenhead
6F Bidston
6G Llandudno Junction
6H Bangor
6J Holyhead
6K Rhyl

8A **Liverpool Edge Hill**
8B Warrington Dallam
Warrington Arpley
8C Liverpool Speke Junction
8D Widnes
8E Northwich
8F Wigan Springs Branch
8G Sutton Oak, St. Helens
8H Liverpool Allerton

9A **Manchester Longsight**
9B Stockport Edgeley
9D Buxton
9E Manchester Trafford Park
9F Heaton Mersey
9G Manchester Gorton
9H Manchester Reddish

12A **Carlisle Kingmoor**
12B Carlisle Upperby
Penrith
12C Carlisle Canal
12E Barrow-in-Furness
12F Workington
12G Oxenholme
12H Tebay

14A **London Cricklewood**
14B London Kentish Town
14D London Neasden
Aylesbury
14E Bedford
14F London Marylebone

15A **Wellingborough**
15B Kettering
15C Leicester Midland
15D Coalville
15E Leicester Great Central
15F Market Harborough

16A **Nottingham Midland**
16B Kirkby-in-Ashfield
16D Annesley

17A **Derby**
17B Burton-on-Trent
Overseal
17C Rowsley
Cromford
Middleton
Sheep Pasture

18A **Toton**
18B Westhouses
18C Hasland

21A **Birmingham Saltley**
21B Bescot
21C Wolverhampton Bushbury
21D Birmingham Aston
21E Birmingham Monument Lane
21F Walsall

24A **Accrington**
24B Rose Grove
24C Lostock Hall
24D Lower Darwen
24E Blackpool Central
24F Fleetwood
24G Skipton
24H Hellifield
24J Lancaster Green Ayre
24L Carnforth

26A **Manchester Newton Heath**
26B Manchester Agecroft
26C Bolton
26D Bury
26E Lees, Oldham
26F Manchester Patricroft

27A **Liverpool Bank Hall**
27B Liverpool Aintree
27C Southport
27D Wigan L & Y
27E Liverpool Walton-on-the-Hill

CW Crewe Works

HW Horwich Works

WW Wolverton Works

ACL AC Electric Lines
(West Coast Route)

One of the four named Stanier 4-6-0s, No 45154 *Lanarkshire Yeomanry* is at Carnforth shed awaiting repair in June 1961. Built by Armstrong Whitworth in June 1935, it was first allocated to Crewe North before transfer to Scotland and naming in 1937. No 45154 spent many years allocated to Glasgow St Rollox before being transferred to Manchester Newton Heath in April 1957 along with another named class member, No 45156 *Ayrshire Yeomanry*. In December 1963 No 45154 transferred to Aintree and later served from Lancaster before going to Speke Junction in March 1965, from where withdrawal took place during the week ended 12 November 1966. Stored at Speke Junction until March 1967, it was then sold to Draper's at Hull for scrap. *Pictorail*

Eastern Region

30A London Stratford
30F Parkeston

31A Cambridge
Ely
31B March
Wisbech East

32A Norwich
Dereham
32B Ipswich
Stowmarket
32C Lowestoft
32D Yarmouth South Town
32E Yarmouth Vauxhall
33B Tilbury
Plaistow
33C Shoeburyness

34A London Kings Cross
34B London Hornsey
34D Hitchin (Diesels)
34E Peterborough New England
34F Grantham
34G London Finsbury Park (Diesels)

36A Doncaster
36C Frodingham
36E Retford

40A Lincoln
40B Immingham
40E Nottingham Colwick
40F Boston
Sleaford

41A Sheffield Darnall
41D Canklow
41E Staveley Barrow Hill
41F Mexborough
Wath
41H Staveley Great Central
41J Langwith Junction

North Eastern Region

50A **York**
50B Hull Dairycoates
Alexandra Dock
50C Hull Botanic Gardens
50D Goole

51A **Darlington**
51C West Hartlepool
51F West Auckland
51J Northallerton
51L Thornaby

52A **Gateshead**
Bowes Bridge
52B Heaton
52C Blaydon
52D Tweedmouth
Alnmouth
52E Percy Main
52F North and South Blyth
52G Sunderland
52H Tyne Dock
52J South Gosforth (DMU Depot)
52K Consett

55A **Leeds Holbeck**
55B Leeds Stourton
55C Leeds Farnley Junction
55D Royston
55E Normanton
55F Bradford Manningham
Keighley
55G Huddersfield
55H Leeds Neville Hill

56A **Wakefield**
56B Ardsley
56C Leeds Copley Hill
56D Mirfield
56E Sowerby Bridge
56F Bradford Low Moor
56G Bradford Hammerton Street

Scottish Region

60A **Inverness**
Kyle of Lochalsh
60B Aviemore
60C Helmsdale
Tain
60D Wick
Thurso

61A **Aberdeen Kittybrewster**
61B Aberdeen Ferryhill
61C Keith Junction
Banff

62A **Thornton Junction**
Burntisland
62B Dundee Tay Bridge
Dundee West (Diesels)
Montrose
62C Dunfermline
Alloa

63A **Perth**
Aberfeldy
Blair Atholl
Forfar
63B Fort William
Mallaig
63C Oban
Ballachulish

64A **Edinburgh St Margarets**
Galashiels
Hardengreen
Seafield
64B Edinburgh Haymarket
64C Edinburgh Dalry Road
64F Bathgate
64G Hawick
64H Leith Central (Diesels)

65A **Glasgow Eastfield**
65B Glasgow St. Rollox
65C Glasgow Parkhead
65D Glasgow Dawsholm
Dumbarton
65E Glasgow Kipps
65F Grangemouth
65G Glasgow Yoker
65J Stirling
Killin (Loch Tay)
65K Polmont

66A **Glasgow Polmadie**
66B Motherwell
66C Hamilton
66D Greenock Ladyburn
66E Carstairs

67A **Glasgow Corkerhill**
67B Hurlford
Beith
Muirkirk
67C Ayr
67D Ardrossan

68B Dumfries
68C Stranraer
68D Beattock

Southern Region

70A	**London Nine Elms**
70B	London Feltham
70C	Guildford
70D	Basingstoke
70E	Reading South
70H	Ryde, Isle of Wight
71A	**Eastleigh**
	Andover Junction
	Lymington
	Winchester City
71B	Bournemouth
	Branksome
71G	Weymouth
71I	Southampton Docks
72A	**Exmouth Junction**
	Bude
	Callington
	Exmouth
	Lyme Regis
	Okehampton
	Seaton
72B	Salisbury
72C	Yeovil Town
72E	Barnstaple Junction
	Ilfracombe
72F	Wadebridge
73A	**London Stewarts Lane**
73B	London Bricklayers Arms
73C	London Hither Green
73E	Faversham
73F	Ashford
	St Leonards
73J	Tonbridge
75A	**Brighton**
	Newhaven
75B	Redhill
75C	London Norwood Junction
75E	Three Bridges
	Horsham
75F	Tunbridge Wells West

Western Region

81A	**London Old Oak Common**
81B	Slough
	Marlow
81C	Southall
81D	Reading
81E	Didcot
81F	Oxford
	Fairford
82A	**Bristol Bath Road**
	Wells
82B	Bristol St. Philip's Marsh
82C	Swindon
	Chippenham
82D	Westbury
	Frome
82E	Bristol Barrow Road
82F	Bath Green Park
	Radstock
82G	Templecombe
83A	**Newton Abbot**
83B	Taunton
83C	Exeter
	Tiverton Junction
83D	Plymouth Laira
	Launceston
83E	St Blazey
	Bodmin
83F	Truro
83G	Penzance
	Helston
83H	Plymouth Friary
84A	**Wolverhampton Stafford Road**
84B	Wolverhampton Oxley
84C	Banbury
84D	Leamington Spa
84E	Birmingham Tyseley
	Stratford-on-Avon
84F	Stourbridge Junction
84G	Kidderminster
84H	Wellington (Salop)
85A	**Worcester**
	Kingham
85B	Gloucester Horton Road
	Brimscombe
	Cheltenham
	Cirencester
	Lydney
	Tetbury
85C	Gloucester Barnwood
	Dursley
	Tewkesbury
85D	Bromsgrove
	Redditch
86A	**Newport Ebbw Junction**
86B	Newport Pill
86C	Hereford
	Leominster
	Ross-on-Wye
86E	Severn Tunnel Junction
86F	Aberbeeg
86G	Pontypool Road
87A	**Neath**
	Glyn Neath
	Neath N&B
87B	Duffryn Yard
87D	Swansea East Dock
	Gurnos
	Upper Bank
87E	Swansea Landore
87F	Llanelly
	Burry Port
	Llandovery
	Pantyffynon
87G	Carmarthen
87H	Neyland
	Cardigan
	Milford Haven
	Pembroke Dock
	Whitland
87J	Goodwick
88A	**Cardiff Canton**
88B	Cardiff Radyr
88C	Barry
88D	Merthyr
	Dowlais Cae Harris
	Dowlais Central
	Rhymney
88E	Abercynon
88F	Treherbert
	Ferndale
88G	Llantrisant
88H	Tondu
88J	Aberdare
88K	Brecon
89A	**Shrewsbury**
	Builth Road
	Craven Arms
	Knighton
89B	Wrexham Croes Newydd
	Bala
	Penmaenpool
89C	Machynlleth
	Aberayron
	Aberystwyth
	Portmadoc
	Pwllheli
89D	Oswestry
	Llanidloes
	Moat Lane
CAT	Cardiff Cathays
CED	Cardiff East Dock
DG	Swansea Danygraig

British Railways Locomotive Allocations at 1 January 1962

1000 'County' Class 4-6-0 6MT

Loco	Shed
1000*	82B
1001*	83G
1002*	81E
1003*	83D
1004*	83G
1005*	82B
1006*	83D
1007*	81E
1008*	83G
1009*	82B
1010*	82C
1011*	82B
1012*	82C
1013*	89A
1014*	87H
1015*	81E
1016*	89A
1017*	89A
1018*	81E
1019*	82C
1020*	87H
1021*	82B
1022*	89A
1023*	82C
1024*	82B
1025*	89A
1026*	89A
1027*	87H
1028*	82B
1029*	82C

Ex Powlesland and Mason 0-4-0ST OF

Loco	Shed
1151	87D

Ex-Cardiff Railway 0-4-0ST OF

Loco	Shed
1338	87D

1361 Class 0-6-0ST OF

Loco	Shed
1363	83D
1365	82C

1366 Class 0-6-0PT 1F

Loco	Shed
1367	71G
1368	71G
1369	71G

1400 Class 0-4-2T 1P

Loco	Shed
1409	85B
1420	83C
1421	81D
1424	85B
1426	85B
1432	89D
1434	83C
1435	81F
1438	89D
1440	84C
1442	81F
1444	81F
1445	81B
1447	89B
1450	81F
1451	83C
1453	84C
1455	84C
1458	89D
1462	83C
1466	83C
1468	83C
1470	83C
1471	83C
1472	85B
1473	85B
1474	81C

1500 Class 0-6-0PT 4F

Loco	Shed
1500	81A
1503	81A
1504	81A
1505	81A
1506	86A
1507	81A
1508	88A

1600 Class 0-6-0PT 2F

Loco	Shed
1605	85B
1607	87F
1608	83C
1609	87F
1611	87F
1612	88E
1613	87H
1614	87F
1617	86C
1618	89B
1619	84F
1621	82C
1622	87F
1623	85B
1624	83E
1626	85B
1627	85B
1628	89D
1630	85B
1631	85B
1632	85B

Hawksworth-designed 'County' class 4-6-0 No 1008 *County of Cardigan* is at Kingswear being prepared for departure in June 1962. New in December 1945 and first allocated to Old Oak Common, in October 1952 No 1008 moved to Chester GWR shed and then to Penzance in June 1958. Subsequent moves were to Neyland in September 1962, Shrewsbury in March 1963 and finally Swindon in September 1963, from where withdrawal was actioned one month later. Cashmore's at Newport carried out the scrapping. *G. W. Sharpe*

Ex-Powlesland & Mason 0-4-0ST No 1151 is in store at Swansea East Dock shed on Saturday 13 October 1962. This was a Peckett-built locomotive dating from September 1916 and originally numbered 779. After withdrawal in August 1963 it was sold to Hayes at Bridgend for further use until it was finally retired in May 1966. *G. W. Sharpe*

Ex-Cardiff Railway 0-4-0ST No 1338 is at work in Swansea Docks in March 1962. This unique Kitson-built engine dated from 1898 and was based at Taunton for many years for work in the docks at Bridgwater. It had moved to Swansea East Dock in June 1960 from where it was withdrawn in September 1963. Saved from the scrapyard, No 1338 can still be seen at Didcot Railway Centre. *G. W. Sharpe*

'1361' class 0-6-0ST No 1363 is in store at Plymouth Laira shed in April 1963 after withdrawal in 1962. This was a 1910 Churchward design and was a Laira-based engine for many years. It remained in storage until August 1964 when it was rescued for preservation and can be seen at Didcot Railway Centre. *P. H. Groom*

'1366' class 0-6-0PT No 1369 is shunting at Boscarne Junction in April 1963. This was the Collett development of the '1361' class dating from 1934. In August 1962 No 1369 moved to Wadebridge from Weymouth and was withdrawn in November 1964. It was rescued for preservation and is now to be seen at the South Devon Railway. *P. H. Groom*

'1400' class 0-4-2T No 1432 is being prepared for work at Oswestry shed in March 1962. This was a Collett design and No 1432 was new in July 1934, first allocated to Newton Abbot. After operating from a number of sheds in the West Country, No 1432 was reallocated to Oswestry in February 1938 and remained there until withdrawn on 27 July 1963. Swindon Works carried out the scrapping the following September. *G. W. Sharpe*

'1500' class 0-6-0PT No 1505 is on an empty stock working near Old Oak Common, London, in April 1961. New from Swindon Works in August 1949, it was allocated to Old Oak Common and spent its entire working life at 81A, withdrawal coming in 1962. Scrapping was carried out at Wolverhampton Works. *R. H. G. Simpson*

'1600' class 0-6-0PT No 1653 is in store at Newport Ebbw Junction shed on Monday 4 March 1963 after withdrawal in December 1962. It had a short working life of only eight years, going new to Ebbw Junction from Swindon Works in December 1954 and remaining on allocation until withdrawn. The nearby Cashmore's yard carried out the cutting up in June 1963. *G. W. Sharpe*

1633	87F
1636	89D
1638	87F
1639	85A
1641	88E
1642	85B
1643	87F
1645	87A
1646	60C
1648	87H
1649	60C
1650	85B
1651	87F
1653	86A
1654	87F
1655	87F
1656	86A
1657	86C
1658	82C
1660	89B
1661	85A
1662	86C
1663	87F
1664	82C
1665	87F
1666	87H
1667	86C
1668	89D
1669	87H

2251 Class 0-6-0 3MT

2200	82D
2201	84D
2204	89C
2209	86A
2210	84D
2211	84D
2212	81D
2214	89A
2216	87G
2217	89C
2218	86A
2219	83B
2221	81E
2222	89C
2223	86A
2224	82B
2229	82E
2230	81E
2231	86E
2232	82B
2234	85A
2236	89C
2239	89C
2240	86A
2241	86C
2242	86C
2243	86A
2244	89C
2245	85B
2246	85A
2247	86A
2248	87G
2249	86C
2250	82C
2251	89D
2253	85B
2255	89C
2256	86C
2257	84D
2261	81D
2268	82D
2271	87J
2273	85B
2276	89C
2277	82G
2283	87H
2286	89C
2287	89C
2289	85B
2291	82C
2292	86E
2294	89C
2295	86C
2298	89C

2800 Class 2-8-0 8F

2807	86E
2818	86A
2822	83B
2834	81E
2836	81E
2839	86G
2841	81D
2842	81E
2845	86G
2849	81E
2851	83B
2852	82C
2853	81D
2854	86E
2855	89B
2856	84B
2857	86E
2858	86E
2859	86G
2860	86E
2861	86E
2862	86E
2865	86E
2866	86G
2867	86G
2871	83B
2872	86E
2873	88J
2874	88J
2875	82D
2876	88J
2879	82C
2882	83B
2883	82D

2884 Class 2-8-0 8F

2884	86A
2885	84F
2886	88J
2887	86E
2888	84C
2889	84C
2890	82C
2891	88A
2892	86E
2893	81E
2894	86A
2895	86E
2896	86E
2897	86A
2898	81E
2899	83D

2251 Class 0-6-0 3MT

3200	89D
3201	89B
3203	85B
3204	89A
3205	89A
3206	87J
3207	85A
3208	89D
3209	89D
3210	82G
3211	86A
3212	82D
3213	89C
3214	89D
3215	82G
3216	82G
3217	84C
3218	82B
3219	81D

9400 Class 0-6-0PT 4F

3400	89A
3401	88B
3402	88B
3403	88B
3404	88B
3405	88B
3406	88B
3407	88B
3408	88B
3409	88B

5700 Class 0-6-0PT 3F

3600	89D
3601	84G
3602	89A
3603	88J
3604	82B
3605	84F
3606	82E
3607	84G
3608	81B
3610	88J
3611	87A
3612	88G
3613	87B
3614	82D
3615	84A
3616	88H
3617	88G
3618	81C
3619	84D
3620	81C
3621	87A
3622	81C
3623	82B
3624	87H
3625	84E
3626	84H
3627	88J
3628	86G
3629	82D
3630	89C
3631	84B
3632	82B
3633	70A
3634	86A
3635	83G
3636	86A
3637	87J
3639	87H
3640	86G
3641	87D
3642	87B
3643	82B
3644	88G
3645	82C
3646	81A
3647	86F
3648	88H
3650	87A
3651	86G
3652	86B
3653	81F
3654	87H
3655	88J
3656	88G
3658	84F
3659	83A
3660	84E
3661	86A
3662	86A
3663	88A
3664	86F
3665	81E
3666	82C
3668	88H
3669	83B
3671	72C
3672	88B
3673	84E
3674	86B
3675	82B
3677	82B
3678	87H
3679	72A
3680	88G
3681	88B
3682	82C
3683	86F
3684	82C
3685	86G
3686	83D
3687	87A
3688	87B
3689	89B
3690	88H
3691	86A
3692	87B
3693	87G
3694	86A
3695	88J
3696	82B
3697	81B
3698	87F
3699	88J
3700	86A
3701	87F
3702	82B
3703	86G
3705	86B
3706	86A
3707	88E
3708	86G
3709	83F
3710	88C
3711	82C
3712	86F
3713	87F
3714	86A
3715	84A
3716	88J
3717	86G
3718	87B
3719	87F
3720	82G
3721	85B
3722	86A
3723	81D
3725	85A
3726	82B
3727	88C
3728	88C
3729	86C
3730	88E
3731	83E
3732	84H
3733	72C
3734	88E
3735	82D
3736	83B
3737	71G
3738	88H
3739	82C
3741	87A
3742	82F
3743	84F
3744	84H
3745	84F
3746	82C
3747	86A
3748	88A
3749	89B
3750	81A
3751	81E
3752	82E
3753	88J
3754	81A
3755	88A
3756	88H
3757	87A
3758	82C
3759	71G
3760	89B
3761	87J
3762	87B
3763	82C
3764	86A
3765	82B
3766	87A
3767	86A
3768	87A
3769	89A
3770	89D
3771	87F
3772	86A
3773	82B
3774	87A
3775	85B
3776	84E
3777	87F
3778	84A
3779	86G
3780	82C
3781	88H
3782	89A
3783	88E
3784	88A
3785	87D
3786	86E
3787	83B
3788	89A
3789	89D
3790	83E
3791	87B
3792	84A
3794	83C
3795	82G
3796	83A
3797	87D
3798	86A

2884 Class 2-8-0 8F

3800	86A
3801	86E
3802	84B
3803	86E
3804	88A
3805	86A
3806	86A
3807	86A
3808	86A
3809	84C
3810	88A
3811	87F
3812	86E
3813	84B
3814	81F
3815	89B
3816	84E
3817	84C
3818	86A
3819	81E
3820	81E
3821	84C
3822	86E
3823	81F
3824	86A
3825	84F
3826	86G
3827	86A
3828	89B
3829	86G
3830	86A
3831	84B
3832	86A
3833	86A
3834	86E
3835	86E
3836	89A
3837	86A
3838	86E
3839	84E
3840	81E
3841	86E
3842	82C
3843	86E
3844	86G
3845	86E
3846	89B
3847	86E
3848	86E
3849	88A
3850	88J
3851	87F
3852	86E
3853	86A
3854	86G
3855	84C
3856	86E
3857	86E
3858	81D
3859	86G
3860	88A
3861	86G
3862	83D
3863	86E
3864	86E
3865	84B
3866	88J

4073 'Castle' Class 4-6-0 7P

4037*	83A
4074*	82C
4076*	87F
4077*	82B
4078*	87F
4079*	82B
4080*	88A
4081*	87F
4082*	81A
4085*	81A
4086*	81D
4087*	83D
4088*	82C
4089*	81A
4090*	87A
4093*	87A
4094*	87G
4095*	83D
4096*	81A
4098*	83A
4099*	87A

5101 Class 2-6-2T 4MT

4100	85B
4101	85B
4102	82C
4103	83B
4104	84F
4105	84E
4106	85B
4107	87H

4108	88H
4109	85B
4110	84E
4111	84E
4112	84D
4113	85A
4114	84G
4115	86C
4116	85B
4118	84D
4119	86E
4120	84H
4121	88H
4122	87H
4124	85A
4125	84E
4126	84E
4127	86E
4128	83B
4129	84G
4130	86E
4131	82B
4132	87G
4133	84E
4134	87A
4135	86G
4136	86E
4137	86E
4140	84F
4141	85B
4142	85B
4143	83B
4144	88H
4145	86E
4146	86A
4147	84G
4148	81F
4149	84C
4150	83A
4151	86E
4152	86E
4153	84G
4154	84C
4155	84E
4156	86E
4157	84E
4158	84H
4159	87H
4160	88B
4161	84F
4163	85B
4165	83C
4166	88B
4167	84E
4168	84F
4169	87A
4171	84D
4172	84E
4173	84F
4174	83A
4175	84G
4176	84D
4177	88B
4178	84H
4179	84A

4200 Class 2-8-0T 7F

4213	87B
4214	86B
4218	88H
4222	88H
4225	88J
4227	86A
4228	88J
4230	87F
4232	87D
4233	86B
4235	86A
4236	88H
4237	86F
4238	86B
4241	86E
4242	88A
4243	88H
4246	86F
4247	86F
4248	82B
4250	87B
4251	88H
4252	86A
4253	86B
4254	88A
4255	87A
4256	87B
4257	88J
4258	86A
4259	86B
4262	88J
4263	88H
4264	86B
4265	86A
4266	86A
4267	88G
4268	88G
4269	88H
4270	88A
4271	87D
4272	87F
4273	83E
4274	88H
4275	87A
4276	86B
4277	86F
4278	87B
4279	87F
4280	86B
4282	87A
4283	86A
4284	87A
4285	86F
4286	87B
4289	88J
4290	86A
4291	86F
4292	87F
4293	86A
4294	86B
4295	87F
4296	87B
4297	86A
4298	87F
4299	87B

4500 Class 2-6-2T 4MT

4507	72C
4555	83A
4557	87H
4558	87H
4561	83D
4564	83G
4566	83D
4567	82D
4569	87H
4570	83G
4574	83A

4575 Class 2-6-2T 4MT

4588	83D
4591	83D
4593	83B

5700 Class 0-6-0PT 3F

4600	86G
4601	70A
4602	84F
4603	86G
4604	83B
4605	84H
4606	81B
4607	82D
4608	81C
4609	81D
4610	70B
4611	86A
4612	83B
4613	85A
4614	85C
4615	81A
4616	70D
4617	89B
4618	88C
4619	82B
4620	88G
4621	87A
4622	83F
4623	89A
4624	71G
4625	84B
4626	72B
4627	86F
4628	85A
4629	84G
4630	72B
4631	73A
4632	88D
4633	88A
4634	70A
4635	88D
4636	82D
4637	88G
4638	81B
4639	86G
4640	87B
4641	84G
4642	86G
4643	86B
4644	83B
4645	89B
4646	84F
4647	82D
4648	84E
4649	81F
4650	86F
4651	82C
4652	86F
4653	87A
4654	87H
4655	83B
4656	72C
4657	86A
4658	83D
4659	86C
4660	82B
4661	81D
4662	88G
4663	83B
4664	85A
4665	83E
4666	72F
4667	88C
4668	86G
4669	88H
4670	81D
4671	86A
4672	70A
4673	83F
4674	88G
4675	88H
4676	87F
4677	87J
4678	86C
4679	83D
4680	85B
4681	70A
4682	86B
4683	89B
4684	87B
4685	86F
4687	84F
4688	82B
4689	71G
4690	88D
4691	82G
4692	70A
4693	89A
4694	72F
4695	87B
4696	84F
4697	82C
4698	70A
4699	87H

4700 Class 2-8-0 7F

4700	81C
4701	81A
4702	81C
4703	82B
4704	81A
4705	82B
4706	82B
4707	81C
4708	81A

4900 'Hall' Class 4-6-0 5MT

4902*	81E
4903*	84B
4904*	83B
4905*	82B
4906*	84B
4907*	85A
4908*	81F
4909*	83C
4910*	81E
4912*	84B
4913*	86C
4914*	82B
4915*	81E
4916*	86G
4917*	82D
4918*	88A
4919*	81A
4920*	83A
4921*	81D
4922*	82B
4923*	84B
4924*	83C
4925*	81C
4927*	87A
4928*	88A
4929*	85B
4930*	83C
4931*	88A
4932*	83B
4933*	82D
4934*	83A
4935*	88A
4936*	83A
4937*	86G
4938*	87F
4939*	81E
4941*	82D
4942*	82B
4943*	86G
4944*	83C
4946*	89A
4947*	87J
4948*	82C
4949*	82B
4950*	81E
4951*	84B
4952*	88A
4953*	82B
4954*	84E
4955*	83B
4956*	88A
4957*	82D
4958*	86G
4959*	81E
4960*	82B
4961*	82D
4962*	87G
4963*	85A
4964*	84C
4965*	81E
4966*	84B

Ex-works on Shrewsbury shed in 1960 is '2251' class 0-6-0 No 2217. Dating from July 1940, No 2217 had first been allocated to Carmarthen. Machynlleth received No 2217 from Carmarthen in July 1954 and here it remained until transfer to Bristol Barrow Road in December 1962 and finally Templecombe a year later, from where it was withdrawn in November 1964. *G. W. Sharpe*

Another view at Shrewsbury shed, this time in May 1962 with '2800' class 2-8-0 No 2839 in the yard. This was a Churchward design, with No 2839 dating from October 1912. At nationalisation No 2839 was allocated to Bristol St Philips Marsh, and in April 1951 a move to Severn Tunnel Junction was made. In February 1957 a further transfer saw No 2839 operating from Newport Ebbw Junction until December 1959 when Pontypool Road shed became the final allocation before withdrawal in June 1964. Scrapping was carried out at Bird's yard at Risca. *G. W. Sharpe*

'57xx' class 0-6-0PT No 3669 is at Taunton station on Tuesday 31 July 1962. New in March 1940, No 3669 was first allocated to Neath. At nationalisation it was based at Old Oak Common, moving to Taunton shed in July 1948. Here it remained until November 1963, when a transfer to Westbury was authorised, and it was here that withdrawal came in September 1965. Ward's at Briton Ferry carried out the scrapping. *G. W. Sharpe*

Side-windowed-cab '2884' class 2-8-0 No 3808 is at London Old Oak Common shed in May 1962. New in September 1939, its first allocation was Llanelly. By 1 January 1948 it was based at Severn Tunnel Junction and moved to Newport Ebbw Junction in May 1954, where it remained until withdrawn in July 1965. Bird's at Morriston carried out the scrapping. *G. W. Sharpe*

'4073' 'Castle' class 4-6-0 No 4037 *The South Wales Borderers* at Swindon station on an express in July 1961. This was one of the older 'Castles' dating from June 1926 and was allocated to Newton Abbot when this photograph was recorded, moving to Exeter in July 1962 from where it was withdrawn two months later and cut up at Cashmore's at Newport. *R. H. G. Simpson*

'5101' class 2-6-2T No 4115 is seen at Hereford shed in September 1960, its home shed at the time. New to stock in September 1936, No 4115 was first allocated to Wolverhampton Stafford Road. Withdrawn in June 1965 after transfer to Severn Tunnel Junction in February 1963, it languished at Barry Docks until rescued for preservation and is now at the Barry Steam Railway. Alongside is Pontypool Road-based '2884' class 2-8-0 No 3818 which was also a 1965 withdrawal, going in May. *R. H. G. Simpson*

Churchward '4200' class 2-8-0T No 4290, with inside steam pipes, at Newport Ebbw Junction shed in 1962. This member of the class entered service in September 1921 and at nationalisation was based at Cardiff Canton. Subsequent moves saw the engine operating from a number of South Wales sheds until settling at Ebbw Junction in June 1953 where, apart from one month at Duffryn Yard in 1961, it remained until withdrawn in February 1963. *R. H. G. Simpson*

Churchward-designed '4500' class 2-6-2T No 4507 at Yeovil Town station in August 1961. Entering traffic in May 1907, this was the oldest class member in service in 1962 and survived until October 1963, still based at Yeovil. It was stored at Swindon Works until April 1964 when it was sold to Bird's at Risca for scrap. *G. W. Sharpe*

'4500' class 2-6-2T No 4557 at Whitland station in April 1962. This was a 1962 withdrawal and the engine had been in service since September 1924. Placed in store at Neyland from September 1962 until July 1963, No 4557 was then sold to Hayes at Bridgend for cutting up. *G. W. Sharpe*

'4700' class 2-8-0 No 4704 is ex-works at Shrewsbury shed in 1960. Dating from April 1922, most of its working life was at Old Oak Common from where it was withdrawn in May 1964. It was eventually scrapped at King's yard in Norwich. *G. W. Sharpe*

'4900' 'Hall' class 4-6-0 No 4959 *Purley Hall* at Didcot shed in May 1962. Dating from 1929, allocation at nationalisation was Birmingham Tyseley, moving to Wolverhampton Oxley in October 1952 and on to Bristol Bath Road in May 1955. The final move was to Didcot in September 1958, from where withdrawal was authorised in December 1964. Stored at Didcot until February 1965, the engine was then sold to Buttigieg's at Newport for scrapping. *R. H. G. Simpson*

'4900' 'Hall' class 4-6-0 No 4964 *Rodwell Hall*, paired with a high-sided tender, is at Shrewsbury shed in July 1961. Built in 1929, during its British Railways days, it served from a variety of sheds until going to Pontypool Road from Wolverhampton Stafford Road in September 1962, from where it was withdrawn in October 1963. *G. W. Sharpe*

4967* 83C
4968* 82B
4969* 81C
4970* 83C
4971* 88A
4972* 82C
4973* 88A
4974* 85B
4975* 81D
4976* 81E
4977* 88A
4978* 83A
4979* 81F
4980* 82B
4981* 87J
4982* 83D
4983* 81A
4984* 83C
4985* 83B
4986* 81C
4987* 81C
4988* 87A
4989* 85B
4990* 86C
4991* 83B
4992* 83B
4993* 83C
4994* 81E
4995* 81C
4996* 83C
4998* 81D
4999* 82B

4073 'Castle' Class 4-6-0 7P

5000* 82C
5001* 81A
5002* 82C
5003* 83A
5004* 87A
5006* 87G
5007* 85B
5008* 81A
5011* 81A
5012* 81F
5013* 87A
5014* 81A
5015* 81A
5016* 87F
5017* 85B
5018* 81D
5019* 84A
5020* 88A
5021* 88A
5022* 84A
5023* 82C
5024* 83A
5025* 81F
5026* 84A
5027* 87G
5029* 83D
5030* 87G
5031* 84A
5032* 81A
5033* 81F
5034* 81A
5035* 82C
5036* 81A
5037* 87A
5038* 89A
5039* 87G
5040* 82B
5041* 87A
5042* 81A
5043* 81A
5044* 88A
5045* 84A
5046* 84A
5047* 84A
5048* 87A
5049* 82B
5050* 82B
5051* 87A
5052* 82B
5053* 88A
5054* 87G
5055* 83A
5056* 81A
5057* 81A
5058* 85B
5059* 89A
5060* 81A
5061* 88A
5062* 87A
5063* 84A
5064* 85B
5065* 81A
5066* 81A
5067* 81D
5068* 82C
5069* 83D
5070* 89A
5071* 85B
5072* 84A
5073* 88A
5074* 87A
5075* 87A
5076* 81D
5077* 87F
5078* 87A
5080* 87F
5081* 88A
5082* 81A
5084* 81A
5085* 82B
5087* 87F
5088* 84A
5089* 84A
5090* 81A
5091* 88A
5092* 88A
5093* 81A
5094* 82B
5095* 89A
5096* 88A
5097* 88A
5098* 83D
5099* 88A

5101 Class 2-6-2T 4MT

5101 84D
5151 84G
5152 84A
5153 83A
5154 83A
5164 86G
5167 84C
5173 85B
5180 87G
5181 86E
5182 85B
5183 84A
5184 84D
5187 84F
5188 86A
5190 84F
5191 86E
5192 84D
5193 87H
5199 84A

4200 Class 2-8-0T 7F

5200 86B
5201 87F
5202 86B
5203 87F
5204 87A

5205 Class 2-8-0T 8F

5205 86A
5206 86F
5208 88H
5209 87F
5210 87D
5211 87D
5212 86E
5213 86A
5214 86E
5215 82B
5216 87B
5217 86A
5218 86F
5219 87F
5220 88A
5221 87A
5222 87A
5223 87F
5224 86E
5225 88A
5226 85A
5227 86A
5228 86A
5229 86A
5230 87B
5231 86B

'4073' 'Castle' class 4-6-0 No 5014 *Goodrich Castle*, also paired with a high-sided tender, is at Old Oak Common shed in October 1962. Entering traffic in June 1932, it was first allocated to Newton Abbot. Its British Railways days were spent allocated to Old Oak Common until June 1964 when it transferred to Birmingham Tyseley, from where it was withdrawn during the week ended 6 February 1965. It later went to Cashmore's at Great Bridge for scrapping. *G. W. Sharpe*

5232	87B
5233	86A
5234	86A
5235	86B
5236	86A
5237	88J
5238	86A
5239	87A
5240	88J
5241	86F
5242	87A
5243	86E
5244	86B
5245	85A
5246	87B
5247	87F
5248	87F
5249	88J
5250	86B
5251	86A
5252	86B
5253	86E
5254	87B
5255	86A
5256	86B
5257	86A
5258	88J
5259	86A
5260	87F
5261	88A
5262	87F
5263	88J
5264	86F

4300 Class 2-6-0 4MT

5306	86A
5322	86G
5326	82B
5330	86A
5336	86E
5357	87H
5358	85A
5369	82C
5376	82B
5380	81E
5385	82B
5399	89B

5400 Class 0-6-0PT 1P

5410	82D
5412	83C
5416	82D
5420	85B
5421	89D

4575 Class 2-6-2T 4MT

5508	83G
5518	83E
5520	87H
5521	83D
5525	83A
5526	82D
5531	83E
5532	83D
5537	83F
5539	83E
5541	83D
5544	83D
5545	83G
5547	82C
5548	72C
5549	87H
5550	87H
5554	83B
5555	83C
5560	83C
5562	83F
5563	72C
5564	83A
5568	83D
5569	83D
5570	82C
5571	83B
5572	83D
5573	83A

5600 Class 0-6-2T 5MT

5600	88F
5601	88E
5602	87F
5603	88D
5604	87F
5605	88D
5606	84B
5607	88F
5608	88F
5609	87D
5610	88D
5611	88F
5612	87F
5613	88F
5614	85A
5615	88E
5616	87D
5617	88E
5618	88D
5619	88C
5620	86E
5621	88C
5622	88D
5623	87D
5624	88J
5625	86G
5626	88D
5627	88E
5628	87D
5629	88H
5630	88E
5631	87D
5632	88F
5633	88J
5634	88C
5635	88B
5636	88D
5637	88C
5638	86G
5639	88C
5640	82B
5641	88E
5642	88J
5643	88C
5644	88E
5645	86G
5646	88F
5647	88E
5648	88B
5649	88J
5650	88D
5651	89B
5652	88D
5653	88F
5654	88F
5655	88D
5656	87F
5657	86A
5658	84E
5659	86G
5660	88D
5661	88D
5662	88D
5663	88B
5664	88C
5665	88F
5666	88D
5667	88C
5668	88C
5669	88B
5670	87B
5671	88D
5672	88D
5673	87A
5674	88F
5675	87D
5676	88F
5677	88D
5678	88F
5679	86G
5680	88E
5681	88D
5682	88E
5683	88B
5684	88F
5685	88A
5686	88E
5687	88F
5688	87B
5689	82D
5690	88H
5691	88F
5692	87F
5693	88F
5694	88F
5695	88F
5696	88D
5697	88B
5698	88J
5699	88E

5700 Class 0-6-0PT 3F

5720	87A
5728	87B
5744	83F
5746	81E
5749	88A
5758	86B
5761	87A
5766	81B
5773	87A
5774	89B
5775	86G
5778	87A
5779	82B
5783	87D
5787	87B
5789	86G
5793	83B
5798	83B

4900 'Hall' Class 4-6-0 5MT

5900*	84A
5901*	81C
5902*	87G
5903*	88A
5904*	82B
5905*	87J
5906*	81D
5908*	87J
5909*	88A
5910*	84B
5911*	88A
5912*	84C
5913*	83C
5914*	81C
5916*	84B
5917*	83D
5918*	81F
5919*	84B
5920*	82D
5921*	82D
5922*	81F
5923*	81F
5924*	82B
5925*	81C
5926*	84E
5927*	84E
5928*	87J
5929*	81A
5930*	85A
5931*	81A
5932*	81A
5933*	81F
5934*	82B
5935*	88A
5936*	81D
5937*	87G
5938*	87G
5939*	81A
5940*	82B
5941*	82B
5942*	89A
5943*	82C
5944*	85A
5945*	81C
5946*	83C
5947*	84C
5948*	86G
5951*	85B
5952*	86C
5953*	82B
5954*	82B
5955*	81F
5956*	85A
5957*	81F
5958*	81A
5959*	84E
5960*	81F
5961*	88A
5962*	88A
5963*	82D
5964*	82C
5965*	84E
5966*	81F
5967*	81A
5968*	85B
5969*	87G
5970*	86G
5971*	89A
5972*	87A
5973*	81D
5974*	82D
5975*	82B
5976*	81D
5977*	81D
5978*	82C
5979*	81D
5980*	85A
5981*	83A
5982*	81D
5983*	84E
5984*	88A
5985*	84B
5986*	81D
5987*	81E
5988*	84C
5989*	87A
5990*	84C
5991*	89A
5992*	83B
5993*	81D
5994*	83C
5995*	84B
5996*	84B
5997*	82C
5998*	86C
5999*	82D

6000 'King' Class 4-6-0 8P

6000*	81A
6001*	84A
6002*	81A
6003*	88A
6004*	88A
6005*	84A
6006*	84A
6007*	84A
6008*	84A
6009*	81A
6010*	88A
6011*	84A
6012*	81A
6013*	84A
6014*	84A
6015*	81A

'4073' 'Castle' class 4-6-0 No 5073 *Blenheim* at Shrewsbury shed in March 1962, seen here fitted with a double chimney. First allocated to Plymouth Laira in July 1938, at nationalisation it was allocated to Shrewsbury and stayed there until April 1958. It then transferred to Bristol Bath Road, later moved to Cardiff Canton in September 1961 and then went across the city to East Dock shed when Canton closed to steam in September 1962. Here it remained until withdrawn in February 1964, making its last journey to Hayes yard at Bridgend in May 1964 for scrap. *G. W. Sharpe*

'5101' class 2-6-2T No 5180 seen at Saundersfoot in July 1959 when allocated to Neyland. Entering traffic in February 1931, this engine spent many years allocated to Stourbridge Junction before moving to Neyland in June 1958 and then to Carmarthen in December 1959. Westbury became No 5180's home in January 1962 from where it was withdrawn later in the year. Swindon Works carried out the scrapping after five months in storage. *G. W. Sharpe*

'5205' class 2-8-0T No 5231 at its home shed Newport Pill in June 1960. Note the Stanier 2-6-2Ts in storage after closure of their home shed Tredegar on 11 June. No 5231 dated from June 1924 and was a powerful Churchward design, ideally suited to heavy freight workings in the steeply graded South Wales valley lines. No 5231 moved from Newport to Aberbeeg in May 1962 and finally to Cardiff East Dock in October 1963, from where it was withdrawn in April 1964 and cut up at Cashmore's, Newport. *R. H. G. Simpson*

'5400' class 0-6-0PT No 5420 at Gloucester Barnwood shed in September 1963. A Collett design for passenger work, No 5420 entered traffic in December 1935, going new to Southall, and spent most of its time there, moving to Banbury in January 1958 and Gloucester Horton Road in November 1961. No 5420 moved 'over the road' to Gloucester Barnwood in July 1963 from where it was withdrawn two months later, after a brief spell at Yeovil in August. Stored at Barnwood until March 1964, No 5420 then went to Coopers Metals at Sharpness for scrapping. *P. H. Groom*

'4575' class 2-6-2T No 5563 at Yeovil Town shed in March 1963. This was a modified version of the '4500' type, with increased water capacity and other improvements. No 5563 was built in December 1928 and at nationalisation was based at Swindon then moved to Yeovil Pen Mill shed, the ex-GWR establishment, in October 1952. Here it remained until 5 January 1959 when Pen Mill closed, and transferred to Yeovil Town shed, the ex-Exeter & Yeovil Railway depot. Here it remained until withdrawn in September 1964, going to Bird's yard at Llanelly for scrapping. *G. W. Sharpe*

'5600' class 0-6-2T No 5634, in lined green livery and with its front numberplate missing, is inside Llanelly shed in September 1961. No 5634 had only a short stay at Llanelly, coming from Barry just before this photograph was taken, and returning to Barry two months later. Neyland shed became its home in September 1962, from where it was withdrawn in July 1964 and placed in store until November when it was sold to Bird's at Morriston for scrap. *G. W. Sharpe*

'4900' 'Hall' class 4-6-0 No 5992 *Horton Hall* is on a westbound local at Exeter St Davids station in June 1961. New in December 1939, No 5992's first allocation was Banbury, and it was still there at nationalisation. A move to Bristol St Philips Marsh was made in August 1949 and then to Taunton in November 1953, Exeter in July 1954, and back to Taunton three months later. Here it remained until October 1964, when it returned to Exeter, then to Gloucester Horton Road in January 1965 and finally to Newport Ebbw Junction in July 1965, from where it was withdrawn two months later. Scrapping was carried out at Bird's, Morriston, in October 1965. *G. W. Sharpe*

'6000' 'King' class 4-6-0 No 6000 *King George V* at London Old Oak Common shed in October 1962. All the 'Kings' were withdrawn during 1962, removing a familiar sight from the ex-GWR main lines. No 6000 was added to stock on 29 June 1927, costing £6,383 to build, and went new to Old Oak Common. The bell was added to the locomotive when it was in America in September–October 1927 when taking part in the Baltimore & Ohio Railroad's centenary celebrations. After withdrawal, No 6000 was saved for preservation and is on display at STEAM—Museum of the GWR, Swindon. *P. H. Groom*

'6000' 'King' class 4-6-0 No 6002 *King William IV* at Wolverhampton Stafford Road shed on Thursday 20 April 1961 when allocated to Old Oak Common. It became part of Stafford Road's allocation on 15 June 1962 and lasted in service a further three months. After withdrawal it was stored at Stafford Road until January 1963, when it was sent to the nearby Cox & Danks yard at Langley Green, Oldbury, for scrapping. *K. Wheal*

6016*	81A
6017*	84A
6018*	81A
6019*	88A
6020*	84A
6021*	81A
6022*	84A
6023*	88A
6024*	88A
6025*	81A
6026*	81A
6027*	81A
6028*	88A
6029*	81A

6100 Class 2-6-2T 4MT

6101	84E
6103	81D
6106	81F
6107	81D
6108	88B
6109	81E
6110	81C
6111	81F
6112	81C
6113	83B
6114	87H
6115	86G
6116	84E
6117	81B
6118	86E
6119	81D
6120	81E
6122	81D
6123	81F
6124	81E
6125	87H
6126	85B
6127	81B
6128	84G
6129	81F
6130	81E
6131	81D
6132	81C
6133	81C
6134	81D
6135	81A
6136	81E
6137	85B
6138	81F
6139	81E
6140	86E
6141	81A
6142	81A
6143	81B
6144	84G
6145	81A
6146	83C
6147	82B
6148	83B
6149	81F
6150	81F
6151	81B
6152	81B
6153	81D
6154	81F
6155	83B
6156	81F
6157	83B
6158	86E
6159	81E
6160	84E
6161	81D
6162	81C
6163	81A
6164	81A
6165	81C
6166	83A
6167	81B
6168	81A
6169	81A

4300 Class 2-6-0 4MT

6301	83D
6302	81E
6304	85B
6309	82C
6310	87F
6312	82B
6314	84G
6316	87G
6317	84C
6319	82B
6320	86E
6324	81D
6326	88A
6327	82C
6330	85B
6335	86G
6336	89C
6337	83B
6338	86E
6339	89B
6340	83B
6342	89A
6344	71G
6345	88A
6346	82E
6347	87G
6348	86C
6349	88A
6350	81E
6353	89C
6356	82B
6357	89B
6361	88J
6362	86E
6363	81E
6364	82B
6365	85B
6366	86A
6367	84C
6368	85A
6369	86E
6370	86G
6372	83B
6373	86E
6374	89A
6375	85A
6376	82E
6378	89C
6379	81D
6380	89A
6381	85B
6384	86E
6385	81D
6386	86E
6387	85A
6388	84G
6390	83B
6391	81D
6394	85B
6395	89C

6400 Class 0-6-0PT 2P

6400	83D
6403	84C
6408	88H
6410	81B
6412	86A
6416	88D
6418	84A
6419	88H
6421	84H
6422	84A
6424	86E
6429	84H
6430	88B
6431	88J
6433	88D
6434	86A
6435	88E
6436	88D
6437	85B
6438	88B

5600 Class 0-6-2T 5MT

6600	88G
6601	82B
6602	87D
6603	88B
6604	84E
6605	88J
6606	88B
6607	88B
6608	88B
6609	84E
6610	87H
6611	89B
6612	88B
6613	87D
6614	88B
6615	89B
6616	87H
6617	89B
6618	84D
6619	88F
6620	87B
6621	86F
6622	88J
6623	87H
6624	88B
6625	82D
6626	88B
6627	87H
6628	88J
6629	88D
6630	82B
6631	84E
6632	89B
6633	88B
6634	86G
6635	88B
6636	86G
6637	88B
6638	88B
6639	88G
6640	84B
6641	87A
6642	86E
6643	88C
6644	84F
6645	84B
6646	84F
6647	88B
6648	88B
6649	87A
6650	87D
6651	88J
6652	88J
6653	87F
6654	82B
6655	88C
6656	86A
6657	88B
6658	88C
6659	88B
6660	88B
6661	88J
6662	87D
6663	84F
6664	88J
6665	88B
6666	86E
6667	84F
6668	84E
6669	85B
6670	85A
6671	85A
6672	86E
6673	88H
6674	89B
6675	86G
6676	86G
6677	84F
6678	84F
6679	84G
6680	87B
6681	82B
6682	88B
6683	84F
6684	88B
6685	86G
6686	87B
6687	88J
6688	88B
6689	88B
6690	86G
6691	87B
6692	84F
6693	86G
6694	89B
6695	87A
6696	88C
6697	88C
6698	89B
6699	88B

6700 Class 0-6-0PT 3F

6714	87D
6724	86B
6738	87D
6739	86B
6741	87D
6742	86B
6749	87D
6754	86A
6755	87D
6757	87D
6758	86B
6760	86B
6762	87D
6763	86B
6764	87D
6765	87D
6767	87D
6768	87D
6769	82C
6770	87D
6772	86B
6777	87D
6778	87D

6800 'Grange' Class 4-6-0 5MT

6800*	83G
6803*	84E
6804*	83D
6806*	85A
6807*	85A
6808*	83G
6809*	82B
6810*	86G
6811*	82B
6812*	83G
6813*	86A
6814*	83G
6815*	83D
6816*	82B
6817*	85A
6818*	87F
6819*	86G
6820*	86A
6821*	86G
6822*	88A
6823*	84B
6824*	83G
6825*	83G
6826*	83G
6827*	82B
6828*	84B
6829*	86A
6830*	82B
6831*	82B
6832*	87A

Left: '6100' class 2-6-2T No 6122 at Southall shed in November 1962 after transfer from Reading, still awaiting the fitting of a shed plate. Behind is 'Modified Hall' 4-6-0 No 6982 *Melmerby Hall*, a visitor from Bristol St Philips Marsh. Added to stock in October 1931, No 6122 was withdrawn in September 1964 after transfer to Swindon shed the previous month. After three months in store it was sent to Cashmore's at Newport for scrap. *R. H. G. Simpson*

'4300' class 2-6-0 No 6310 runs into Shrewsbury on a mixed freight working in March 1961. Built at Swindon in January 1921 to a Churchward design dating from 1911, No 6310 was withdrawn in 1962 and sold to Cashmore's at Newport for scrap. *G. W. Sharpe*

'6400' class 0-6-0PT No 6437 is at Gloucester Horton Road shed in May 1962. This was another Collett design for light passenger work. No 6437 was added to stock in April 1937 and first allocated to Aberdare. It was still at this South Wales shed at nationalisation and moved to Gloucester in May 1960, where it remained until withdrawn in July 1963. Storage at Barnwood followed, with scrapping at Swindon Works then being carried out. *G. W. Sharpe*

'5600' class 0-6-2T No 6692 runs through Birmingham Snow Hill station on a northbound freight on Saturday 12 August 1961. No 6692 was built in 1928 and came to the West Midlands area from Aberdare, being based at Stourbridge Junction in December 1953. It remained at Stourbridge until withdrawn in September 1965 and after storage went to Cohen's at Kettering for scrap in February 1966. *L. Hanson*

'6700' class 0-6-0PT No 6724 is at its home shed Newport Pill in June 1960, with '5205' class 2-8-0Ts Nos 5235 and 5231 behind. The '6700s' were virtually the same design as the '57xxs' but were fitted only with steam brakes and no ATC equipment. No 6724 was built in October 1930 and spent many years allocated to Barry shed, moving to Newport Pill in September 1957 and to Swansea East Dock in October 1962, from where it was withdrawn in November 1963. Scrapping was actioned at Swindon Works. *R. H. G. Simpson*

'6800' Grange class 4-6-0 No 6864 *Dymock Grange* is seen at Old Oak Common shed in April 1962. Placed in traffic in January 1939, Old Oak Common was the first allocation. At nationalisation it was based at Reading and then ensued a number of moves until May 1965, when the final transfer from Wolverhampton Oxley to Birmingham Tyseley was authorised. No 6864 was withdrawn during the week ended 9 October the same year. *P. H. Groom*

'4900' 'Hall' class 4-6-0 No 6913 *Levens Hall* at Crewe South shed on Saturday 23 June 1962. Dating from 1941, No 6913 spent its British Railways days at Plymouth Laira before moving to Reading in September 1960 and finally to Gloucester Horton Road in March 1963. Withdrawal came during the week ended 29 June 1964 and, after storage at Gloucester until the following November, No 6913 was scrapped at Bird's yard at Morriston. *G. W. Sharpe*

6833*	88A
6834*	82B
6835*	82B
6836*	86G
6837*	87F
6838*	86G
6839*	84B
6840*	86G
6841*	82B
6842*	82B
6843*	87F
6844*	87A
6845*	84B
6846*	82B
6847*	88A
6848*	86G
6849*	82B
6850*	86A
6851*	84B
6852*	82B
6853*	84E
6854*	84B
6855*	84E
6856*	85A
6857*	84B
6858*	84E
6859*	88A
6860*	83D
6861*	84E
6862*	84B
6863*	83D
6864*	88A
6865*	82B
6866*	84E
6867*	86G
6868*	83G
6869*	83G
6870*	84B
6871*	84B
6872*	86G
6873*	83D
6874*	82B
6875*	83G
6876*	86G
6877*	85A
6878*	82B
6879*	84E

4900 'Hall' Class 4-6-0 5MT

6900*	82B
6901*	86G
6903*	86G
6904*	84C
6905*	87A
6906*	84C
6907*	84B
6908*	82B
6909*	88A
6910*	81E
6911*	84C
6912*	88A
6913*	81D
6914*	83B
6915*	89A
6916*	89A
6917*	84B
6918*	88A
6919*	82B
6920*	81A
6921*	83D
6922*	89A
6923*	81D
6924*	81D
6925*	84B
6926*	84E
6927*	81F
6928*	86G
6929*	84C
6930*	84E
6931*	84A
6932*	88A
6933*	84B
6934*	89A
6935*	88A
6936*	88A
6937*	81E
6938*	83D
6939*	88A
6940*	83A
6941*	83D
6942*	81A
6943*	88A
6944*	88A
6945*	84A
6946*	86G
6947*	85A
6948*	85A
6950*	88A
6951*	85A
6952*	84C
6953*	81D
6954*	82B
6955*	82D
6956*	85B
6957*	88A
6958*	86G

6959 'Modified Hall' Class 4-6-0 5MT

6959*	81A
6960*	81D
6961*	81A
6962*	81A
6963*	81A
6964*	89A
6965*	83C
6966*	81A
6967*	81C
6968*	82D
6969*	81E
6970*	81F
6971*	84E
6972*	82B
6973*	81A
6974*	81C
6975*	84B
6976*	84C
6977*	82B
6978*	81A
6979*	84C
6980*	84B
6981*	82B
6982*	82B
6983*	81E
6984*	85A
6985*	85B
6986*	82C
6987*	84A
6988*	82A
6989*	85A
6990*	81A
6991*	81C
6992*	85A
6993*	85B
6994*	83C
6995*	88A
6996*	81E
6997*	82B
6998*	81A
6999*	83B

4073 'Castle' Class 4-6-0 7P

7000*	85B
7001*	84A
7002*	85A
7003*	85B
7004*	85A
7005*	85A
7006*	85A
7007*	85A
7008*	81A
7009*	81A
7010*	81A
7011*	85A
7012*	84A
7013*	85A
7014*	81A
7015*	89A

7016* 88A
7017* 81A
7018* 81A
7019* 84A
7020* 81A
7021* 81A
7022* 83D
7023* 85A
7024* 84A
7025* 89A
7026* 84A
7027* 85A
7028* 87F
7029* 83A
7030* 81A
7031* 82C
7032* 81A
7033* 81A
7034* 85B
7035* 85B
7036* 81A
7037* 82C

7200 Class 2-8-2T 8F

7200 87F
7201 86G
7202 88B
7203 88J
7204 87A
7205 88B
7206 86E
7207 84C
7208 88J
7209 81F
7210 86G
7211 87F
7212 86E
7213 84B
7214 86A
7215 87D
7216 88J
7217 86E
7218 84B
7219 86A
7220 86G
7221 88J
7222 86A
7223 86A
7224 86A
7225 87D
7226 87D
7227 86G
7228 86E
7229 86A
7230 89B
7231 86A
7232 87F
7233 86A
7234 86A
7235 87F
7236 84C
7237 86A
7238 85A
7239 81F
7240 86A
7241 88C
7242 88B
7243 87B
7244 87A
7245 86A
7246 86G
7247 87A
7248 87D
7249 87B
7250 86A
7251 86G
7252 88B
7253 86A

4300 Class 2-6-0 4MT

7300 89A
7301 82B
7302 86G
7303 71G
7304 83B
7305 83B
7306 87G
7307 87F
7308 86E
7309 89A
7310 89B
7311 83C
7312 87G
7313 89B
7314 89A
7315 85A
7316 83C
7317 82B
7318 87H
7319 87F
7320 87G
7321 87G
7323 82B
7324 81E
7325 86A
7326 83B
7327 81E
7328 86E
7329 89A
7330 89A
7331 81D
7332 88A
7333 83B
7334 87G
7335 85B
7336 89A
7337 82C
7338 85A
7339 89B
7340 87H
7341 89B

7400 Class 0-6-0PT 2F

7402 87G
7403 86E
7404 81F
7405 89D
7406 89C
7407 87G
7408 87G
7412 81F
7413 86C
7414 89B
7418 86C
7422 87G
7423 88J
7424 84E
7425 87G
7426 84E
7427 86E
7428 89C
7430 84F
7431 89B
7432 84F
7434 89D
7435 84F
7436 83B
7437 86C
7439 87G
7440 89B
7441 84F
7442 89C
7443 89B
7444 87G
7445 81F
7446 83E
7448 87G
7449 84F

5700 Class 0-6-0PT 3F

7713 83B
7715 83E
7718 87F
7720 88J
7721 86B
7724 86G
7729 82B
7732 88H
7736 86A
7739 87A
7744 88E
7749 82B
7753 88H
7755 86F
7762 84F
7764 86E
7765 87F
7780 71G
7782 71G
7783 82B
7784 82D
7785 87F
7786 87A
7788 81D
7790 82B
7796 86G
7799 87A

7800 'Manor' Class 4-6-0 5MT

7800* 89D
7801* 89D
7802* 89C
7803* 89C
7804* 87G
7805* 88A
7806* 84F
7807* 89D
7808* 84E
7809* 89D
7810* 89D
7811* 89B
7812* 89B
7813* 84E
7814* 89C
7815* 89C
7816* 84F
7817* 84F
7818* 89C
7819* 89D
7820* 88A
7821* 89B
7822* 89D
7823* 89C
7824* 84F
7825* 87H
7826* 87G
7827* 89D
7828* 89B
7829* 87G

6959 'Modified Hall' Class 4-6-0 5MT

7900* 81F
7901* 82B
7902* 81A
7903* 81A
7904* 81A
7905* 84C
7906* 81D
7907* 87J
7908* 84E
7909* 83A
7910* 81C
7911* 81F
7912* 84E
7913* 88A
7914* 81D
7915* 84B
7916* 83D
7917* 82D
7918* 84E
7919* 81D
7920* 85A
7921* 81A
7922* 89A
7923* 81C
7924* 83B
7925* 88A
7926* 85B
7927* 88A
7928* 85A
7929* 84C

8100 Class 2-6-2T 4MT

8100 84D
8102 87A
8103 87G
8104 87A
8106 85A
8107 85A
8109 84E

9400 Class 0-6-0PT 4F

8400 85D
8401 85D
8402 85D
8403 85D
8405 85D
8407 87B
8409 85D
8414 87D
8415 85A
8416 87B
8418 87A
8420 88B
8422 81C
8425 88A
8426 84A
8428 84B
8430 81D
8431 87D
8433 82C
8435 81A
8436 86F
8437 88H
8438 88B
8439 87A
8440 86F
8444 86F
8445 88J
8446 88C
8449 89A
8452 84A
8453 88H
8456 81C
8458 81A
8459 81A
8461 86G
8464 84B
8465 82C
8466 88A
8467 87F
8469 88B
8470 88B
8471 88B
8472 82C
8474 87F
8475 87D
8477 87F
8478 88B
8479 82B
8480 85A
8481 88C
8482 87B
8483 87D
8484 88A
8486 83F
8487 85D
8488 87D
8489 85B
8490 87B
8491 85B
8493 86G
8494 81E

8495 86G
8496 81D
8497 88A
8498 84A
8499 86F

5700 Class 0-6-0PT 3F

8700 84E
8701 85B
8702 83E
8707 86G
8709 86G
8710 88H
8711 82C
8712 88H
8713 84E
8714 82B
8715 87A
8716 86G
8717 85B
8718 84G
8719 83E
8720 81E
8723 88A
8724 87B
8725 82E
8727 89B
8728 88A
8729 85B
8730 88E
8731 81C
8732 87A
8733 83E
8734 89B
8735 88E
8736 87F
8737 83E
8738 87H
8739 87H
8741 82B
8742 84F
8743 85B
8744 82D
8745 72C
8746 82B
8747 82B
8748 88H
8749 87F
8750 87D
8751 86A
8752 81C
8753 81A
8756 81A
8757 81A
8759 81A
8760 86A
8761 81A
8763 81A
8764 88C
8765 81A
8766 86A
8767 81A
8768 81A
8770 81C
8771 81A
8773 81A
8776 88A
8779 82C
8780 88B
8781 86C
8783 82C
8784 87A
8785 87F
8786 86F
8788 87A
8790 82B
8791 86B
8792 84F
8793 82C
8794 87D
8795 82B
8797 84F
8799 71G

9400 Class 0-6-0PT 4F

9401 85A
9404 81D
9405 81A
9406 81B
9407 81A
9408 87F
9409 81C
9410 81A
9411 81A
9412 87A
9413 81C
9415 81B
9416 87D
9418 81A
9419 81A
9420 81A
9421 81B
9422 81B
9423 81A
9424 86A
9425 88C
9426 88A
9429 85A
9430 85D
9431 87D
9433 83G
9435 84A
9437 88A
9440 83A
9441 87D
9442 87B
9444 86F
9446 87A
9448 87A
9450 81E
9451 88H
9452 87A
9453 85B
9454 87B
9455 81F
9456 87B
9457 87B
9460 86F
9461 88A
9463 89A
9464 87B
9465 87F
9466 82B
9467 83D
9469 81A
9470 84A
9471 85B
9472 89A
9473 87A
9475 83G
9476 82C
9477 81A
9478 87A
9479 81A
9480 83C
9482 86A
9483 87B
9484 87D
9485 87F
9486 85A
9487 83C
9488 86A
9489 87D
9490 85A
9493 85D
9494 86F
9495 81C
9497 83C
9498 89A

5700 Class 0-6-0PT 3F

9600 82B
9601 82B
9602 87J
9603 88A
9604 82C
9605 82C
9606 87G
9607 88J
9608 83B
9609 88H
9610 89B
9611 86G
9612 82D
9613 84F
9614 84F
9615 82B
9616 86A
9617 87B
9618 88D
9619 86E
9620 71G
9621 87F
9622 88E
9623 82B
9624 84F
9625 87D
9626 82B
9627 87A
9628 82D
9629 89D
9630 84H
9631 88D
9632 87G
9633 83A
9634 87B
9635 84E
9636 84H
9637 87F
9638 88D
9639 84H
9640 81A
9641 81C
9642 81C
9643 88D
9644 86A
9645 87J
9646 83B
9647 83B
9648 88A
9649 88H
9650 86G
9651 82B
9652 87F
9653 81F
9654 81F
9655 83E
9656 89A
9657 89A
9658 81A
9659 81A
9660 88H
9661 81A
9662 86A
9663 83B
9664 86A
9665 86C
9666 87J
9667 86A
9668 82D
9669 89B
9670 83B
9671 87B
9672 82C
9674 86A
9675 88D
9676 88D
9677 87J
9678 83A
9679 88D
9680 83E
9681 88A
9682 86F
9700 81A
9702 81A
9704 81A
9706 81A
9707 81A
9709 81A
9710 81A
9711 88H
9712 88J
9713 88A
9715 87B
9716 83E
9717 86C
9718 83B
9719 84F
9721 82C
9722 81B
9723 88A
9724 84E
9725 81A
9726 81C
9727 88A
9728 88E
9729 82B
9730 86G
9731 88J
9732 72C
9733 84F
9734 87A
9738 88H
9740 82C
9741 84H
9742 87B
9743 87F
9744 87F
9746 86A
9747 88D
9748 83G
9750 87A
9752 84B
9753 84E
9754 82C
9755 83E
9756 71G
9757 83B
9758 81A
9759 88A
9760 87J
9761 87D
9763 81D
9764 72C
9766 87B
9768 84B
9769 82D
9770 70A
9773 82C
9774 84H
9775 88A
9776 88D
9777 87A
9778 88A
9779 87A
9780 88C
9782 84F
9783 87A
9784 81A
9785 87B
9786 87A
9787 87G
9788 87F
9789 81C
9790 82C
9791 81C
9792 87A
9793 89B
9794 88A
9796 86G
9797 86G
9798 84E
9799 87B

'6959' 'Modified Hall' class 4-6-0 No 6961 *Stedham Hall* at its home shed Old Oak Common in August 1961. New in March 1944, No 6961 was first allocated to Westbury shed. By January 1948 it was at Old Oak Common, moving to Southall in February 1949, then back to Old Oak Common in April 1952, where it remained until October 1963 when another transfer to Southall took place. A year later it was back at 81A and then went to Didcot in January 1965 and finally Oxford six months later, from where withdrawal took place in September 1965. Cashmore's at Newport carried out the scrapping. *P. H. Groom*

'4073' 'Castle' class 4-6-0 No 7035 *Ogmore Castle* awaits departure from London Paddington on an express to Gloucester in August 1962. Entering traffic in August 1950, it was first allocated to Shrewsbury. In September 1953 No 7035 moved to Gloucester Horton Road and to Bristol Bath Road in November 1956, Swansea Landore in February 1959, back to Gloucester Horton Road in March 1960, Oxford in November 1962, and finally to Old Oak Common in February 1963. Withdrawal came during the first week of June 1964 — it had a short working life of just under 14 years — and cutting up was carried out at Swindon Works. *G. W. Sharpe*

'7200' class 2-8-2T No 7206 is at its home shed Severn Tunnel Junction on Sunday 24 September 1961, keeping company with '4200' class 2-8-0T No 4293 from Newport Ebbw Junction (which was withdrawn in 1962). No 7206 was first allocated to Neath in October 1934 and spent its days working from sheds in South Wales, ending at Newport Ebbw Junction, from where withdrawal took place during the first week of July 1964. Hayes at its Bridgend yard scrapped No 7206. *Author's collection*

'4300' class 2-6-0 No 7330, nearing the end of its days in a dirty state and with its top feed cover missing, runs into Shrewsbury station on a local freight on Saturday 16 June 1962. It was withdrawn later in the year. Introduced in March 1932, it first carried the number 9308 and was renumbered in June 1957. When new it was allocated to Old Oak Common. After withdrawal, No 7330 went to Swindon Works for cutting up. *G. W. Sharpe*

'7400' class 0-6-0PT No 7449 is seen with a local livery variation at Stourbridge not long before withdrawal in 1963. It was a Collett design for shunting duties and not fitted for push-pull working, unlike the similar '6400' class. No 7449 was the last to be built and was placed in service on 18 April 1950 at Stourbridge Junction shed, where it remained allocated for the whole of its working life. Withdrawal came at the end of May 1963 and scrapping was at Cashmore's at Newport. *R. H. G. Simpson*

'7800' 'Manor' class 4-6-0 No 7819 *Hinton Manor* is at its home shed Oswestry in April 1962. This was the last 'Manor' to be built by the GWR, entering traffic in February 1939 at Carmarthen. The next one, No 7820, was built by British Railways, coming into stock in November 1950. No 7819 had been on Oswestry's allocation since October 1946 and moved to Shrewsbury at the end of 1962. Then, in March 1963, Machynlleth took over the maintenance, No 7819 being based at Aberystwyth sub-shed. Finally, in January 1965, transfer to Shrewsbury was actioned, with withdrawal coming on 6 November 1965. Sold as scrap to Woodham's at Barry, No 7819 was saved for preservation, arriving at the Severn Valley Railway in January 1973. *G. W. Sharpe*

'6959' 'Modified Hall' class 4-6-0 No 7905 *Fowey Hall* is on shed at Wolverhampton Stafford Road in September 1962. This engine was built at Swindon Works under British Railways and went new to Plymouth Laira in April 1949, where it stayed until transferred to Banbury in November 1959. Here it remained until withdrawn during the week ended 23 May 1964. It was scrapped at Cashmore's, Great Bridge. *P. H. Groom*

'8100' class 2-6-2T No 8106 at home at Worcester shed in August 1961. This was a Collett rebuild from Churchward 2-6-2T No 5126 and entered traffic in June 1939. It was withdrawn from Worcester shed at the end of November 1963 after spending most of its working life at 85A. Swindon Works reduced No 8106 to scrap metal in March 1964. *G. W. Sharpe*

'57xx' class 0-6-0PT No 8720, along with 'Hall' 4-6-0 No 4959 *Purley Hall*, at their home shed Didcot on Thursday 25 July 1963. No 8720 dated from March 1931 and during its British Railways days operated from Swansea Danygraig, moving to Swansea Victoria in January 1952, and back to Danygraig a month later, where it stayed until transfer to Didcot in December 1959. Here it remained until withdrawn in September 1964 and it returned to South Wales for cutting up at Bird's yard at Risca. *K. C. H. Fairey*

'9400' class 0-6-0PT No 9479 is photographed at Old Oak Common shed in July 1962. New in July 1952, built by R. Stephenson & Hawthorn Ltd, No 9479's first allocation was Llanelly. In March 1957 a transfer to Southall took place and in November 1958 it moved to Old Oak Common, from where No 9479 was withdrawn in July 1963 and later scrapped at Swindon Works. *R. H. G. Simpson*

'57xx' class 0-6-0PT No 9636 is at Wellington (Salop) station on a local trip working on Saturday 10 February 1962. No 9636 was added to stock in January 1946 and allocated to Stourbridge Junction. It remained there until September 1960, when transfer to Wellington took place. Here it stayed until withdrawn in October 1963 and it was then sent to Swindon Works for scrapping. *G. W. Sharpe*

'57xx' class 0-6-0PT No 9702, fitted with condensing apparatus for working on London's Metropolitan Widened Lines, is at Old Oak Common in July 1961. New in September 1933, it spent its whole time allocated to Old Oak Common, withdrawal coming in 1962. Scrapping was carried out at Cashmore's Newport yard. *P. H. Groom*

An interesting line-up of locomotives at Eastleigh shed on Sunday 11 November 1962 shows 'M7' class 0-4-4T No 30032, '0298' class 2-4-0WT No 30587 and 'W' class 2-6-4T No 31916. No 30032 dated from March 1898 and was withdrawn from Eastleigh shed on 7 July 1963, whilst No 30587 was a 1962 withdrawal and survives in preservation at the Bodmin & Wenford Railway. No 31916 was also withdrawn in July 1963 from Exmouth Junction shed. *G. W. Sharpe*

M7 Class 0-4-4T 2P

30021	72B
30024	72A
30025	72A
30028	71A
30029	71A
30031	71B
30032	70B
30033	72B
30034	83H
30035	70B
30036	83H
30039	70A
30045	72A
30048	72A
30049	70C
30050	71B
30051	70A
30052	70A
30053	75E
30055	75E
30056	71B
30057	71B

USA Class 0-6-0T 3F

30061	71I
30062	71I
30063	71I
30064	71I
30065	71I
30066	71I
30067	71I
30068	71I
30069	71I
30070	71I
30071	71I
30072	71I
30073	71I
30074	71I

B4 Class 0-4-0T 1F

30089	70C
30096	71A
30102	71A

M7 Class 0-4-4T 2P

30105	71B
30107	71B
30108	71B
30110	71B
30111	71B
30112	71B

T9 Class 4-4-0 3P

30120	71A

M7 Class 0-4-4T 2P

30125	72A
30127	71B
30129	72C
30131	72C
30132	70C
30133	71A

O2 Class 0-4-4T 0P

30193	83H
30199	71A
30200	71A
30225	83H

M7 Class 0-4-4T 2P

30241	70A
30245	70A
30249	70A
30251	72E
30254	72E

700 Class 0-6-0 3F

30306	71A
30309	72B
30315	72B
30316	71A

M7 Class 0-4-4T 2P

30320	70A
30321	70A

700 Class 0-6-0 3F

30325	75A
30326	75A

M7 Class 0-4-4T 2P

30328	71B

700 Class 0-6-0 3F

30339	70C
30346	70C
30350	70C
30368	70D

M7 Class 0-4-4T 2P

30375	71A
30377	71A
30378	70C
30379	71B

N15 'King Arthur' Class 4-6-0 5P

30451*	72B

M7 Class 0-4-4T 2P

30480	71A

G16 Class 4-8-0T 8F

30494	70B
30495	70B

S15 Class 4-6-0 6F

30496	70B
30497	70B
30498	70B
30499	70B
30500	70B
30501	70B
30502	70B
30503	70B
30504	70B
30505	70B
30506	70B
30507	70B
30508	70B
30509	70B
30510	70B
30511	70B
30512	70B
30513	70B
30514	70B
30515	70B

H16 Class 4-6-2T 6F

30516	70B
30517	70B
30518	70B
30519	70B
30520	70B

Q Class 0-6-0 4F

30530	71A
30531	71A
30532	71A
30533	75A
30534	75A
30535	75A
30536	71A
30537	75A
30538	75A
30539	71B
30540	75E
30541	71B
30542	71A

'M7' class 0-4-4T No 30036, dating from May 1898, is not likely to go far without its wheels at Plymouth Friary shed in July 1961. It was reallocated to Bournemouth in January 1963, withdrawn on 12 January 1964, then stored for a time at Eastleigh Works before being sold to Ward's at Briton Ferry for scrapping. *G. W. Sharpe*

The 'USA' 0-6-0Ts were acquired by the Southern Railway from the War Department in December 1946 and were initially all based at Southampton Docks, still being there in 1962. One of the class that acquired lined out livery, No 30073, is seen here outside Southampton Docks engine shed in June 1961. Transferred to Eastleigh in June 1963, it was withdrawn on 8 January 1967 and, after storage at Eastleigh and Salisbury, was cut up at Cashmore's, Newport. *G. W. Sharpe*

Guildford shed pilot, 'B4' class 0-4-0T No 30089, is the centre of attention in this scene captured on film on Friday 21 April 1961. Built in November 1892, and originally named *Trouville*, for working in Southampton Docks, No 30089 came to Guildford from Eastleigh in February 1959 and spent the remaining service days acting as shed pilot. Withdrawal came on 10 March 1963, ousted by a 'USA' 0-6-0T, No 30072. Not a candidate for preservation, No 30089 was broken up at Eastleigh Works. *K. Wheal*

'O2' class 0-4-4T No 30199 is at home at Eastleigh shed in June 1962 in the company of Ivatt 2-6-2T No 41320. New in June 1891, No 30199 spent a number of years at Exmouth Junction before transferring to Eastleigh in November 1961, where it remained until withdrawn at the end of 1962. Stored for a further year, it was then scrapped at Eastleigh Works. *R. H. G. Simpson*

In store at Basingstoke shed on Saturday 29 September 1962 is '700' class 0-6-0 No 30368. All the remaining '700s' were withdrawn during 1962, No 30368 being one of the last to go. Dating from June 1897, No 30368 spent all its British Railways days allocated to Basingstoke. Cutting up was carried out at Eastleigh Works. *G. W. Sharpe*

The last of the original batch of 'N15' 'King Arthur' class 4-6-0s, No 30451 *Sir Lamorak* is at Basingstoke in 1960. All the 'N15s' were gone by the end of 1962, with No 30451 staying in traffic until June. It had entered traffic in June 1925 and spent its British Railways days allocated either to Basingstoke or Salisbury. The end came under the cutters' torch at Eastleigh Works within a month of withdrawal. *G. W. Sharpe*

Another 'last of class' photograph — this time 'G16' 4-8-0T No 30495. This is a March 1961 view recorded in Willesden yards with the engine and crew awaiting return to the Southern Region on a transfer freight. Designed by Urie and intended for use as 'hump' shunters in Feltham yard, only four were built, No 30495 entering traffic in August 1921. The remaining two were withdrawn in 1962. *G. W. Sharpe*

'S15' class 4-6-0 No 30514 at Salisbury shed in the summer of 1962. This was another Urie design for work on mixed traffic duties, and was used on the many heavy freight workings from and to the London Division. No 30514 was added to stock in March 1921 and spent its entire British Railways career based at Feltham shed. Withdrawal came on 7 July 1963 and after storage at Feltham No 30514 was dispatched to Cohen's at Kettering for scrapping in March 1964. *Pictorail*

All the 'H16' class 4-6-2Ts were withdrawn during 1962. This example, No 30520, at its home shed Feltham, had only seven weeks left on the active list when this photograph was taken on 27 September 1962. Only five were built, No 30520 coming into service in February 1922, and all spent their British Railways days at Feltham, none making it into preservation. *G. W. Sharpe*

'Q' class 0-6-0 No 30532 stands alongside the manual coaling stage at Eastleigh in April 1962. Twenty were built to a Maunsell design, No 30532 entering traffic in June 1938 and based at Eastleigh when new. It served from 71A for many years, moving to Salisbury in December 1962, from where it was withdrawn on 5 January 1964 and sent to Ward's yard at Killamarsh for scrap. *R. H. G. Simpson*

Another 'Q' class 0-6-0, No 30549, this time fitted with a stovepipe chimney, is shunting at Three Bridges in June 1963. This was the last of the class to be built, in September 1939, and was allocated new to London Nine Elms. No 30549 had been transferred to Three Bridges shed in June 1962 from Brighton shed and was withdrawn on 21 July 1963. Cohen's at Kettering handled the scrapping. *P. H. Groom*

Beattie Well Tank No 30585 is seen at Eastleigh shed on Saturday 29 September 1962. All three remaining examples were withdrawn at the end of 1962, being replaced at their Wadebridge home by ex-GWR '1366' class 0-6-0PTs Nos 1367, 1368 and 1369. No 30585 survived into preservation and can be seen at the Buckinghamshire Railway Centre. *G. W. Sharpe*

30543	71A
30544	75A
30545	75E
30546	75E
30547	75E
30548	71B
30549	75A

0298 Class 2-4-0T 0P

30585	72F
30586	72F
30587	72F

M7 Class 0-4-4T 2P

30667	72A
30670	72E

700 Class 0-6-0 3F

30689	72A
30690	70C
30692	72B
30695	71A
30697	72A
30698	70C
30700	72A

N15 'King Arthur' Class 4-6-0 5P

30765*	70D
30770*	71A
30773*	71A
30781*	71B
30782*	71B
30788*	71A
30793*	70D
30795*	70D
30796*	72B
30798*	72B
30804*	71A

S15 Class 4-6-0 6F

30823	72B
30824	72B
30825	72B
30826	72B
30827	72B
30828	72B
30829	72B
30830	72B
30831	72B
30832	72B
30833	70B
30834	70B
30835	75B
30836	75B
30837	70B
30838	70B
30839	70B
30840	70B
30841	72A
30842	72A
30843	72A
30844	72A
30845	72A
30846	72A
30847	75B

LN 'Lord Nelson' Class 4-6-0 7P

30850*	71A
30852*	71A
30853*	71A
30856*	71A
30857*	71A
30860*	71A
30861*	71A
30862*	71A
30863*	71A
30864*	71A

V 'Schools' Class 4-4-0 5P

30900*	75A
30901*	75A
30902*	70A
30903*	70C
30906*	70C
30909*	70C
30911*	75B
30912*	70A
30913*	70A
30915*	75B
30916*	75B
30917*	75A
30921*	70A
30923*	75A
30924*	75B
30925*	70D
30926*	70D
30927*	70A
30928*	75A
30929*	75A
30930*	75A
30934*	70D
30935*	70A
30936*	70A
30937*	70A

Z Class 0-8-0T 6F

30950	72A
30951	72A
30952	72A
30953	72A
30954	72A
30955	72A
30956	72A
30957	72A

H Class 0-4-4T 1P

31005	75F

C Class 0-6-0 2F

31112	73F
31218	73F

H Class 0-4-4T 1P

31263	73J

C Class 0-6-0 2F

31267	73B
31268	73F
31271	73B

H Class 0-4-4T 1P

31278	75F

C Class 0-6-0 2F

31280	73F
31293	73B

H Class 0-4-4T 1P

31305	73B
31308	73J

C Class 0-6-0 2F

31317	73A

H Class 0-4-4T 1P

31324	73J

N Class 2-6-0 4P5F

31400	75A
31401	75A
31402	75A
31403	75A
31404	72B
31405	71G
31406	71G
31407	71G
31408	72B
31409	72A
31410	73A
31411	73A
31412	73A
31413	71A
31414	70C

C Class 0-6-0 2F

31510	73B

H Class 0-4-4T 1P

31518	73J
31521	75F
31522	75F
31530	75E
31533	75F
31542	73A
31543	75F
31544	75F
31551	75E

C Class 0-6-0 2F

31584	73A
31588	73F
31592	73F

U Class 2-6-0 4P3F

31610	70C
31611	70D
31612	70A
31613	71A
31614	72C
31615	70C
31616	75B
31617	70A
31618	71A
31619	71A
31620	71A
31621	70A
31622	70C
31623	70C
31624	70A
31625	70C
31626	71A
31627	70C
31628	70C
31629	71A
31630	70C
31631	70C
31632	72C
31633	70C
31634	70A
31635	70C
31636	70A
31637	72C
31638	70C
31639	71A

C Class 0-6-0 2F

31686	73F
31689	73B
31690	73F
31717	73B
31719	73B
31721	73F
31722	70C
31723	70C
31724	73F

L1 Class 4-4-0 3P

31786	70A

U Class 2-6-0 4P3F

31790	70C
31791	71A
31792	72C
31793	71A
31794	71A
31795	71A
31796	70A
31797	70C
31798	72C
31799	75B
31800	70C
31801	71A
31802	72C
31803	71A
31804	71A
31805	72C
31806	70D
31807	75B
31808	71A
31809	71A

N Class 2-6-0 4P5F

31810	71A
31811	70C
31812	70C
31813	72B
31814	72B
31815	70C
31816	71A
31817	75B
31818	71A
31819	70C
31820	70C
31821	70C

N1 Class 2-6-0 4P5F

31822	73J

N Class 2-6-0 4P5F

31823	73A
31824	73A
31825	73B
31826	73B
31827	73B
31828	73B
31829	73B
31830	72A
31831	72A
31832	72A
31833	72A
31834	72A
31835	72A
31836	72A
31837	72A
31838	72A
31839	72A
31840	72A
31841	72A
31842	72A
31843	72A
31844	72A
31845	72A
31846	72A
31847	72A
31848	72A
31849	72A
31850	75B
31851	75B
31852	75B
31853	72A
31854	73A
31855	72A
31856	72A
31857	72A
31858	70C
31859	70C
31860	72A
31861	75B
31862	75B
31863	75B
31864	75B
31865	75B
31866	75B
31867	75B
31868	75B
31869	75B
31870	75B
31871	75B
31872	75B
31873	73B
31874	72A
31875	72A

Yeovil Town shed in October 1962 sees 'M7' class 0-4-4T No 30667 and 'U' class No 31619 on view. No 30667 was a visitor from Exmouth Junction shed and moved to Bournemouth in April 1963, from where it was withdrawn on 17 May 1964. No 31619 was another visitor, being based at the time at Eastleigh. It moved to Norwood Junction in November 1962 and Guildford in December 1963, from where withdrawal took place on 19 December 1965. The shed at Yeovil Town, with its distinctive side brickwork, dated from the 1860s and closed in June 1965. A stream running alongside was a natural source of water for the shed to use. The steel cylinder, seen beside the engines, capped the 'well', with a pipe connecting the shed to the stream. *G. W. Sharpe*

'N15' 'King Arthur' class 4-6-0 No 30770 *Sir Prianius* at London Nine Elms shed in November 1961. Dating from June 1925, No 30770 was at Dover shed at nationalisation, moving to Stewarts Lane in May 1952, Basingstoke in August 1955, Eastleigh in May 1956, and back to Basingstoke in August 1962, seeing out its last days until withdrawal. Eastleigh Works carried out the dismantling. *Pictorail*

'S15' class 4-6-0 No 30823 is at Yeovil on a van train on Monday 29 October 1962, carrying out shunting duties. This was one of the later batch to be built, when Maunsell was in charge of engine building. These were fitted with higher pressure boilers, smaller grates and modified footplating. No 30823 was the first of the 15 built in 1927, with a further 10 in 1936. This engine was at Exmouth Junction at nationalisation, moving to Salisbury in June 1951 and Feltham in December 1963, from where it was withdrawn on 29 November 1964 and sent to Cashmore's at Newport for scrap. G. W. Sharpe

Left: Another 'S15' 4-6-0, No 30837, is here paired with a 'Schools' class tender on Eastleigh shed in August 1962. This was the last of the 1927 build and did not enter traffic until January 1928. At nationalisation No 30837 was at Feltham and moved to Redhill in July 1951, moving back to Feltham in June 1961, from where it was withdrawn on 19 September 1965. After nearly a year in storage at Feltham it left for its last journey to Cashmore's at Newport. *P. H. Groom*

All the remaining 'Lord Nelson' class 4-6-0s were withdrawn during 1962. This is No 30856 *Lord St Vincent* at its home shed Eastleigh on Wednesday 22 August 1962 with only four weeks to go before withdrawal. No 30856 dated from November 1928 and spent most of its British Railways days based at Eastleigh and was cut up at the works. *G. W. Sharpe*

All the remaining 'Schools' class 4-4-0s were also withdrawn during 1962. A long way from its Basingstoke home on Sunday 13 May 1962, No 30925 *Cheltenham* is at Darlington shed. It was being serviced before returning to Nottingham Victoria after working in on an RCTS East Midlands Branch special, double-heading with Bescot-based LMS 2P 4-4-0 No 40646. The tour participants were enjoying a visit to the works and shed. No 30925 had been requested as Cheltenham was where the RCTS was first formed in 1928. No 30925 entered service in July 1934 and was first allocated to Fratton. At nationalisation it was at Dover shed, moving to London Bricklayers Arms in May 1951, then Stewarts Lane in January 1961 and Basingstoke eight months later. The locomotive survived cutting up and is now part of the collection of engines at the National Railway Museum, York. *G. W. Sharpe*

Another 'Schools' class 4-4-0, No 30926 *Repton*, is in immaculate condition at London Stewarts Lane shed on Wednesday 6 June 1962 ready for Royal Race Day duty. Also dating from 1934, *Repton* entered traffic at Eastleigh and served from a number of sheds before going to its last home, Basingstoke, in December 1961. No 30926 was eventually preserved in America before returning to England and is now at the North Yorkshire Moors Railway. *G. W. Sharpe*

Another class that was banished to the scrapyard in 1962 was the 'Z' class 0-8-0Ts, with all eight being withdrawn. This is No 30956, the last to go, at Exeter Central station on Friday 24 August 1962 taking a rest from banking duties for trains climbing the severe gradient from St David's station. Dating from 1929, this was a Maunsell design for heavy shunting work and by the end of 1959 all were allocated to Exmouth Junction. All were scrapped at Eastleigh Works, except No 30952, which, after a protracted time in storage, went to Cashmore's at Newport. *G. W. Sharpe*

'C' class 0-6-0 No 31293 at its home shed London Bricklayers Arms in March 1961, with one of the running foremen posing for the camera. A Wainwright design for the South East & Chatham Railway (SE&CR), the first were introduced in 1900, with No 31293 coming into traffic in June 1908. It had come to Bricklayers Arms from Guildford in April 1950, where it remained until withdrawn in 1962. Ashford Works carried out the cutting up. *G. W. Sharpe*

Another view at Bricklayers Arms in 1961 and another 1962 withdrawal — 'H' class 0-4-4T No 31305. H. S. Wainwright designed these attractive tank engines for the SE&CR, the first taking to the rails in 1904. No 31305 entered traffic in May 1906 and under British Railways control operated from Ashford, Faversham and Gillingham, going to the 'Brick' in September 1955 and finally to Stewarts Lane in June 1962. Ward's at Briton Ferry reduced the engine to scrap metal after it was stored at Stewarts Lane from withdrawal until July 1963. *R. H. G. Simpson*

'N' class 2-6-0 No 31403 is at Hove in 1962. This was one of the last batch of this Maunsell design, built in 1932, with No 31403 entering traffic at its first shed, Ashford, in August. It spent most of its working life at Ashford, moving to Guildford in May 1961 and Brighton in December 1961, from where it was withdrawn on 30 June 1963. Eastleigh Works carried out the scrapping. *G. W. Sharpe*

'U' class 2-6-0 No 31635 at Guildford shed on Saturday 1 April 1961. Another Maunsell design, No 31635 entered traffic in April 1931 and worked at a number of sheds before settling at Guildford in January 1957, from where it was withdrawn on 1 December 1963. It made its last journey to Eastleigh Works soon after. *G. W. Sharpe*

The last 'L1' class 4-4-0 in service, No 31786, is at Eastleigh shed on Sunday 4 February 1962 after arriving from Nine Elms for withdrawal and scrapping. The 'L1s' were introduced in 1926 and were a post-Grouping development of the Wainwright 1914 design, being built by the North British Locomotive Co. No 31786 had been transferred to Nine Elms in June 1959 from Gillingham, displaced from its usual haunts by electrification. By January 1961 the class had been reduced to only nine members, all at Nine Elms, with eventually all going for scrap. *G. W. Sharpe*

'N' class 2-6-0 No 31831 is a visitor to Eastleigh shed from Exmouth Junction in April 1962. Dating from July 1924, No 31831 was an Exmouth Junction engine from August 1950 to August 1962 when it was added to Brighton's fleet. Redhill acquired the engine in December 1963 and then Guildford in December 1964, from where it was withdrawn on 25 April 1965. This was another candidate for the workers at Cashmore's, Newport, to reduce to scrap metal. *Pictorail*

The 'N1' class 2-6-0s were a three-cylinder development of the 'N' class, with only six being built. All were withdrawn in 1962. This is 'N1' No 31876, dating from March 1923, on a down extra near St Mary Cray Junction in June 1959 when allocated to Tonbridge. No 31876 moved to Stewarts Lane in June 1962, but this was a 'paper' move as it was placed in store at Hove goods yard until July 1963. That month it was moved to Brighton for further storage until September, when it went to Eastleigh Works for cutting up. *P. H. Groom*

N1 Class 2-6-0 4P5F	
31876	73J
31877	73J
31878	73J
31879	73J
31880	73J

U1 Class 2-6-0 4P3F	
31890	75C
31891	75E
31892	75E
31893	75E
31894	75E
31895	75C
31896	75C
31897	75C
31898	75C
31899	75C
31900	75C
31901	75C
31902	75C
31903	75C
31904	75C
31905	75C
31906	75C
31907	75C
31908	75C
31909	75C
31910	75C

W Class 2-6-4T 6F	
31911	71A
31912	71A
31913	71A
31914	75C
31915	75C
31916	71A
31917	75C
31918	75C
31919	75C
31920	75C
31921	75C
31922	71A
31923	70B
31924	70B
31925	75C

E2 Class 0-6-0T 3F	
32101	71I
32103	71I
32104	71I
32105	71I
32106	71I
32109	71I

K Class 2-6-0 4P5F	
32337	75A
32338	75A
32339	75A
32340	75A
32341	75A
32342	75A
32343	75A
32344	75A
32345	75E
32346	75E
32347	75E
32348	75E
32349	75E
32350	75E
32351	75E
32352	75E
32353	75E

E6 Class 0-6-2T 3F	
32408	70B
32416	70B
32417	75A
32418	75A

E4 Class 0-6-2T 2MT	
32468	75A
32470	75E
32472	70A
32473	70A
32474	75E
32479	75A
32487	70A
32500	70A
32503	75A
32509	75A
32510	71A

C2X Class 0-6-0 2F	
32523	75E
32525	75E
32535	75E

E4 Class 0-6-2T 2MT	
32557	70A
32580	75A
32581	75A

A1X 'Terrier' Class 0-6-0T 0P	
32635	75A
32636	75A
32640	71A
32646	71A
32650	71A
32661	71A
32662	75A
32670	75A
32678	71A

Q1 Class 0-6-0 5F	
33001	70B
33002	70B
33003	70B
33004	70B
33005	70C
33006	70B
33007	70B
33008	70B
33009	70B
33010	70B
33011	70B
33012	70B
33013	70B
33014	70B
33015	70B
33016	70B
33017	70B
33018	70B
33019	70C
33020	71A
33021	71A
33022	70C
33023	71A
33024	70B
33025	70C
33026	70B
33027	70B
33028	73J
33029	73J
33030	73J
33031	73J
33032	73J
33033	73J
33034	70C
33035	70C
33036	70C
33037	71A
33038	70B
33039	71A
33040	70B

'West Country' Class 4-6-2 7P6F	
34001*	70A
34002*	72A
34003*	72B
34004*	71A
34005*	72B

'U1' class 2-6-0 No 31890 is at West Hoathly with a train of condemned wagons in March 1960. No 31890 was the prototype of the class, being rebuilt from a 2-6-4T in June 1928 and was a three-cylinder development of the 'U' class. At the beginning of 1962 the class was intact, but 17 were withdrawn during the year, leaving only four still on the active list, including No 31890 which was withdrawn on 30 June 1963 from Brighton shed and cut up at Eastleigh Works.
G. W. Sharpe

'W' class 2-6-4T No 31917 at its home shed Norwood Junction in May 1962, but strangely carrying an Eastleigh 71A shedplate. This was a Maunsell design and a development of the 'N1' class 2-6-0 for cross-London freight traffic. This example was placed in traffic in April 1935 and first allocated to London Stewarts Lane. In November 1962 No 31917 was reallocated to Exmouth Junction, along with other members of the class, to take up banking duties at Exeter, replacing the 'Z' class 0-8-0Ts. However, No 31917 did not stay long, for it returned to the London area at Feltham on 27 January 1963. No 31923 was sent from Feltham to Exmouth Junction on the same day as a replacement, but it is doubtful if it ever actually reached Exmouth as it was withdrawn on 2 February. No 31917 remained at Feltham until withdrawn on 5 January 1964. Bird's at Morriston, Swansea, carried out the scrapping after No 31917 had been stored at Feltham until June 1964.
R. H. G. Simpson

'E2' class 0-6-0T No 32104, with No 32109 behind, is in store at Eastleigh on Sunday 11 November 1962. By this date these were the last two survivors of the class and were allocated to Southampton Docks, going there from Norwood Junction during the period 10 November to 8 December 1961. No 32104 had been introduced in January 1914 and No 32109 in October 1916, being designed by L. B. Billinton for the LB&SCR. Both were withdrawn on 28 April 1963 and cut up at Eastleigh Works. *G. W. Sharpe*

Another class to be completely withdrawn in 1962 was the Billinton designed 'K' class 2-6-0s. This is No 32351, which was built at Brighton Works in January 1921, about to carry out shunting duties at Hailsham on Tuesday 12 June 1962. From November 1959 the entire class was allocated to either Brighton or Three Bridges. None survived into preservation. *G. W. Sharpe*

'E6' class 0-6-2T No 32418 at Seaford is paired with 'A1X' 'Terrier' 0-6-0T No 32636 on the RCTS 'Sussex Special Railtour' on Sunday 7 October 1962. The special had started from London Bridge station and had been hauled to Brighton by 'Schools' class 4-4-0 No 30925 *Cheltenham*. The two tank engines had taken over at Brighton for a run to Seaford and back via Lewes. No 32418 had been built at Brighton to an R. J. Billinton design in December 1905 and was a 1962 withdrawal, along with the remaining members of the class. After storage in Hove goods yard until May 1963, No 32418 went to Eastleigh for scrapping. *G. W. Sharpe*

A view of the 'A1X' 'Terrier' 0-6-0T No 32636 on the RCTS 'Sussex Special Railtour', this time at Lewes during a water stop. Designed by Stroudley and dating from September 1872, No 32636 was rebuilt in April 1913 by Marsh with a new boiler and extended smokebox. Withdrawn on 4 November 1963 from Eastleigh shed, it was saved for preservation and can be seen at the Bluebell Railway. *G. W. Sharpe*

A 'Terrier' in full cry on the Hayling Island branch near North Hayling in June 1963. This is No 32646, fitted with a spark arrester chimney. Originally built in January 1877, it was rebuilt in 1932 and was also withdrawn on 4 November 1963 from Eastleigh. Previously it had been part of the Isle of Wight stock, going to the island in March 1914 and returning to the mainland in May 1949. After withdrawal it was purchased from BR by Sadler Rail Car Co and resold to Brickwoods Brewery who preserved it as 'Newington' outside the 'Hayling Billy' public house on Hayling Island. It was later restored to working order after going back to the Isle of Wight at the steam centre at Haven Street. *P. H. Groom*

'E4' class 0-6-2T No 32487 is on shed pilot duties at London Nine Elms in April 1962. This was another R. J. Billinton design, with No 32487 entering traffic in June 1899. It was one of 10 withdrawn during 1962. Stored at Nine Elms from December 1962 to July 1963, it was then sent to Eastleigh Works for scrapping. *R. H. G. Simpson*

The three remaining 'C2X' class 0-6-0s were withdrawn in February 1962, and No 32535, seen here at Three Bridges shed in 1959, was one of them. This was a Marsh rebuild of the original R. J. Billinton 'C2' class with a larger boiler and extended smokebox. After withdrawal all three were quickly cut up at Ashford Works. *R. H. G. Simpson*

Bulleid's 'Austerity'-design 'Q1' class 0-6-0 No 33008 is at Feltham shed in June 1962. This example had entered traffic in July 1942 and was first allocated to Guildford. September 1948 saw a move to Feltham and here it remained until withdrawn on 25 August 1963. Storage at Feltham then took place until May 1964 when No 33008 was sold to Cohen's at Kettering for scrap. *Pictorail*

34006* 70A
34007* 70A
34008* 75A
34009* 70A
34010* 70A
34011* 72A
34012* 73B
34013* 73B
34014* 73B
34015* 72A
34016* 71A
34017* 70A
34018* 70A
34019* 75A
34020* 70A
34021* 71B
34022* 71A
34023* 72A
34024* 72A
34025* 71A
34026* 72B
34027* 75A
34028* 71B
34029* 71B
34030* 72A
34031* 70A
34032* 72A
34033* 72A
34034* 71A
34035* 72A
34036* 72A
34037* 71B
34038* 71A
34039* 71B
34040* 71B
34041* 71B
34042* 71B
34043* 71B
34044* 71B
34045* 71B
34046* 71B
34047* 71B
34048* 72B

'Battle of Britain' Class 4-6-2 7P6F

34049* 72B
34050* 70A
34051* 72B
34052* 72B
34053* 71B
34054* 72B
34055* 75A
34056* 72A
34057* 75A
34058* 72A
34059* 72B
34060* 72A
34061* 71A
34062* 72A
34063* 72A
34064* 72A
34065* 72A
34066* 72A
34067* 72B
34068* 72B
34069* 72A
34070* 72A
34071* 70A
34072* 72A
34073* 70A
34074* 72A
34075* 72A
34076* 72A
34077* 70A
34078* 72A
34079* 72A
34080* 72A
34081* 72A
34082* 70A
34083* 72A
34084* 72A
34085* 71B
34086* 72A
34087* 70A
34088* 70A
34089* 73A
34090* 70A

'West Country' Class 4-6-2 7P6F

34091* 72B
34092* 72B
34093* 70A
34094* 70A
34095* 70A
34096* 72A
34097* 72A
34098* 72A
34099* 72B
34100* 73A
34101* 73B
34102* 71B
34103* 71B
34104* 71A
34105* 71B
34106* 72A
34107* 72A
34108* 72A

'Battle of Britain' Class 4-6-2 7P6F

34109* 72A
34110* 72A

'Merchant Navy' Class 4-6-2 8P

35001* 70A
35002* 71B
35003* 72A
35004* 72B
35005* 71B
35006* 72B
35007* 72B
35008* 71B
35009* 72A
35010* 72A
35011* 71B
35012* 70A
35013* 72A
35014* 70A
35015* 70A
35016* 70A
35017* 70A
35018* 70A
35019* 70A
35020* 70A
35021* 71B
35022* 72A
35023* 71B
35024* 71B
35025* 72A
35026* 72A
35027* 71B
35028* 70A
35029* 70A
35030* 70A

Locomotives Allocated to the Isle of Wight

O2 Class 0-4-4T 0P

14* 70H
16* 70H
17* 70H
18* 70H
20* 70H
21* 70H
22* 70H
24* 70H
25* 70H
26* 70H
27* 70H
28* 70H
29* 70H
30* 70H
31* 70H
32* 70H
33* 70H
35* 70H
36* 70H

Unrebuilt 'West Country' 4-6-2 No 34011 *Tavistock* runs through Clapham Junction with empty milk tankers on their way to Devon in April 1962. No 34011 had entered traffic in October 1945 and went new to Exmouth Junction shed, then to Plymouth Friary in April 1948, Nine Elms in April 1951, and back to Exmouth Junction in March 1959, remaining on allocation until withdrawn at the end of November 1963. Cutting up was carried out at Eastleigh Works in April 1964. *G. W. Sharpe*

Rebuilt 'West Country' 4-6-2 No 34025 *Whimple* is at London Nine Elms shed in September 1962 among the remains of the old coal stage. Added to stock in March 1946 and allocated to Ramsgate, it was rebuilt in October 1957. No 34025 was one of the last of the class in service, withdrawal coming on 9 July 1967 when allocated to Bournemouth. Storage at Salisbury shed then took place until February 1968 when No 34025 went to Cashmore's at Newport for scrap. *P. H. Groom*

Rebuilt 'Battle of Britain' 4-6-2 No 34062 *17 Squadron* is at Exmouth Junction shed in July 1962. Allocated to Ramsgate in May 1947 when new, it moved to Stewarts Lane in June 1948, Nine Elms in March 1950 and settled at Exmouth Junction in 1951, where it remained until withdrawn on 8 August 1964. Rebuilding was carried out during a visit to Eastleigh Works in February/March 1959. After withdrawal No 34062 was sent to Bird's Bridgend yard for cutting up. *G. W. Sharpe*

The second 'Merchant Navy' 4-6-2 to be built, No 35002 *Union Castle*, drifts through Clapham Junction on an express from Bournemouth in June 1962. Placed in service at Salisbury on 16 June 1941, it was rebuilt at Eastleigh during a works visit in April/May 1958. Withdrawal came on 23 February 1964 after transfer to Nine Elms from Bournemouth the previous month. No 35002 was then stored at 70A until July, when it was towed away to Rotherham to the Slag Reduction Co for breaking up. *G. W. Sharpe*

On the Isle of Wight at Ryde Pier is 'O2' class 0-4-4T No 36 *Carisbrooke* waiting to proceed light engine to Ryde Esplanade station in July 1961. The 'O2s' were the staple power on the island until steam was withdrawn in 1967. No 36, however, lasted in service only until 14 June 1964, when it was withdrawn and then went into storage at Ryde Works. It was not cut up until October 1965. It had entered traffic on the mainland in April 1891 and became No 198 before moving to the island in April 1949. *Pictorail*

Fowler 2-6-2T 3MT

40006	1A
40009	9F
40022	14B
40024	14B
40026	14E
40031	14B
40063	26A

Stanier 2-6-2T 3MT

40072	24D
40073	16B
40078	6H
40080	21B
40082	55E
40083	21B
40085	6A
40086	24L
40087	2B
40088	16B
40089	16B
40090	27C
40093	6G
40098	6A
40099	24D
40100	14B
40104	2B
40105	9F
40106	6A
40109	24E
40110	1A
40112	56C
40113	9F
40114	56C
40116	6H
40117	50E
40119	14B
40120	24D
40122	6G
40128	1A
40135	2B
40137	6G
40138	2B
40145	27C
40146	16B
40147	56A
40148	55D
40150	60D
40151	67B
40152	68B
40153	65D
40154	65D
40157	1A
40158	65D
40159	65D
40164	24D
40170	68B
40173	21B
40174	24E
40176	65D
40177	65D
40179	55E
40180	21D
40181	55D
40185	6G
40186	65D
40187	65D
40188	65D
40189	65D
40190	51A
40191	27C
40193	55D
40196	27C
40197	27C
40198	27C
40200	65D
40201	1A
40202	6G
40203	14B
40205	6H
40206	24L
40207	2B

Johnson/Fowler 4-4-0 2P

40453	26F
40537	84D
40540	85C

LMS 4-4-0 2P

40563	82G
40564	82G
40634	82G
40638	68C
40646	21B
40657	1C
40664	68C
40665	67B
40670	68B
40672	1C
40681	26F
40694	21B
40696	82F
40697	82F
40700	82F

Ivatt 2-6-2T 2MT

41200	6H
41201	84H
41202	82E
41203	82E
41204	84H
41205	27A
41206	83H
41207	82E
41208	82E
41209	41D
41210	8B
41211	8B
41212	1A
41213	8B
41214	83H
41215	24J
41216	83H
41217	8D
41218	2E
41219	6H
41220	5A
41221	8D
41222	1E
41223	1C
41224	14E
41225	14E
41226	6C
41227	16D
41228	15C
41229	5A
41230	8D
41231	84D
41232	84H
41233	6H
41234	6H
41235	6G
41236	6G
41237	8D
41238	72A
41239	1B
41240	82E
41241	84H
41242	82F
41243	82F
41244	8D
41245	41D
41246	41D
41247	50F
41248	82E
41249	82E
41250	56F
41251	50F
41252	55H
41253	56F
41254	55C
41255	55C
41256	55C
41257	55F
41258	55C
41259	55H
41260	75A
41261	75A
41262	50B
41263	56F
41264	56F
41265	50F
41266	55F
41267	55A
41268	27A
41269	27A
41270	72A
41271	15C
41272	72A
41273	55F
41274	56F
41275	83D
41276	6K
41277	27C
41278	2E
41279	15C
41280	16D
41281	55H
41282	55H
41283	75A
41284	72A
41285	84D
41286	9D
41287	75A
41288	8B
41289	1E
41290	72E
41291	75A
41292	72A
41293	71A
41294	72E
41295	83H
41296	82E
41297	72E
41298	72E
41299	72A
41300	75A
41301	75A
41302	83H
41303	75A
41304	82E
41305	71A
41306	72A
41307	72A
41308	72A

The last Fowler 2-6-2T to be withdrawn in 1962 was No 40022, seen here at London Kentish Town shed in 1961. This was one of the class fitted with condensing gear, allowing workings through the tunnels on London's Metropolitan Widened Lines. No 40022 had been built at Derby Works and had been added to stock in January 1931 and at first carried the number 15521, being renumbered 22 in 1934 and 40022 in July 1949. At nationalisation No 40022 was a Kentish Town engine, moving to St Albans during the first week in January 1948. Here it remained until January 1960, when it returned to the care of Kentish Town shed and finally to Cricklewood in September 1962 for its final few months in service. Derby Works carried out the cutting up in March 1963. *R. H. G. Simpson*

All the remaining 72 Stanier 2-6-2Ts were withdrawn during 1962, including No 40201 here in store with No 40157 at London Willesden shed on Thursday 2 August 1962. New in February 1938, and built at Crewe Works, its first allocation was Nuneaton. Subsequent transfers saw it based at a number of depots including Stoke, Widnes, Birkenhead and, finally, Willesden from August 1961. After withdrawal and storage at Willesden, it was sent to Horwich Works for scrapping in November 1962. *G. W. Sharpe*

Also withdrawn during 1962 was No 40203, which was fitted with a larger boiler in 1942 to improve its steaming capacity. This view was recorded in June 1960 at Kentish Town shed. Northampton was its first allocation when new from Crewe Works in February 1938 and during its BR days it worked from Warwick, Liverpool Brunswick and, from September 1959, Kentish Town. After withdrawal Horwich Works carried out the scrapping in February 1963. *P. H. Groom*

LMS 2P 4-4-0 No 40646 at Leighton Buzzard on the SLS 'Seven Branch Line Tour' on Saturday 14 April 1962. The tour started from Birmingham New Street at 10.00am with No 40646 in charge. Then the route was through Nuneaton, the Coventry avoiding line, Rugby, Northampton and Bedford where privately preserved GN 0-6-0T No 1247 (ex-68846) took over for the section to Hitchin, Hertford North, Welwyn Garden City, Hatfield and Luton. Here No 40646 resumed its duty and returned to Birmingham via Dunstable, Leighton Buzzard, Weedon, Leamington Spa and Berkswell, arriving back at 8.00pm. Over 300 SLS members took part, each paying 30s 6d (£1.52) for the 240-mile tour. All the remaining LMS 2P 4-4-0s were withdrawn during 1962, No 40646 going one month after this tour. After storage at Bescot, it was sold in August 1962 to Cashmore's at Great Bridge for scrapping. *G. W. Sharpe*

Backing onto Watford shed in March 1962 is LMS 2P 4-4-0 No 40672, with seven months to go before withdrawal. On shed is Watford-allocated LMS 4F 0-6-0 No 44340. No 40672 dated from February 1932 and had been built at Derby Works. It spent the whole of its BR service based at Watford and returned to Derby for cutting up. *R. H. G. Simpson*

Ex-works at Crewe North shed in June 1962 is Ivatt 2MT 2-6-2T No 41243, with an incorrect shedplate of 82A. The correct code was 82F, Bath Green Park. Placed in traffic during the week ended 15 October 1949, and built at Crewe Works, No 41243 went new to Bath Green Park and was a familiar sight on the Somerset & Dorset (S&D), spending its entire life on the line. Its only move was to Templecombe in August 1962, from where it was withdrawn on 18 July 1965 and later scrapped at Cohen's South Wales yard at Morriston. *G. W. Sharpe*

41309	72A
41310	72E
41311	71A
41312	72E
41313	72E
41314	72E
41315	83H
41316	83H
41317	83H
41318	72A
41319	71A
41320	72A
41321	72A
41322	72A
41323	72A
41324	75A
41325	75A
41326	75A
41327	75A
41328	71A
41329	71A

Deeley 0-4-0T 0F

41528	41E
41531	41E
41533	41E
41535	85C
41537	85C

Johnson 0-6-0T 1F

41702	9G
41708	41E
41712	16B
41734	41E
41739	41E
41763	41E
41769	41E
41804	41E
41835	41D
41844	16B
41875	41E

Stanier 0-4-4T 2P

41900	85C

LT&S 0-6-2T 3F

41981	33B

Fairburn 2-6-4T 4MT

42050	9E
42051	24H
42052	55A
42053	21A
42054	16A
42055	66A
42056	66A
42057	66A
42058	66A
42059	66A
42060	66D
42061	6A
42062	2A
42063	27C
42064	9E
42065	9E
42066	1E
42067	12C
42068	1A
42069	5C
42070	14D
42071	1E
42072	55F
42073	56C
42074	6H
42075	33C
42076	33C
42077	8C
42078	8C
42079	5A
42080	16B
42081	12C
42082	21A
42083	56E
42084	56F
42085	51A
42086	14D
42087	14D
42088	15C
42089	16B
42090	14D
42091	16A
42092	14D
42093	55F
42094	56E
42095	12C
42096	1C
42097	1C
42098	12G
42099	1C
42100	1C
42101	1C
42102	1C
42103	2A
42104	2A
42105	1E
42106	1E
42107	56F
42108	56F
42109	56F
42110	24B
42111	9E
42112	9E
42113	9E
42114	26E
42115	26E
42116	56F
42117	1A
42118	1A
42119	12E
42120	12E
42121	8A
42122	67C
42123	67D
42124	67D
42125	66B
42126	66B
42127	66B
42128	66C
42129	66B
42130	68D
42131	65D
42132	27C
42133	9F
42134	9F
42135	24J
42136	24J
42137	9A
42138	55A
42139	55F
42140	16A
42141	55F
42142	66E
42143	66A
42144	66A
42145	66E
42146	17A
42147	24D
42148	24E
42149	56E
42150	56E
42151	56E
42152	56D
42153	24E
42154	24D
42155	8A
42156	14B
42157	14D
42158	24C
42159	9F
42160	5D
42161	16A
42162	66E
42163	66E
42164	66C
42165	66C
42166	66C
42167	66A
42168	60B
42169	66B
42170	66A
42171	66A
42172	64C
42173	66E
42174	17A
42175	66D
42176	66D
42177	66E
42178	14D
42179	12E
42180	27D
42181	17A
42182	87D
42183	8C
42184	17A
42185	16A
42186	8C
42187	24C
42188	55H
42189	55F
42190	67D
42191	67D
42192	68D
42193	67D
42194	67D
42195	65D
42196	67C
42197	65D
42198	6A
42199	65B
42200	66B
42201	65D
42202	6A
42203	67D
42204	66E
42205	68D
42206	24E
42207	26C
42208	66B
42209	6A
42210	12C
42211	6H
42212	6A
42213	6A
42214	68D
42215	68D
42216	66A
42218	33C
42219	33C
42221	33C
42222	16B
42223	33C
42224	33C
42225	21A
42226	33C
42227	33C
42228	17C
42229	6A
42230	21A
42231	16B
42232	16B
42233	12A
42234	1A
42235	8F
42236	6A
42237	14B
42238	12G
42239	66E
42240	6A
42241	66D
42242	66D
42243	66A
42244	66A
42245	66D
42246	66A
42247	6A
42248	9G
42249	9G
42250	14D
42251	14D
42252	14D
42253	14D
42254	33B
42255	33B
42256	9G
42257	33B
42258	66D
42259	66D
42260	66D
42261	66D
42262	66D
42263	66D
42264	66D
42265	66D
42266	66D
42267	21E
42268	66A
42269	68B
42270	6A
42271	66E
42272	64C
42273	64C
42274	66A
42275	66A
42276	66A
42277	66A
42278	24H
42279	14D
42280	26A
42281	14D
42282	33C
42283	33C
42284	21A
42285	56D
42286	24C
42287	26E
42288	26A
42289	26C
42290	27C
42291	14D
42292	27C
42293	27C
42294	24E
42295	24B
42296	24C
42297	27D
42298	24C
42299	27D

Fowler 2-6-4T 4MT

42301	12A
42303	8F
42304	12A
42305	87D
42306	9D
42309	5C
42310	55G
42311	56F
42313	12A
42314	9D
42315	5D
42316	9B
42317	55G
42318	12E
42319	24L
42320	12A
42322	12G
42323	5D
42324	56F
42327	5C
42331	15C
42333	17A
42334	14B
42335	14B
42336	14B
42337	9B

Deeley 0F 0-4-0T No 41537 is at Gloucester Docks in September 1962 on shunting duties. Constructed at Derby Works in May 1922, it was the last one to be built. The first batch, Nos 41528 to 41533, had been built in 1907 and the three survivors in 1962 were at work at Staveley Barrow Hill. The two survivors of the second batch were at Gloucester Barnwood. No 41537 was withdrawn in September 1963 and scrapped at Derby Works. *P. H. Groom*

Johnson 1F 0-6-0T No 41763 is taking a rest from shunting duties at the Staveley Iron Works complex in the summer of 1962. Built in December 1889 at Derby Works, and with a G5-type boiler fitted in December 1946, No 41763 continued in service until 25 December 1966. After storage at Canklow, it was sold to Arnott Young at Rawmarsh for scrap. *G. W. Sharpe*

The last survivor of the class of 0-4-4Ts built when Stanier was new to the office of Chief Mechanical Engineer, No 41900 is seen at Tewkesbury sub-shed in July 1960. New in December 1932, it was first allocated to Nottingham Midland shed. Allocated to Gloucester Barnwood in June 1957, its final allocation was to Leamington Spa, although when withdrawn in 1962 it was in store at Wellington shed and it is unlikely that it saw any work from Leamington. Crewe Works carried out the scrapping. *G. W. Sharpe*

Another last survivor is seen, this time ex-LT&SR (London, Tilbury & Southend Railway) 3F 0-6-2T No 41981 stored at Plaistow shed in August 1962 two months after withdrawal. A Thomas Whitelegg design, No 41981 was built by the North British Locomotive Company in June 1903 as LT&SR No 70 and originally named *Basildon*. Shortly after this photograph was recorded, No 41981 was towed away to Doncaster Works for scrapping. *P. H. Groom*

An unusual visitor to Lincoln on Tuesday 4 June 1963 was Willesden-allocated Fairburn 4MT 2-6-4T No 42234, here in the station parcels bay. New from Derby Works in July 1946, it was first allocated to Manchester Patricroft. At nationalisation it was at Stoke-on-Trent, moving to Bangor during the four-week period ending 12 July 1952, then back to Stoke during the three-week period ended 4 October 1952. Here it remained until December 1957, when No 42234 was transferred to Willesden, from where it was withdrawn during the week ended 15 February 1964 and, unusually, cut up on site at Willesden shed. *G. W. Sharpe*

Fowler 4MT 2-6-4T No 42304 was one of the 37 class members to be withdrawn during 1962 and is seen here at Carlisle Citadel station in March 1961 on a local trip working. New in January 1928, on 1 January 1948 No 42304 was a Watford-based engine, moving to Uttoxeter during the three-week period ended 11 July 1953. Subsequent moves saw the locomotive at Manchester Longsight (January 1956), Willesden (September 1958), and back to Longsight (July 1959), before settling at Carlisle Kingmoor in March 1960. After withdrawal, No 42304 was stored at Kingmoor for around eight months before going to McLellan's yard at Langloan, near Coatbridge in Scotland, for scrapping. *G. W. Sharpe*

Stanier 4MT 2-6-4T No 42446 is at home at Bangor shed in March 1962. Dating from June 1936 and built at Derby Works, No 42446 had first been allocated to Watford, later serving from a number of sheds including Bletchley, Rugby and Market Harborough, before going to Bangor in August 1960. Here it remained until withdrawn during the week ended 25 April 1964 and was then stored until November before being dispatched to the Slag Reduction Co at Rotherham for scrapping. *Pictorail*

42338	14B
42339	17A
42340	12E
42342	14B
42343	9B
42347	12E
42350	1A
42351	2E
42352	15C
42353	2E
42355	15C
42357	12B
42358	5F
42359	24L
42361	15C
42362	5D
42366	1A
42367	1A
42368	1A
42369	12G
42370	9D
42371	9D
42372	9B
42374	9G
42375	5F
42376	12E
42378	5D
42379	9D
42381	2E
42384	55G
42385	87D
42387	87D
42388	87D
42389	5C
42391	9B
42392	5D
42393	12B
42394	87D
42396	12H
42400	21A
42401	12E
42402	12E
42403	12H
42405	56E
42406	56D
42407	56D
42408	55A
42409	55A
42410	55G
42411	56C
42412	55G
42413	55G
42414	12H
42415	12E
42416	21A
42417	21A
42419	21A
42420	12E
42421	21A
42422	21A
42424	12H

Stanier 2-6-4T 4MT

42425	9A
42426	12B
42429	9G
42430	2A
42431	6A
42432	12E
42433	24C
42434	24C
42435	27C
42436	50D
42437	15E
42439	26F
42440	12C
42441	6C
42442	26F
42443	5D
42444	26D
42445	8C
42446	6H
42447	24J
42448	9E
42449	12C
42451	27C
42452	16A
42453	15E
42454	1E
42455	24E
42456	8F
42457	12G
42458	26F
42459	6C
42460	26D
42461	24E
42462	8F
42463	6A
42464	12G
42465	8F
42466	9E
42468	26F
42469	9E
42470	1A
42472	9G
42473	27D
42474	26B
42476	24C
42477	51A
42478	1A
42480	24C
42481	24C
42482	6A
42483	24D
42484	24H
42485	27C
42486	17C
42487	6H
42488	21E
42489	6H
42491	24H
42492	24H
42493	6C
42494	26F

Stanier Three-cylinder 2-6-4T 4MT

42500	33C
42501	33C
42502	33C
42503	33C
42504	33C
42505	33C
42508	33C
42509	33C

42511 33C
42513 33C
42514 33C
42515 33C
42516 33C
42517 33C
42518 33C
42519 33C
42520 33C
42522 33C
42523 33C
42525 33C
42526 33C
42527 33C
42528 33C
42529 33C
42530 33C
42532 33C
42533 33C
42535 33C
42536 33C

Stanier 2-6-4T 4MT

42537 27C
42538 6A
42540 27E
42541 2A
42542 6C
42543 5D
42544 21E
42546 24B
42547 24B
42548 26A
42550 26D
42551 27C
42553 51A
42554 27D
42555 27D
42556 15E
42557 27D
42558 24E
42559 24E
42560 9E
42561 26F
42562 2A
42563 26C
42564 5D
42565 26C
42566 84D
42567 6H
42568 17C
42569 27D
42571 12G
42572 8F
42573 2A
42574 26F
42575 5A
42576 1A
42577 6H
42578 24L
42579 1E
42580 8C
42581 12E
42582 21C
42583 6C
42584 8C
42585 1A
42586 1E
42587 16A
42588 16A
42589 24J
42590 5D
42591 12E
42592 27D
42593 5D
42594 12G
42595 14B
42596 9E
42597 6C
42598 8C
42599 8A
42600 5D
42601 6H
42602 6C
42603 5D
42604 1A
42605 5F
42606 6C
42607 8F
42608 6C
42609 5D
42610 14B
42611 1A
42612 8C
42613 12G
42614 27D
42615 1E
42616 1C
42617 14B
42618 16B
42619 26A
42620 26A
42621 27D
42622 56F
42623 26A
42624 27D
42625 24E
42626 26C
42628 16A
42629 16B
42630 26C
42631 27D
42632 27D
42633 26C
42634 24C
42636 16A
42638 24E
42639 51A
42640 27D
42641 27D
42642 27D
42643 24E
42644 27D
42645 27C
42646 26B
42647 26B
42649 56A
42650 56A
42651 26A
42652 26C
42653 26C
42654 26C
42655 26C
42656 26C
42657 24E
42658 6C
42659 21C
42660 26F
42661 24C
42662 27C
42663 5D
42664 12B
42665 5F
42666 12E
42667 5D
42668 5D
42670 5D
42671 5D
42672 5D

Fairburn 2-6-4T 4MT

42673 12E
42674 5D
42675 9E
42676 9E
42677 5A
42678 33C
42679 33C
42680 14E
42681 33C
42682 14E
42684 33C
42685 14B
42686 14E
42687 33C
42688 68D
42689 68B
42690 65B
42691 66D
42692 66D
42693 68D
42694 65D
42695 66B
42696 26A
42697 26A
42698 26A
42699 66B

Hughes/Fowler 2-6-0 6P5F

42700 26D
42701 26A
42702 55F
42703 24B
42704 26A
42705 26A
42706 24B
42707 24F
42708 26A
42709 26A
42710 26A
42711 27B
42712 26D
42713 55C
42714 26A
42715 27B
42716 24B
42717 24B
42718 24D
42719 26D
42720 12A
42721 27B
42722 24F
42723 26B
42724 26B
42725 26B
42726 26A
42727 27B
42728 24D
42729 24D
42730 26D
42731 27D
42732 24D
42733 26A
42734 27D
42735 67B
42736 67C
42737 67C
42738 66A
42739 67B
42740 66D
42741 66D
42742 67D
42743 67B
42744 67B
42745 67C
42746 67B
42747 1A
42748 9G
42749 68C
42750 26A
42751 12A
42752 12A
42753 26B
42754 9G
42755 26B
42756 16A
42757 12A
42758 9G
42759 9G
42760 9G
42761 9G
42762 55F
42763 17B
42764 15B
42765 24F
42766 55C
42767 9G
42768 9G
42769 16A
42770 55F
42771 55A
42772 6C
42773 2B
42774 55C
42775 9G
42776 5B
42777 5D
42778 5D
42779 9B
42780 67C
42781 5A
42782 5D
42783 2B
42784 16A
42785 1A
42786 2B
42787 5D
42788 9G
42789 55C
42790 21A
42791 9G
42792 9G
42793 12A
42794 27D
42795 55C
42796 24D
42797 6C
42798 55A
42799 17B
42800 67C
42801 67C
42802 67C
42803 67C
42804 6C
42805 67C
42806 67D
42807 67C
42808 67C
42809 67C
42810 1A
42811 2B
42812 1A
42813 9G
42814 6C
42815 5B
42816 9G
42817 9B
42818 17B
42819 26B
42820 26D
42821 27D
42822 17B
42823 21A
42824 17B
42825 17B
42826 16A
42827 21A
42828 6C
42829 17B
42830 12A
42831 12A
42832 12A
42833 12A
42834 12A
42835 12A
42836 12A
42837 12A
42838 24D
42839 16A
42840 24F
42841 24F
42842 24F
42843 24F
42844 24F

42845	27B
42846	9G
42847	9G
42848	9B
42849	9B
42850	66A
42851	24J
42852	1A
42853	6C
42854	9B
42855	16A
42856	5D
42857	9G
42858	5D
42859	1A
42860	26B
42861	56A
42862	56A
42863	56A
42865	55C
42866	55C
42867	24F
42868	26B
42869	24B
42870	1A
42871	26A
42872	16A
42873	9G
42874	9G
42875	12A
42876	5D
42877	6C
42878	27B
42879	67C
42880	67B
42881	12A
42882	12A
42883	12A
42884	12A
42885	5D
42886	9B
42887	5D
42888	5D
42889	1A
42890	9G
42891	5D
42892	9B
42894	5D
42895	24J
42896	16A
42897	16A
42898	24B
42899	12A
42900	21A
42901	26B
42902	9G
42903	21A
42904	9B
42905	12A
42906	12A
42907	12A
42908	68B
42909	68B
42910	67C
42911	67D
42912	67C
42913	68B
42914	67C
42915	68B
42916	67C
42917	67C
42918	68B
42919	68B
42920	5D
42921	9B
42922	16A
42923	5A
42924	5D
42925	1A
42926	5A
42927	67C
42928	24J
42929	5D
42931	9B
42932	9B
42933	5A
42934	5A
42935	1A
42936	6C
42937	5D
42938	9B
42939	2B
42940	5B
42941	9B
42942	9B
42943	9B
42944	9B

Stanier 2-6-0 6P5F

42945	2B
42946	6C
42947	21D
42948	5B
42949	5B
42950	6C
42951	2B
42952	5B
42953	2B
42954	2B
42955	2B
42956	21D
42957	21D
42958	6C
42959	5B
42960	2B
42961	5B
42962	5B
42963	5B
42964	2B
42965	2B
42966	21D
42967	6A
42968	6C
42969	6C
42970	6C
42971	6C
42972	5B
42973	6C
42974	21D
42975	2B
42976	2B
42977	5B
42978	2B
42979	21D
42980	5B
42981	6C
42982	6A
42983	5B
42984	5B

Ivatt 2-6-0 4MT

43000	12B
43001	2B
43002	2B
43003	2B
43004	12F
43005	2B
43006	12F
43007	24J
43008	12F
43009	12H
43010	15A
43011	12B
43012	21A
43013	21A
43014	50A
43015	51C
43016	55F
43017	21A
43018	12A
43019	14A
43020	2B
43021	24J
43022	2B
43023	12A
43024	2B
43025	12F
43026	12F
43027	12A
43028	12B
43029	12H
43030	55F
43031	14A
43032	40E
43033	21A
43034	2B
43035	12H
43036	21A
43037	41D
43038	55B
43039	55A
43040	21A
43041	21A
43042	15B
43043	55A
43044	55B
43045	12C
43046	21A
43047	21A
43048	15B
43049	21A
43050	51A
43051	55H
43052	24J
43053	51C
43054	55H
43055	50A
43056	51A
43057	51L
43058	40F
43059	40F
43060	40A
43061	40F
43062	40F
43063	2F
43064	40F
43065	40F
43066	40F
43067	34E
43068	40F
43069	50B
43070	51L
43071	50A
43072	51A
43073	12B
43074	55E
43075	51L
43076	50B
43077	50B
43078	50B
43079	50B
43080	40F
43081	34E
43082	34E
43083	40F
43084	34E
43085	40F
43086	31A
43087	41H
43088	34E
43089	34E
43090	41E
43091	40F
43092	40F
43093	40F
43094	34E
43095	40A
43096	50B
43097	50D
43098	50D
43099	51A
43100	51C
43101	51L
43102	51A
43103	12A
43104	40A
43105	31A
43106	2F
43107	40F
43108	40F
43109	40F
43110	40F
43111	41E
43112	24J
43113	24J
43114	55E
43115	24J
43116	55E
43117	55A
43118	14A
43119	14A
43120	14A
43121	14A
43122	21A
43123	51C
43124	55A
43125	50D
43126	50A
43127	36E
43128	51C
43129	51A
43130	55A
43131	50B
43132	65E
43133	65E
43134	65E
43135	65D
43136	65D
43137	65F
43138	64G
43139	12C
43140	65D
43141	64G
43142	40F
43143	40F
43144	40F
43145	41H
43146	34E
43147	40F
43148	40F
43149	31A
43150	34E
43151	34E
43152	40E
43153	34E
43154	40A
43155	40E
43156	40E
43157	36E
43158	40F
43159	41E
43160	40E
43161	40E

Johnson 0-6-0 3F

43213	9D
43216	82G
43240	8B
43242	21A
43254	17B
43257	8B
43261	9G
43263	21A
43282	8B
43342	17C
43389	21A
43400	9G
43410	8B
43428	14E
43435	21A
43436	24B
43446	55D
43449	14E
43453	21A
43464	5B

All the remaining 29 Stanier three-cylinder 4MT 2-6-4Ts that operated on the LT&SR were withdrawn in 1962 when the line was electrified. This is No 42513, with domed boiler, in store inside Plaistow shed in July 1962 after withdrawal. New from Derby Works in July 1934, Leicester Midland was the first allocation before transfer to the LT&SR. Scrapping took place at Doncaster Works in September 1962. *P. H. Groom*

In 1959 the Stanier three-cylinder 2-6-4Ts were still receiving heavy repairs and repaints at Derby Works and on Sunday 30 August 1959 No 42536 looks superb on Derby shed, awaiting return to Plaistow. This was the last of the class to be built at Derby in December 1934 and was first allocated to Manchester Trafford Park. After withdrawal, scrapping was carried out at Doncaster Works in March 1963. *Author's collection*

The Stanier two-cylinder 2-6-4Ts were looked after at Crewe Works, and on Crewe North shed on Sunday 9 September 1962 is No 42626 ex-works awaiting return to its home shed Bolton. Dating from August 1938, Bolton was No 42626's first allocation where it spent most of its working life. Withdrawal came during the week ended 23 October 1965 at Bolton shed and after storage it was scrapped at Cashmore's, Great Bridge, in July 1966. *L. Hanson*

One of the first batch of Fairburn 4MT 2-6-4Ts, No 42680 out of steam at its home depot, Bedford, on Sunday 24 March 1963. New in May 1945, Wigan Lancashire & Yorkshire Railway (L&YR) shed was its first allocation. During the British Railways period, No 42680 was allocated to Nottingham, Kentish Town, St Albans, Cricklewood and Bedford from May 1960 to August 1963. It then returned to its first home, moved on to Wigan Springs Branch in April 1964, and finally, a month later, went to Carnforth. Here it was withdrawn during the week ended 27 March 1965 and then sent to Draper's yard at Hull for scrapping. *G. W. Sharpe*

Hughes/Fowler 6P5F 2-6-0 No 42810 is at Crewe South shed on Sunday 9 September 1962. Dating from April 1929, at nationalisation Speke Junction was the allocation, then Crewe South during June 1948, Aston in February 1953, Nuneaton in June 1953, Lancaster in November 1954, Stockport Edgeley in October 1960, Willesden two months later, and finally Birkenhead in March 1962. Withdrawal came during the week ended 14 December 1963 and scrapping at Crewe Works. *K. C. H. Fairey*

Stanier 6P5F 2-6-0 No 42959 is at Shrewsbury shed in May 1962. Entering traffic in January 1934, its first allocation was Kentish Town. By nationalisation No 42959 was based at Nuneaton, then went to Mold Junction during the week ended 12 February 1949. Here it remained until February 1957, when Crewe South became its operating base. November 1962 saw it at Stoke-on-Trent and in, December 1963, Wigan Springs Branch, where withdrawal was authorised during the week ended 25 December 1965. After storage, Cashmore's at Great Bridge scrapped the engine in June 1966. *G. W. Sharpe*

Ivatt 4MT 2-6-0 No 43029 is at Oxenholme station in September 1963 during its time allocated to Tebay shed. Built at Horwich Works, No 43029 went new to Crewe South during the week ended 19 March 1949, moving to Sutton Oak two weeks later. Here it had a long stay until January 1957 when the move to Tebay was actioned. Apart from a brief spell at Carlisle Upperby in June 1960, No 43029 remained at Tebay until April 1967 when Lostock Hall became its final home. Withdrawn during the week ended 30 September 1967, it was stored until January 1968 and then sold to the Motherwell Machinery & Scrap Co for dismantling. *Pictorail*

Johnson 3F 0-6-0 No 43342 is seen at Rowsley shed on Sunday 28 February 1960. This was a design dating from 1885, with No 43342 being built in 1891 at Derby Works. By the end of 1962 only seven remained in traffic, including this example. It had been allocated to Rowsley since nationalisation and before, moving to Bedford in December 1962. No 43342 ended its career at Derby shed after transfer in May 1963, withdrawal coming the following August during the week ending the 24th and was cut up at the works. *B. K. B. Green/Initial Photographics*

Fowler 4F 0-6-0 No 43942 is seen at its home shed Royston in February 1962. Built by Armstrong Whitworth & Co Ltd in 1921, No 43942 spent its entire British Railways working life allocated to Royston and was withdrawn on 23 December 1963, going to Darlington Works for scrapping. *Pictorail*

43496	17C
43499	9G
43510	17A
43514	9D
43521	21A
43565	14E
43583	21A
43585	24H
43586	55F
43593	85C
43599	21A
43608	17B
43615	8B
43618	6K
43620	21A
43621	17A
43637	17B
43645	85C
43657	8B
43658	17A
43668	21A
43669	17B
43679	17A
43680	21A
43682	82G
43687	21A
43709	17B
43714	55E
43721	9G
43734	24B
43754	85C
43756	24H
43760	9D
43763	9G
43766	14E

Deeley 0-6-0 3F

43789	9G
43793	9G
43808	14E
43822	9D
43825	17C

Fowler 0-6-0 4F

43844	41E
43845	18A
43848	66B
43849	66B
43850	18B
43853	85C
43854	15D
43855	9G
43856	9G
43859	14B
43861	15D
43865	18A
43869	41E
43870	16A
43871	55B
43876	15D
43880	26D
43882	41D
43885	16B
43887	85C
43888	16A
43893	24G
43899	67B
43902	12A
43903	16B
43906	55D
43908	24L
43913	26D
43914	55D
43915	9G
43917	18B
43918	16A
43923	16B
43924	85C
43925	17A
43928	16A
43929	15A
43931	55B
43932	9G
43933	16B
43935	14E
43937	15C
43938	21A
43940	21A
43942	55D
43945	9F
43947	14A
43949	21A
43950	17A
43951	21A
43952	27D
43953	17A
43954	16A
43955	17A
43957	CW
43958	17A
43960	24G
43963	21A
43964	14B
43967	18C
43968	55B
43969	15C
43971	18A
43972	16B
43975	21A
43976	24D
43977	2B
43979	15D
43981	6K
43982	18C
43983	55D
43985	21A
43986	18C
43987	55B
43988	27E
43991	17B
43994	18A
43995	15A
43996	67D
43999	24G
44001	67A
44003	55B
44004	21A
44007	24G
44008	12A
44009	12A
44010	41E
44011	66A
44012	18A
44013	15C
44015	9G
44016	12B
44020	15A
44022	26A
44023	27E
44025	9G
44026	17B

LMS 0-6-0 4F

44027	21B
44028	55B

44030	15C	44070	41E	44115	5D	44157	12F	44192	8G
44034	15C	44071	41D	44117	8G	44158	15C	44193	66A
44035	12F	44074	5D	44118	18B	44159	67B	44194	65B
44036	41E	44075	8G	44119	24D	44160	21A	44195	9E
44038	27E	44076	8F	44121	8F	44162	18A	44196	66B
44039	55F	44078	9G	44122	18C	44164	17A	44197	24G
44040	27E	44079	5E	44123	85C	44165	21A	44198	67B
44041	24G	44080	17C	44124	17B	44166	15D	44199	65B
44042	17C	44081	12B	44125	8F	44167	85C	44200	18A
44043	18A	44083	24L	44126	5E	44168	21A	44202	16B
44044	55B	44085	15D	44127	8G	44169	9G	44203	17C
44045	85C	44086	8G	44128	41D	44170	55E	44205	41E
44046	17C	44087	55D	44129	41E	44171	14E	44207	55B
44047	17A	44089	41D	44130	18B	44172	17C	44208	5E
44048	5E	44091	16B	44131	18B	44174	41D	44209	85C
44049	17A	44092	21A	44132	16A	44176	17A	44210	14B
44051	14A	44094	55B	44133	18A	44177	18B	44211	21A
44053	18C	44096	26B	44134	17C	44178	18A	44212	41D
44054	18C	44097	55F	44135	82E	44179	21A	44213	21A
44055	55F	44098	55E	44137	21A	44180	15D	44214	17A
44056	56D	44099	55E	44138	17A	44181	12A	44215	16A
44057	21B	44100	17B	44139	16A	44182	15C	44216	55F
44059	9D	44101	17C	44143	21A	44183	12A	44218	27E
44060	12B	44102	82G	44146	82F	44184	21A	44219	2E
44061	8B	44104	41E	44149	24H	44185	21A	44220	24G
44062	56A	44106	18A	44150	15D	44186	12E	44221	27D
44063	8B	44109	15D	44151	17A	44187	21A	44222	27D
44065	12F	44110	21D	44153	55B	44188	27E	44223	16A
44066	41E	44112	21A	44154	18B	44189	67C	44224	18A
44068	5D	44113	15D	44155	8E	44190	9G	44226	21A
44069	8F	44114	9G	44156	15A	44191	18B	44228	14E

At Stoke-on-Trent shed on Sunday 9 September 1962 is LMS 4F 0-6-0 No 44355 with a covered tender for use on snowplough duties. Built in June 1927 by Kerr Stuart & Co Ltd, No 44355 was withdrawn during the week ended 18 September 1965 from Westhouses shed after transfer there in December 1964. Scrapping was carried out at Ward's, Killamarsh. *L. Hanson*

44229	18B
44231	15C
44232	8B
44233	18B
44234	65F
44235	14B
44236	9G
44237	8B
44238	55B
44239	2E
44240	27D
44241	17B
44242	5E
44243	14B
44244	18B
44245	41D
44246	5D
44247	2E
44248	16A
44250	9F
44251	66A
44252	16B
44253	63A
44254	63A
44255	63B
44256	66A
44257	63A
44258	60A
44259	14A
44260	15D
44261	18C
44262	17C
44263	21A
44264	85C
44265	41D
44266	8G
44267	41E
44268	16B
44269	82E
44270	18A
44271	5D
44272	85C
44273	31B
44274	55D
44275	9E
44276	24H
44277	24G
44278	15A
44279	15D
44280	8F
44281	67B
44282	24G
44283	66A
44284	9G
44286	9F
44287	41D
44288	18C
44289	17A
44290	55D
44292	12F
44294	14B
44295	18A
44296	85C
44297	14A
44299	5E
44300	8G
44301	21D
44302	21B
44303	8F
44304	16A
44305	12A
44307	5D
44308	5D
44309	5D
44310	5D
44311	26D
44312	67B
44314	63A
44315	8G
44318	66A
44320	65F
44321	18B
44322	66A
44323	67A
44325	67B
44327	17C
44328	63A
44329	67C
44330	67A
44331	67C
44332	17B
44333	15D
44334	17C
44335	55B
44336	55E
44337	55E
44338	55E
44339	9D
44340	1C
44341	8E
44342	5E
44344	5D
44345	12E
44346	12B
44347	12E
44348	1C
44349	5E
44350	8G
44351	12E
44352	5E
44353	2E
44354	5E
44355	5F
44356	8B
44358	21B
44359	6B
44362	18B
44363	CW
44364	1E
44367	6K
44368	55B
44370	1E
44373	CW
44374	CW
44376	18A
44377	5B
44378	9E
44379	9F
44380	17B
44381	14B
44384	8B
44386	5E
44387	18B
44388	18A
44389	6G
44390	12F
44392	9E
44393	5D
44394	17A
44395	5D
44396	9E
44397	1E
44398	24D
44399	24L
44400	55F
44401	16A
44402	9E
44403	15C
44404	41E
44405	5E
44407	9F
44408	55E
44411	82E
44413	17C
44414	15C
44416	16B
44417	82G
44418	16B
44419	17C
44420	17A
44421	17A
44422	82G
44424	5D
44425	17A
44426	41D
44428	17C
44429	17C
44431	26A
44432	5D
44433	17A
44434	17B
44435	17B
44436	17B
44437	41D
44439	12F
44440	1C
44441	14A
44442	1C
44443	12E
44444	21E
44445	24L
44446	55D
44447	1E
44448	21B
44449	12F
44450	5E
44451	12A
44452	5B
44454	12E
44455	5D
44456	8E
44457	56A
44458	55E
44460	24D
44461	12F
44462	27E
44463	18C
44464	27D
44465	15A
44466	82E
44467	55B
44468	24G
44469	24L
44470	16B
44472	16A
44475	41E
44476	15A
44478	6H
44479	24D
44481	27E
44482	41E
44484	21B
44485	56A
44486	27D
44487	12E
44489	9E
44490	8F
44491	2E
44492	21D
44493	8G
44494	8B
44497	8G
44499	5D
44500	5D
44501	9F
44504	6H
44505	12F
44508	9D
44509	31B
44512	21B
44514	21E
44516	21A
44517	21D
44518	41E
44519	15C
44520	21A
44521	31B
44522	2E
44523	82E
44524	2E
44525	6G
44526	17B
44527	17B
44528	17B
44529	14A
44530	15C
44531	14B
44532	14B
44533	9E
44534	82E
44535	41E
44536	5D
44537	12E
44538	17B
44539	15D
44540	17A
44541	17B
44542	17B
44543	26A
44544	27D
44545	17C
44548	5D
44549	12F
44550	55D
44551	17B
44552	17B
44553	82E
44554	9F
44556	17C
44557	82G
44558	82F
44559	82F
44560	82G
44561	82F
44562	17B
44564	9E
44565	9E
44566	9E
44567	24G
44568	41D
44569	82E
44570	55B
44571	21A
44572	14B
44573	41E
44574	15A
44575	15A
44576	41D
44577	16A
44578	17A
44579	24G
44580	21A
44581	14A
44582	55D
44583	21A
44584	55B
44586	55B
44587	9E
44588	17C
44589	8B
44591	17B
44592	5B
44593	5D
44594	12A
44595	6B
44596	8G
44597	17B
44598	18B
44599	17B
44601	12E
44602	17C
44603	18C
44604	55E
44605	27E
44606	41E

Stanier 4-6-0 5MT

44658	16A
44659	21A
44660	21A
44661	6J
44662	55A
44663	21A
44664	17A
44665	9E

44666	21A
44667	15C
44668	12A
44669	12A
44670	12A
44671	12A
44672	12A
44673	12A
44674	12A
44675	12A
44676	12E
44677	65B
44678	5A
44679	5A
44680	5A
44681	5A
44682	8A
44683	5A
44684	5A
44685	5A
44686	6G
44687	6G
44688	14B
44689	27C
44690	15C
44691	14E
44692	27C
44693	56F
44694	56F
44695	56F
44696	26A
44697	26A
44698	63A
44699	67A
44700	66E
44701	66E
44702	65A
44703	61B
44704	63A
44705	63A
44706	67A
44707	65A
44708	26F
44709	24L
44710	21D
44711	2A
44712	2A
44713	5B
44714	5A
44715	2A
44716	2A
44717	9E
44718	67B
44719	66A
44720	63A
44721	63A
44722	63A
44723	67A
44724	63A
44725	12A
44726	12A
44727	12A
44728	27C
44729	27C
44730	24E
44731	24E
44732	24E
44733	24E
44734	26A
44735	26A
44736	26A
44737	24E
44738	6G
44739	6G
44740	6G
44741	8C
44742	8C
44743	27A
44744	27A
44745	27A
44746	26A
44747	9A
44748	9A
44749	8C
44750	8C
44751	8C
44752	9B
44753	55A
44754	8C
44755	9B
44756	55A
44757	55A
44758	8A
44759	5A
44760	2A
44761	5A
44762	5A
44763	5A
44764	5A
44765	5A
44766	21B
44767	27A
44768	8A
44769	8A
44770	5A
44771	2A
44772	8A
44773	8A
44774	14A
44775	21A
44776	21A
44777	14A
44778	24E
44779	24E
44780	1A
44781	26B
44782	26B
44783	66A
44784	60A
44785	60A
44786	65B
44787	65A
44788	63A
44789	68C
44790	12A
44791	67A
44792	12A
44793	66E
44794	61B
44795	12A
44796	63A
44797	63A
44798	67A
44799	63A
44800	6B
44801	67A
44802	6J
44803	26A
44804	21A
44805	21A
44806	16A
44807	6J
44808	26F
44809	9E
44810	21A
44811	15C
44812	21A
44813	21A
44814	21A
44815	15C
44816	14A
44817	14B
44818	21A
44819	15E
44820	66B
44821	14B
44822	14B
44823	26B
44824	55A
44825	21A
44826	55A
44827	8B
44828	55A
44829	21C
44830	15E
44831	2A
44832	5B
44833	2A
44834	5B
44835	89A
44836	2A
44837	21D
44838	8A
44839	21A
44840	21B
44841	21A
44842	6B
44843	15C
44844	1A
44845	26A
44846	14B
44847	15E
44848	15C
44849	55A
44850	66B
44851	17A
44852	55A
44853	55A
44854	55A
44855	8A
44856	16A
44857	55A
44858	21A
44859	21A
44860	2A
44861	16A
44862	2A
44863	2A
44864	8C
44865	21D
44866	2A
44867	5D
44868	9B
44869	2E
44870	2A
44871	5D
44872	21D
44873	21B
44874	24L
44875	21B
44876	21D
44877	12A
44878	12A
44879	63A
44880	65B
44881	65B
44882	12E
44883	12A
44884	12A
44885	68B
44886	12A
44887	27C
44888	21A
44889	24B
44890	26A
44891	26A
44892	24L
44893	26A
44894	24B
44895	26A
44896	55C
44897	2A
44898	12A
44899	12A
44900	12A
44901	12A
44902	12A
44903	12A
44904	24L
44905	24L
44906	8A
44907	8A
44908	65A
44909	2A
44910	21B
44911	9B
44912	56C
44913	6H
44914	21B
44915	2A
44916	1A
44917	6B
44918	16A
44919	21A
44920	21A
44921	63A
44922	65B
44923	65B
44924	63A
44925	63A
44926	24E
44927	24E
44928	27A
44929	26B
44930	24E
44931	63A
44932	16D
44933	26A
44934	26A
44935	6B
44936	2E
44937	9B
44938	2A
44939	12B
44940	24B
44941	14A
44942	21D
44943	55A
44944	21A
44945	21A
44946	56F
44947	24E
44948	24B
44949	24B
44950	24E
44951	56D
44952	66E
44953	66E
44954	66E
44955	66E
44956	65A
44957	65A
44958	12A
44959	63A
44960	63A
44961	63A
44962	21A
44963	21A
44964	9E
44965	21A
44966	21A
44967	65A
44968	65A
44969	66B
44970	65A
44971	6B
44972	66A
44973	66A
44974	66A
44975	63B
44976	63B
44977	63B
44978	63A
44979	63A
44980	63A
44981	21A
44982	24F
44983	55A
44984	14B
44985	14E
44986	8B
44987	26B
44988	24F
44989	27C
44990	56F

A variation on a Stanier 'Black Five' theme — No 44744 at Willesden shed in August 1963. This was one of a batch of 20 engines fitted with Caprotti valve gear and had been added to stock on 3 July 1948 after construction at Crewe Works. First allocation was Leeds Holbeck. A move to Bristol Barrow Road took place during the week ended 9 July 1949, then it went back to Holbeck during the week ended 18 October 1952, and once again to Barrow Road during the week ended 21 May 1955. Derby became the allocation in May 1957, then Liverpool Bank Hall in June 1958, Southport in March 1962 and finally Manchester Longsight in May 1963. Withdrawn during the week ended 9 November 1963, it returned to Crewe Works for scrapping. *P. H. Groom*

Stanier 5MT 4-6-0 No 44759 is on a southbound freight at Carstairs on Saturday 9 June 1962. New from Crewe Works in September 1947, the first allocation was Perth. This was a short stay as by January 1948 it was based at Crewe North. Subsequent transfers saw No 44759 at Manchester Longsight in June 1950, Chester in February 1951, Crewe North in March 1951, Crewe South in September 1964, Workington in April 1967 and finally Carlisle Kingmoor in September 1967. Withdrawn during the week ended 18 November 1967, it was scrapped at Motherwell Machinery and Scrap Co. Alongside in the platform is another 'Black Five', No 45022, which dated from August 1934 and was also first allocated to Perth. Withdrawal for this locomotive came during the week ended 16 September 1963 from Edinburgh Dalry Road shed. *G. W. Sharpe*

Another 'Black Five' variant, No 44766 with double chimney and Timken roller bearings is at Stafford in ex-works condition in April 1962. This was the last 'Black Five' to be built under the LMS, being released to traffic from Crewe Works during the week ended 27 December 1947 and allocated to Crewe North. Later moves saw No 44766 at Liverpool Edge Hill in April 1949, Crewe North in May 1949, Birmingham Monument Lane in July 1959, Bescot in July 1960, Stourbridge Junction in March 1966, Llandudno Junction in June 1966, Chester in October 1966, and finally Crewe South in May 1967, where withdrawal took place during the week ended 19 August 1967. After storage until December 1967, it then went to Cashmore's at Newport for cutting up. *G. W. Sharpe*

Stanier 5MT 4-6-0 No 45020 is at Nuneaton shed in April 1963, when based at Willesden and shortly before a move to Stoke-on-Trent. This was the first 'Black Five' to enter service in August 1934 after construction at Vulcan Foundry, and was first allocated to Perth. Withdrawal came from Stoke shed during the week ended 11 December 1965 and cutting up was later carried out at Cashmore's, Great Bridge. *Author's collection*

44991	66A	45034	8C	45077	24E	45120	12A	45163	12A
44992	67B	45035	8B	45078	24E	45121	66B	45164	67A
44993	12A	45036	64C	45079	55C	45122	12A	45165	66C
44994	64C	45037	1E	45080	55C	45123	60A	45166	66E
44995	68B	45038	21D	45081	12A	45124	67B	45167	67D
44996	65A	45039	8A	45082	12A	45125	65F	45168	66C
44997	63A	45040	21A	45083	12A	45126	12A	45169	68B
44998	63A	45041	8A	45084	65J	45127	64C	45170	64C
44999	63A	45042	6B	45085	66B	45128	5B	45171	67A
45000	5B	45043	6B	45086	64C	45129	26F	45172	66E
45001	5B	45044	12B	45087	66E	45130	2A	45173	66E
45002	5B	45045	5A	45088	21A	45131	8A	45174	66E
45003	5D	45046	5A	45089	1E	45132	5A	45175	66E
45004	5A	45047	63A	45090	66C	45133	26F	45176	66B
45005	8A	45048	5B	45091	8A	45134	24J	45177	65F
45006	21A	45049	65J	45092	8F	45135	8F	45178	65F
45007	67B	45050	2A	45093	5A	45136	63A	45179	66C
45008	66B	45051	24J	45094	8A	45137	8C	45180	21B
45009	66B	45052	21D	45095	26F	45138	12A	45181	8A
45010	67B	45053	64C	45096	26F	45139	2A	45182	26F
45011	66E	45054	24L	45097	24L	45140	8C	45183	64C
45012	12A	45055	6B	45098	66A	45141	12E	45184	2A
45013	12A	45056	2A	45099	66B	45142	5A	45185	12B
45014	24L	45057	8F	45100	12A	45143	89A	45186	21A
45015	8A	45058	21D	45101	26A	45144	6H	45187	8A
45016	65J	45059	14A	45102	24E	45145	89A	45188	8A
45017	8F	45060	5D	45103	26B	45146	21B	45189	5A
45018	12A	45061	27C	45104	26A	45147	1E	45190	89A
45019	8F	45062	14A	45105	27C	45148	5A	45191	1A
45020	1E	45063	55C	45106	12B	45149	6A	45192	67B
45021	5A	45064	21B	45107	24F	45150	8B	45193	24L
45022	64C	45065	21D	45108	8F	45151	66B	45194	67C
45023	64C	45066	66A	45109	8F	45152	66B	45195	26B
45024	8F	45067	5B	45110	6J	45153	65B	45196	8A
45025	12B	45068	24B	45111	12B	45154*	26A	45197	12B
45026	8F	45069	8A	45112	12A	45155	64C	45198	9B
45027	1A	45070	6B	45113	2A	45156*	26A	45199	26F
45028	6B	45071	8C	45114	21D	45157*	65B	45200	24E
45029	66B	45072	6B	45115	65B	45158*	65B	45201	24E
45030	64C	45073	8C	45116	16D	45159	65B	45202	26A
45031	6B	45074	5B	45117	60A	45160	67C	45203	26A
45032	8C	45075	55C	45118	12A	45161	66E	45204	55C
45033	5A	45076	26A	45119	65B	45162	61B	45205	24B

45206 24F
45207 56D
45208 56D
45209 24B
45210 27A
45211 55C
45212 24F
45213 65J
45214 65J
45215 16D
45216 24B
45217 16D
45218 27C
45219 56C
45220 26A
45221 21A
45222 2A
45223 2F
45224 26A
45225 5A
45226 24F
45227 24E
45228 27C
45229 24B
45230 24L
45231 21D
45232 26A
45233 26A
45234 16D
45235 5A
45236 12B
45237 5A
45238 14E
45239 9E
45240 5A
45241 5A
45242 8A
45243 5A
45244 12B
45245 66E
45246 12B
45247 6H
45248 5B
45249 8A
45250 5A
45251 67D
45252 26F
45253 21A
45254 5A
45255 26A
45256 8B
45257 5A
45258 12E
45259 12B
45260 21A
45261 26B
45262 15C
45263 21A
45264 15C
45265 21A
45266 67B
45267 14B
45268 21A
45269 21A
45270 5A
45271 8B
45272 21A
45273 55C
45274 14A
45275 6B
45276 1A
45277 14B
45278 1A
45279 14A
45280 21A
45281 8F
45282 9A
45283 89A
45284 8A
45285 14A
45286 12B
45287 21B
45288 1A
45289 5A
45290 26A
45291 9B
45292 1E
45293 12B
45294 26F
45295 12B
45296 12B
45297 5B
45298 89A
45299 5B
45300 5B
45301 2E
45302 2E
45303 24L
45304 26F
45305 9A
45306 24L
45307 8A
45308 21C
45309 66B
45310 21C
45311 5A
45312 8C
45313 8F
45314 8F
45315 5B
45316 12B
45317 12B
45318 24E
45319 65F
45320 66A
45321 8B
45322 21D
45323 12B
45324 2A
45325 6B
45326 24L
45327 8A
45328 8B
45329 8C
45330 12A
45331 1E
45332 21D
45333 15C
45334 12A
45335 14A
45336 26A
45337 26B
45338 26B
45339 26A
45340 8A
45341 26A
45342 17A
45343 8B
45344 5A
45345 6H
45346 17A
45347 8F
45348 5A
45349 21D
45350 5D
45351 12B
45352 26F
45353 21D
45354 8B
45355 64C
45356 65B
45357 65J
45358 65B
45359 65J
45360 64C
45361 67A
45362 67A
45363 12A
45364 12F
45365 67A
45366 67A
45367 64C
45368 12B
45369 5A
45370 8C
45371 12B
45372 8F
45373 8F
45374 1A
45375 8C
45376 8A
45377 24E
45378 26F
45379 1E
45380 8B
45381 8B
45382 9B
45383 12E
45384 67D
45385 9A
45386 8C
45387 21B
45388 8F
45389 65J
45390 8A
45391 5B
45392 2E
45393 1E
45394 24L
45395 21D
45396 65J
45397 12B
45398 8A
45399 8A
45400 65J
45402 12B
45403 5B
45404 8C
45405 21C
45406 89A
45407 16A
45408 8F
45409 26F
45410 21B
45411 26F
45412 8A
45413 8A
45414 8B
45415 24E
45416 14E
45417 6H
45418 21D
45419 2A
45420 26F
45421 8A
45422 89A
45423 65J
45424 26F
45425 8F
45426 5A
45427 2E
45428 55C
45429 5A
45430 21D
45431 8F
45432 68B
45433 66B
45434 9A
45435 26A
45436 24E
45437 12B
45438 6B
45439 21C
45440 8A
45441 6J
45442 24E
45443 65B
45444 16D
45445 12E
45446 5A
45447 21A
45448 21D
45449 8F
45450 16D
45451 12B
45452 66E
45453 63A
45454 2E
45455 12A
45456 67D
45457 67D
45458 66A
45459 66A
45460 67A
45461 63A
45462 66B
45463 67D
45464 24E
45465 63A
45466 12A
45467 67B
45468 65B
45469 61B
45470 60A
45471 65B
45472 63A
45473 63A
45474 63A
45475 63A
45476 64C
45477 64C
45478 66A
45479 60A
45480 68B
45481 12A
45482 65F
45483 64C
45484 66B
45485 66B
45486 67C
45487 65F
45488 67A
45489 67B
45490 67D
45491 12A
45492 66B
45493 2A
45494 5B
45495 8B
45496 65F
45497 67D
45498 66B
45499 65B

'Patriot' Class 4-6-0 6P5F

45504* 82E
45505* 12B
45506* 82E
45507* 12B
45510 12B

Rebuilt 'Patriot' Class 4-6-0 7P

45512* 12B

'Patriot' Class 4-6-0 6P5F

45513 8A
45515* 26A
45517 27A
45518* 8A
45519* 82E
45520* 8A

Rebuilt 'Patriot' Class 4-6-0 7P

45521* 8F
45522* 26A
45523* 1A

'Patriot' Class 4-6-0 6P5F

45524* 8A

All the remaining unrebuilt 'Patriot' class 4-6-0s were withdrawn during 1962, including No 45505 *The Royal Army Ordnance Corps* seen here with a high straight-sided tender, which it acquired on 2 April 1960. This is a view at Nuneaton Ashby Junction on Saturday 7 May 1960, when No 45505 was a Longsight-based engine, on a freight working for the Ashby line. No 45505 was built at Crewe in July 1932 and first allocated to Liverpool Edge Hill. From Longsight it moved to Carlisle Upperby in September 1960, then to Lancaster Green Ayre shed during the week ended 10 February 1962. After withdrawal No 45505 was scrapped at Crewe Works.
B. O. Hilton

Another unrebuilt 'Patriot' to be scrapped in 1962 was No 45541 *Duke of Sutherland* seen here on Saturday 2 September 1961 leaving Nuneaton shed's 60ft turntable. Built at Crewe in August 1933, the first allocation was Crewe North. From October 1947 to November 1959 No 45541 was allocated to Carlisle Upperby, then to Rugby and finally to Nuneaton during the week ended 31 December 1960. After withdrawal No 45541 returned to Crewe Works for cutting up.
K. C. H. Fairey

Eighteen 'Patriots' were rebuilt with larger taper boilers, and this is one of them, No 45523 *Bangor*, at Willesden shed in July 1963. First allocated to Camden when new from Crewe Works in March 1933, it was rebuilt in October 1948 and when completed No 45523 went to Crewe North shed. Later transfers were to Camden during the week ended 7 July 1951 and Willesden during the week ended 21 January 1961. Withdrawal took place during the week ended 25 January 1964 and scrapping was carried out at Crewe Works. *R. H. G. Simpson*

Rebuilt 'Patriot' Class 4-6-0 7P

45525* 6G
45526* 12B
45527* 6J
45528* 1A
45529* 1A
45530* 6G
45531* 8A
45532* 21A

'Patriot' Class 4-6-0 6P5F

45533* 8A

Rebuilt 'Patriot' Class 4-6-0 7P

45534* 6G
45535* 8A
45536* 41D

'Patriot' Class 4-6-0 6P5F

45537* 2B
45538* 2B

Rebuilt 'Patriot' Class 4-6-0 7P

45540* 21A

'Patriot' Class 4-6-0 6P5F

45541* 2B
45542 2B
45543* 8A

Rebuilt 'Patriot' Class 4-6-0 7P

45545* 12B

'Patriot' Class 4-6-0 6P5F

45546* 8B
45547 8A
45548* 2B
45549 8B
45550 8B
45551 8A

'Jubilee' Class 4-6-0 6P5F

45552* 5A
45553* 5B
45554* 5A
45555* 5B
45556* 5A
45557* 17B
45558* 26F
45559* 24E
45560* 5A
45561* 14B
45562* 55A
45563* 26F
45564* 55A
45565* 55A
45566* 55A
45567* 5A
45568* 55A
45569* 55A
45570* 41D
45571* 24E
45572* 89A
45573* 55A
45574* 24E
45575* 17A
45576* 41D
45577* 89A
45578* 5A
45579* 17B
45580* 24E
45581* 55C
45582* 24L
45583* 8B
45584* 24E
45585* 17B
45586* 21D
45587* 5A
45588* 12B
45589* 55A
45590* 41D
45591* 5A
45592* 24L
45593* 21D
45594* 41D
45595* 5A
45596* 12B
45597* 55A
45598* 17B
45599* 2B
45600* 26F
45601* 26A
45602* 41D
45603* 2B
45604* 5A
45605* 55A
45606* 24L
45607* 41D
45608* 55A
45610* 17B
45611* 17B
45612* 17B
45613* 5A
45614* 17A
45615* 17B
45617* 5B
45618* 17B
45620* 17B
45621* 67A
45622* 14B
45623* 5B
45624* 2B
45625* 5A
45626* 17B
45627* 41D
45628* 14B
45629* 5A
45631* 5A
45632* 12B
45633* 24L
45634* 5B
45635* 26A
45636* 17B
45638* 8B
45639* 55A
45640* 12A
45641* 17B
45642* 26A
45643* 5A
45644* 5B
45645* 26F
45646* 55C
45647* 21D
45648* 17B
45649* 17B
45650* 17B
45651* 89A
45652* 26A
45653* 24E
45654* 41D
45655* 8B
45656* 41D
45657* 12A
45658* 55A
45659* 55A
45660* 89A
45661* 26A
45662* 89A
45663* 26F
45664* 41D
45665* 67A
45666* 5B
45667* 17B
45668* 17B
45669* 2B
45670* 2A
45671* 8B
45672* 2A
45673* 67A
45674* 5A
45675* 55A
45676* 5A
45677* 67A
45678* 12B
45679* 26A
45680* 12B
45681* 12B
45682* 82E
45683* 41D
45684* 2A
45685* 82E
45686* 24L
45687* 67A
45688* 12B
45689* 5A
45690* 82E
45691* 12B
45692* 67A
45693* 67A
45694* 55A
45695* 55C
45696* 24L
45697* 12A
45698* 27A
45699* 89A
45700* 26A
45701* 26A
45702* 12B
45703* 12B
45704* 2A
45705* 24E
45706* 26A
45707* 67A
45708* 55C
45709* 5B
45710* 26A
45711* 67A
45712* 14B
45713* 12A
45714* 24L
45715* 12A
45716* 12B
45717* 27A
45718* 12A
45719* 27A
45720* 67A
45721* 5A
45722* 2A
45723* 5A
45724* 12A
45725* 41D
45726* 5A
45727* 67A
45728* 12B
45729* 12A
45730* 24L
45731* 12B
45732* 12A
45733* 2A
45734* 12B

Rebuilt 'Jubilee' Class 4-6-0 7P

45735* 1A
45736* 5A

'Jubilee' Class 4-6-0 6P5F

45737* 5A
45738* 12B
45739* 55A
45740* 21D
45741* 12B
45742* 12B

'Royal Scot' Class 4-6-0 7P

46100* 16A
46101* 6G
46102* 66A
46103* 21A
46104* 66A
46105* 66A
46106* 21A
46107* 66A
46108* 12B
46109* 56F
46110* 8A
46111* 1A
46112* 16A
46113* 56D
46114* 6J
46115* 9A
46116* 8A
46117* 56D
46118* 21A
46119* 8A
46120* 6G
46121* 66A
46122* 21A
46123* 21A
46124* 8A
46125* 5A
46126* 1A
46127* 5A
46128* 5A
46129* 12B
46130* 56F
46131* 41D
46132* 21A
46133* 26A
46134* 8A
46135* 5A
46136* 5A
46137* 21A
46138* 6J
46139* 26A
46140* 26A
46141* 21A
46142* 26A
46143* 9E
46144* 6G
46145* 56D
46146* 1A
46147* 41D
46148* 41D
46149* 9A
46150* 6J
46151* 41D
46152* 6G
46153* 9E
46154* 6G
46155* 5A
46156* 6J
46157* 21A
46158* 9E
46159* 1A
46160* 21A
46161* 8F
46162* 21A
46163* 6J
46164* 41D
46165* 8F
46166* 5A
46167* 8F
46168* 8F
46169* 5A
46170* 5A

'Princess Royal' Class 4-6-2 8P

46200* 24L
46201* 12A
46203* 24L
46206* 2A
46208* 8A
46209* 5A

'Jubilee' class 4-6-0 No 45569 *Tasmania* is at Shrewsbury shed in January 1962 just after its last general overhaul at Crewe Works. Built by the North British Locomotive Co Ltd, it was added to traffic in August 1934 and first allocated to Crewe North. Leeds Holbeck added No 45569 to its fleet during the week ended 31 October 1942 and here it remained until withdrawal during the week ended 25 April 1964, and then to Crewe Works for scrapping. *G. W. Sharpe*

'Jubilee' class 4-6-0 No 45638 *Zanzibar* is at Crewe South shed after a visit to Crewe Works for a general overhaul in February 1961, when allocated to Llandudno Junction. Built at Crewe, it entered service in December 1934. By October 1961 it was allocated to Warrington Dallam, from where it was withdrawn during the week ended 14 March 1964. It was another of the class to be cut up at Crewe Works. *Pictorail*

'Jubilee' class 4-6-0 No 45675 *Hardy* with unrebuilt 'Patriots' Nos 45505 and 45507 at Lancaster Green Ayre shed on Saturday 17 March 1962. Built at Crewe, it entered traffic in December 1935 and was another long-time Leeds Holbeck engine, going there during the week ended 2 October 1948 from Crewe North and remaining until withdrawn on 24 June 1967. Cashmore's at Great Bridge carried out the scrapping in October 1967 after storage at Wakefield shed. *G. W. Sharpe*

'Jubilee' class 4-6-0 No 45728 *Defiance*, paired with a smaller Fowler-type tender which it acquired in January 1959, passes Stirling shed on a van train in June 1961. Another Crewe Works production, it had entered traffic in October 1936 and was first allocated to Willesden. Since March 1940 it had been allocated to Carlisle Kingmoor, moving across the city to Upperby during the week ended 26 August 1961 and back again to Kingmoor during the week ended 10 March 1962. The final move was to Manchester Agecroft during the week ended 18 August 1962, with withdrawal following in October 1962. After storage, cutting up was not carried out until November 1963, and this was at Cowlairs Works, Glasgow. *G. W. Sharpe*

Two 'Jubilees' were rebuilt with larger boilers and double chimneys. This is No 45735 *Comet* at Willesden shed in April 1963, where it had been allocated since transfer from Liverpool Edge Hill during the week ended 14 January 1961. During the week ended 12 October 1963 it moved to Annesley, from where it was withdrawn during the week ended 3 October 1964 and scrapped at Cashmore's, Great Bridge. No 45735 had been placed in traffic from Crewe Works in November 1936 and rebuilt during a heavy general repair at Crewe in April/May 1942. The smoke deflectors were added during another works visit in January 1952. *P. H. Groom*

'Royal Scot' class 4-6-0 No 46106 *Gordon Highlander* is at Cricklewood shed early in January 1963, with nameplates removed. This is something of a mystery as No 46106 had been withdrawn in December 1962. It had, presumably, been unofficially reinstated for a short while to cope with the shortage of motive power as a result of the severe winter weather. By April 1963 it had been reduced to scrap metal at Crewe Works. Built by the North British Locomotive Co Ltd, it had entered traffic in September 1927 at Crewe North shed. Rebuilt with a taper boiler in September 1949, it was unique in having the BR-style standard smoke deflectors which had been fitted in July 1954. *P. H. Groom*

'Royal Scot' class 4-6-0 No 46115 *Scots Guardsman* is at Oxenholme in June 1962 on a southbound express. Built by the North British Locomotive Co Ltd in October 1927, it was rebuilt in August 1947. When this photo was taken it was a Manchester Longsight engine, moving to Wigan Springs Branch in May 1964, Carlisle Upperby the following August, and Carlisle Kingmoor three months later. It was the last of the class to be withdrawn during the week ended 1 January 1966 and was saved from the scrapyard. It is still to be seen in preservation. *Pictorail*

The first of the Stanier Pacifics to be built was No 46200 *The Princess Royal* seen here at Camden shed in June 1962. Built at Crewe Works, it was officially on view to the press at Euston station in grey undercoat and without a name on Wednesday 28 June 1933. After being fully completed and painted it powered a special press run on Tuesday 15 August 1933 and was allocated to Camden. Throughout its life it served from Crewe North, Camden and Liverpool Edge Hill until the week ended 2 September 1961, when it was allocated to Carnforth, along with No 46203 *Princess Margaret Rose*, both being placed into store. Both were taken out of storage and returned to traffic at Carlisle Upperby during the week ended 27 January 1962 and reallocated to Carlisle Kingmoor during the week ended 7 April 1962. All the class was withdrawn during 1962 with No 46200 the last to go. After storage at both Kingmoor and Upperby, this magnificent engine was towed to Connell's yard at Coatbridge for scrapping in September 1964. *P. H. Groom*

'Princess Coronation' class 4-6-2 No 46246 *City of Manchester* is at the old Euston station Platform 1 in June 1961 after arrival from the north, still with a good head of steam. Built at Crewe Works and entering traffic in August 1943, No 46246 was first allocated to Camden. A move to Crewe North during the week ended 1 May 1948, returning to Camden during the week ended 11 June 1960, were the only transfers. Placed in store on 5 November 1962, withdrawal was authorised during the week ended 26 January 1963, with storage continuing until April. By the end of May the engine had been reduced to scrap metal at Crewe Works. *R. H. G. Simpson*

'Princess Coronation' class 4-6-2 No 46256 *Sir William A. Stanier, F.R.S.* is at Derby on Saturday 25 August 1962 being removed from display after the works open day, to be prepared for return to its home shed Crewe North. This was the last Pacific to be built under the LMS, taking to the rails on 13 December 1947. The final member of the class, No 46257, did not enter traffic until British Railways days in May 1948. For No 46256, Crewe North was the first and last allocation, with a time at Camden and Carlisle Upperby in between. Withdrawn during the week ended 3 October 1964, this prime candidate for preservation was not spared the cutting torch, being scrapped at Cashmore's, Great Bridge. *K. C. H. Fairey*

'Princess Coronation' Class 4-6-2 8P

46220*	12B
46221*	12A
46222*	66A
46223*	66A
46224*	66A
46225*	12B
46226*	12A
46227*	66A
46228*	5A
46229*	8A
46230*	66A
46231*	66A
46232*	66A
46233*	8A
46234*	12B
46235*	5A
46236*	12B
46237*	12A
46238*	12B
46239*	1B
46240*	1B
46241*	8A
46242*	66A
46243*	8A
46244*	12A
46245*	1B
46246*	1B
46247*	12A
46248*	5A
46249*	66A
46250*	12B
46251*	5A
46252*	12A
46253*	5A
46254*	5A
46255*	12A
46256*	5A
46257*	12A

Ivatt 2-6-0 2MT

46400	31A
46401	89D
46402	17A
46403	15B
46404	15B
46405	27B
46406	26D
46408	50D
46409	50D
46410	24J
46411	26A
46412	27B
46413	56A
46414	26D
46415	50D
46416	26D
46417	26D
46418	26A
46419	26A
46420	2B
46421	21B
46422	8F
46423	21D
46424	1A
46425	21B
46426	24J
46427	21D
46428	8F
46429	5D
46430	5D
46431	1C
46432	12F
46433	12F
46434	12B
46435	56F
46436	26D
46437	26A
46438	56E
46439	27B
46440	17A
46441	24J
46442	12F
46443	21A
46444	15B
46445	2A
46446	2A
46447	2B
46448	8F
46449	24C
46450	41D
46451	67B
46452	24G
46453	55A
46454	21A
46455	12B
46456	21B
46457	12B
46458	12B
46459	21B
46460	63C
46461	64A
46462	64A
46463	62B
46464	62B
46465	31A
46466	31A
46467	67B
46468	63C
46469	31A
46470	8F
46471	52A
46472	1A
46473	52A
46474	52B
46475	51A
46476	52D
46477	51A
46478	50D

46479	52B
46480	50A
46481	50A
46482	52D
46483	56E
46484	26A
46485	26B
46486	26B
46487	26A
46488	12F
46489	12B
46490	21B
46491	12F
46492	21D
46493	55A
46494	31A
46495	17A
46496	15B
46497	17A
46498	55A
46499	17A
46500	17A
46501	24G
46502	17A
46503	89D
46504	89D
46505	89D
46506	82B
46507	89D
46508	89D
46509	89D
46510	89D
46511	89D
46512	89D
46513	89D
46514	89D
46515	89D
46516	89D
46517	82B
46518	89D
46519	89D
46520	89D
46521	89D
46522	89D
46523	89D
46524	89D
46525	82B
46526	89D
46527	89D

LMS/BR 0-4-0ST 0F

47000	17A
47001	27A
47002	24C
47003	18C
47004	18C
47005	6C
47006	17A
47007	17C
47008	24C
47009	6C

Fowler 0-6-0T 2F

47160	6C
47161	24F
47163	66D
47164	6C
47165	26C
47166	8A
47168	66D

Johnson 0-6-0T 3F

47201	24B
47202	14B
47207	26A
47211	14A
47213	14A
47217	26A
47223	14B
47224	26A
47225	27E
47228	27E
47230	27A
47231	18A
47235	27E
47236	17A
47248	14A
47250	18B
47257	17A
47259	27B

LMS 0-6-0T 3F

47261	14B
47264	14E
47266	56A
47267	6H
47269	12B
47270	8F
47272	18C
47273	15A
47275	82F
47276	85D
47278	18C
47279	14E
47280	5D
47281	12A
47283	14B
47284	26A
47285	8A
47286	WW
47287	12E
47288	12B
47289	8A
47290	12F
47292	12B
47293	24C
47294	2B
47295	12B
47297	6A
47298	8G
47300	26F
47302	1A
47304	1A
47305	27B
47306	27A
47307	1C
47308	85D
47310	5C
47313	17B
47314	8C
47316	82F
47317	12E
47318	2E
47319	24C
47320	16A
47321	6J
47322	24L
47324	6C
47325	17A
47326	12B
47327	17A
47328	33B
47330	5B
47332	12A
47333	24B
47336	8A
47338	5B
47340	12B
47341	21E
47342	12B
47343	6F
47344	12F
47345	12E
47348	WW
47349	8D
47350	6K
47351	33B
47353	8A
47354	5B
47355	1C
47356	24J
47357	8A
47358	12A
47359	5C
47360	24C
47361	12F
47362	8B
47365	26F
47366	8G
47367	18A
47368	6J
47371	6A
47372	6C
47373	12E
47375	24L
47376	8G
47377	12B
47378	26F
47379	56E
47380	5D
47381	24J
47383	8C
47384	5B
47385	2B
47386	24C
47388	8C
47389	6A
47390	12F
47391	5B
47392	8F
47393	8G
47395	8F
47396	2B
47397	5B
47399	5E
47400	5B
47402	HW
47404	8A
47406	8B
47408	12B
47410	6B
47412	8A
47413	24C
47414	5B
47415	12B
47416	8A
47417	85C
47419	55C
47422	85C
47423	18C
47424	41E
47425	27B
47426	41E
47427	24G
47428	24G
47429	HW
47430	26F
47431	5B
47432	14A
47433	14A
47434	14A
47435	14A
47437	14B
47439	6J
47441	17A
47442	14B
47444	8F
47445	5B
47447	17C
47449	14B
47450	5B
47451	8C
47452	8G
47453	8G
47454	24G
47455	41E
47457	17C
47458	17B
47459	17C
47460	17C
47461	17C
47464	17B
47465	82F
47466	18B
47467	5B
47468	24J
47469	24J
47470	24J
47471	12A
47472	24C
47473	24L
47474	21B
47475	5C
47476	6J
47478	WW
47479	WW
47480	27A
47481	24J
47482	5B
47483	24J
47485	14B
47487	8A
47488	8A
47490	8G
47491	26F
47492	12A
47493	8C
47494	21E
47495	6F
47496	82F
47497	6C
47499	2E
47500	1E
47501	1A
47502	14B
47503	12E
47504	6A
47505	5B
47506	85C
47507	6C
47511	6H
47512	27B
47514	24L
47515	12A
47516	5B
47517	8F
47518	5C
47519	8A
47520	12E
47521	1E
47522	12F
47524	5B
47526	5B
47530	5B
47531	12E
47532	24J
47533	17A
47534	17A
47535	18C
47536	66B
47539	85C
47542	82G
47543	15C
47544	82E
47545	41E
47546	26A
47547	26A
47548	41D
47549	14E
47550	27A
47551	18A
47552	82E
47554	14B
47555	33B
47556	50A
47557	82F
47558	6G
47562	24B
47564	12E
47565	6C
47566	8A
47572	24C
47574	26B
47577	24G
47578	26B

47579 26B
47581 55C
47582 26A
47583 27A
47584 26D
47587 5D
47588 5C
47589 55C
47590 5C
47592 CW
47593 12F
47594 8B
47596 5E
47597 CW
47598 5E
47599 24J
47601 5B
47602 12B
47603 8B
47604 12F
47606 5E
47608 5B
47609 5D
47610 12F
47611 14B
47612 8C
47614 12B
47615 6B
47616 8D
47618 CW
47621 26D
47622 6F
47623 85C
47627 6C
47628 6F
47629 17A
47630 41E
47631 6G
47633 5E
47638 17A
47640 26A
47641 17B
47642 14B
47643 17B
47644 17A
47645 14B
47646 6B
47647 8C
47648 5B
47649 5C
47651 8C
47653 2B
47654 8B
47655 27B
47656 8A
47657 8B
47658 5D
47659 6C
47660 15A
47661 CW
47662 24J
47664 5B
47665 5C
47666 12B
47667 12A
47668 24L
47669 8B
47671 8F
47673 6B
47674 6C
47675 12E
47676 12E
47677 5B
47678 26B
47679 17C
47680 5B
47681 27E

Stanier 2-8-0 8F

48000 16A
48001 16B
48002 16A
48003 16B
48004 16B
48005 15B
48006 16B
48007 21A
48008 15B
48009 16B
48010 15A
48011 16B
48012 2A
48016 2B
48017 8E
48018 2A
48020 2B
48024 16A
48026 41D
48027 15A
48029 41E
48033 18B
48035 2A
48036 1A
48037 41E
48039 8E
48045 8D
48046 6B
48050 15B
48053 15D
48054 2B
48055 56D
48056 18C
48057 18A
48060 18A
48061 15A
48062 9D
48063 16B
48064 16A
48065 18C
48067 55D
48069 15B
48070 55D
48073 16B
48074 2B
48075 55B
48076 56D
48077 2B
48078 55D
48079 15B
48080 55B
48081 17C
48082 18C
48083 17A
48084 55B
48085 5B
48088 16B
48089 18C
48090 2E
48092 16B
48093 55D
48094 8B
48095 18C
48096 16B
48097 16B
48098 16B
48099 16A
48100 16B
48101 21A
48102 16B
48103 41E
48104 55A
48105 16B
48106 8B
48107 15B
48108 16A
48109 21A
48110 89A
48111 2B
48112 18B
48113 55D
48114 16B
48115 26A
48116 18C
48117 14A
48118 18A
48119 16B
48120 2A
48121 17A
48122 2E
48123 55D
48124 17A
48125 18C
48126 55B
48127 21A
48128 18A
48129 8B
48130 55D
48131 2E
48132 18A
48133 14A
48134 1A
48135 8E
48136 8D
48137 16B
48138 56D
48139 8D
48140 41D
48141 14A
48142 14A
48143 14A
48144 41E
48145 18A
48146 55D
48147 2E
48148 26A
48149 18A
48150 41D
48151 41D
48152 8A
48153 17A
48154 2B
48155 8E
48156 16B
48157 55A
48158 55A
48159 55D
48160 55B
48161 9F
48162 55D
48163 18A
48164 41E
48165 9D
48166 8E
48167 18A
48168 15B
48169 55D
48170 16A
48171 1A
48172 87F
48173 2A
48174 5C
48175 6B
48176 41E
48177 21A
48178 41D
48179 41D
48180 15B
48181 41E
48182 17B
48183 21A
48184 18A
48185 18A
48186 18A
48187 18C
48188 8B
48189 41E
48190 9F
48191 9F
48192 16B
48193 16A
48194 18A
48195 18A
48196 18A
48197 18A
48198 17A
48199 41E
48200 41E
48201 18A
48202 56D
48203 1E
48204 18A
48205 18C
48206 8D
48207 1E
48208 9F
48209 41D
48210 41E
48211 16A
48212 18C
48213 41E
48214 16B
48215 16B
48216 41D
48217 16A
48218 16A
48219 16B
48220 21A
48221 18A
48222 55D
48223 16B
48224 16B
48225 16B
48246 6G
48247 1A
48248 5B
48249 8A
48250 8C
48251 2B
48252 5B
48253 6B
48254 8E
48255 5B
48256 21B
48257 6C
48258 2B
48259 6B
48260 6C
48261 16A
48262 6C
48263 2B
48264 2B
48265 56D
48266 15A
48267 16B
48268 8B
48269 2E
48270 17A
48271 18A
48272 16B
48273 9E
48274 55B
48275 9D
48276 56D
48277 16B
48278 9D
48279 16A
48280 8A
48281 55D
48282 16B
48283 55A
48284 18C
48285 15B
48286 16A
48287 2B
48288 9E
48289 2B
48290 2E
48291 2B
48292 5B
48293 15B
48294 8C
48295 8E
48296 8D
48297 8C
48301 14A

Ivatt 2MT 2-6-0 No 46456 is at Keswick on a local on Thursday 10 August 1961. Built at Crewe Works and sent new to Crewe North for running-in purposes during the week ended 13 May 1950, it then went to Workington shed during the week ended 1 July 1950. Here it remained until transfer to Bescot during the week ended 23 September 1961, from where it was withdrawn during the week ended 25 September 1965 and later cut up at Cashmore's, Great Bridge. *G. W. Sharpe*

Built by Kitson's for the LMS to a design by Stanier, No 47000 was the first such constructed, entering traffic in November 1932 and initially allocated to Gloucester Barnwood. It is seen here at Derby shed in October 1963 after transfer in January 1959 from Rowsley, where it had been sub-shedded to work on the Cromford & High Peak line. Apart from a short stay at Westhouses in May 1960, No 47000 remained at Derby until withdrawn during the week ended 8 October 1966, and was then sold to Cashmore's at Great Bridge for scrap. *Pictorail*

From the same class, but different in design to the earlier Nos 47000 to 47004, this is No 47005, with increased coal space and shorter saddle tanks, at Birkenhead shed in July 1961. Built at Horwich Works, it was allocated new to Birkenhead during the week ended 31 October 1953 and transferred to Staveley Barrow Hill in June 1963. On 4 October 1965, when Barrow Hill closed, No 47005 was transferred to Langwith Junction but in reality placed in store at Canklow and later at Rotherham Masboro', along with the remaining Staveley tank engines Nos 41528, 41533, 41708, 41734, 41763, 41804, 41835 and 47001. Withdrawal came on 25 December 1966 and it was later sold to Arnott Young at Rawmarsh for scrapping. *Pictorail*

Designed by Fowler for the LMS for dock shunting duties, 0-6-0T No 47163 is here at Greenock Ladyburn shed in July 1961 buffered up to sister engine No 47168. No 47163 was built at Derby Works in December 1928 and spent a number of years at Edinburgh Dalry Road shed before going to Greenock in October 1960. Both Nos 47163 and 47168 were withdrawn in 1962 and later scrapped, No 47163 at Campbell's Airdrie yard and No 47168 at Inverurie Works.
G. W. Sharpe

London Kentish Town shed in November 1961 is the setting for Cricklewood-allocated Johnson-designed 3F 0-6-0T No 47211, fitted with condensing gear. Built at Vulcan Foundry in February 1900, No 47211 had a long stay in London before moving to Manchester Gorton shed in July 1962 and to Carlisle Kingmoor in January 1963. It then moved to Lostock Hall in June 1963 and finally Rose Grove in September 1964, from where it was withdrawn during the week ended 28 November 1964. Stored at Rose Grove until March 1965, No 47211 then went to Smith's at Ecclesfield for scrapping.
R. H. G. Simpson

LMS 'Jinty' 3F 0-6-0T No 47345 at Barrow-in-Furness shed stands outside the unique style of coaling stage in April 1962. Dating from September 1926, No 47345 had been built by the North British Locomotive Co Ltd and carried the original number 16428, becoming 7345 in 1934 and 47345 in April 1950. It came to Barrow from Manchester Longsight in November 1959 and moved to Carlisle Upperby during the week ended 6 October 1962, from where it was withdrawn during the week ended 3 October 1964. Sold to Hughes, Bolckow Ltd at North Blyth, No 47345 was cut up the following December. *Pictorail*

A portrait of a Stanier 8F 2-8-0 No 48084, allocated to Leeds Stourton shed, at rest at Lancaster Green Ayre shed in March 1962. This was one of the class built at Vulcan Foundry in January 1937 and first allocated to Normanton shed. It was still at Normanton when British Railways was nationalised, not moving until June 1957 for a short spell at Wakefield, before going to Stourton three months later. Here it stayed until January 1967, when it became part of Royston's allocation until withdrawn on 4 November 1967. Stored until February 1968, No 48084 then went to Cashmore's at Great Bridge for scrapping. *Pictorail*

A number of Stanier 8F 2-8-0s were fitted with smaller Fowler-type tenders, as seen here on No 48479 at its home shed, Willesden, on Tuesday 5 June 1963. This engine dated from July 1945 and was built at the GWR Swindon Works, going new to Reading shed. No 48479's last allocation was Sutton Oak, withdrawal coming during the week ended 12 February 1966. It was another Cashmore's purchase. *P. H. Groom*

Another tender variation on a Stanier 8F 2-8-0 is this high-sided example, paired with No 48600, also at home at Willesden shed, this time in September 1962. This was a Southern Railway Eastleigh Works-built engine, entering traffic in December 1942 and going new to Willesden, which heralded a long stay at 1A until October 1963, when a move to Woodford Halse was made. Westhouses was allocated No 48600 in March 1964, Annesley in October 1966 and finally Aintree in November 1966, it being promptly withdrawn during the week ended 26 November. This time, Draper's at Hull was the scrap merchant. *P. H. Groom*

48302	9F	48367	14A	48432	16B	48511	8E	48617	15A
48303	18A	48368	1A	48433	8A	48512	8A	48618	41E
48304	14A	48369	89A	48434	87F	48513	8A	48619	15D
48305	2E	48370	18A	48435	2B	48514	21B	48620	18A
48306	14A	48371	18C	48436	89A	48515	41D	48621	16B
48307	87F	48372	26A	48437	9B	48516	5B	48622	55B
48308	8D	48373	8B	48438	87F	48517	14A	48623	2B
48309	87F	48374	15A	48439	55D	48518	1A	48624	1A
48310	9B	48375	21B	48440	2E	48519	9D	48625	14A
48311	55B	48376	15B	48441	6C	48520	8C	48626	5B
48312	2B	48377	16A	48442	16B	48521	8E	48627	15A
48313	14A	48378	14A	48443	55D	48522	8C	48628	1A
48314	18A	48379	16B	48444	82B	48523	21A	48629	1A
48315	15D	48380	15B	48445	2E	48524	87F	48630	5B
48316	9F	48381	15A	48446	1E	48525	87F	48631	8E
48317	16B	48382	15D	48447	16B	48526	2A	48632	1A
48318	8A	48383	16B	48448	6C	48527	18C	48633	5B
48319	18A	48384	18A	48449	2B	48528	16B	48634	9F
48320	2B	48385	15A	48450	84F	48529	8D	48635	18A
48321	12A	48386	15A	48451	9D	48530	18A	48636	18A
48322	9D	48387	18A	48452	87F	48531	1A	48637	18A
48323	8A	48388	21A	48453	5C	48532	55D	48638	16A
48324	14A	48389	9D	48454	55A	48533	41E	48639	16A
48325	1A	48390	9F	48455	6C	48534	1E	48640	16A
48326	8D	48391	41D	48456	2B	48535	8C	48641	55B
48327	9F	48392	16B	48457	8A	48536	12A	48642	41D
48328	87F	48393	16A	48458	6B	48537	55D	48643	16B
48329	9F	48394	55B	48459	84F	48538	18A	48644	15D
48330	84F	48395	16B	48460	84F	48539	41E	48645	15B
48331	41E	48396	41D	48461	87F	48540	55D	48646	1E
48332	18A	48397	41D	48462	8E	48541	16B	48647	18A
48333	18A	48398	2B	48463	87F	48542	55C	48648	6C
48334	16B	48399	55A	48464	12A	48543	9F	48649	1A
48335	1A	48400	87F	48465	9D	48544	1E	48650	18A
48336	21A	48401	16A	48466	55D	48545	18A	48651	15A
48337	55D	48402	84F	48467	15B	48546	41E	48652	55B
48338	9F	48403	9F	48468	89A	48547	18C	48653	16A
48339	21A	48404	82B	48469	55D	48548	5B	48654	17C
48340	8E	48405	16B	48470	87F	48549	1E	48655	6G
48341	41E	48406	9F	48471	89A	48550	1E	48656	1E
48342	16B	48407	41E	48472	12A	48551	1A	48657	1E
48343	2B	48408	1E	48473	55D	48552	16B	48658	2B
48344	9E	48409	87F	48474	89A	48553	26A	48659	5B
48345	2A	48410	81A	48475	82B	48554	8D	48660	89A
48346	41E	48411	2A	48476	6C	48555	8E	48661	18A
48347	82F	48412	81A	48477	21B	48556	21B	48662	17B
48348	6B	48413	16B	48478	89A	48557	9F	48663	41E
48349	2E	48414	18A	48479	8C	48558	9D	48664	55C
48350	18A	48415	84F	48490	16A	48559	2A	48665	1A
48351	21A	48416	1A	48491	26A	48600	1A	48666	16A
48352	55B	48417	84F	48492	15A	48601	1A	48667	6B
48353	18B	48418	89A	48493	2E	48602	21B	48668	1E
48354	89A	48419	87F	48494	18C	48603	1A	48669	21A
48355	15B	48420	82B	48495	15A	48604	16A	48670	55D
48356	15B	48421	9D	48500	8D	48605	8E	48671	15A
48357	56D	48422	2E	48501	9F	48606	18A	48672	18A
48358	56D	48423	6C	48502	5B	48607	15B	48673	16B
48359	18C	48424	84F	48503	9F	48608	56D	48674	21B
48360	2E	48425	8D	48504	2B	48609	15B	48675	16A
48361	18A	48426	8E	48505	5B	48610	1E	48676	9F
48362	18A	48427	1E	48506	8C	48611	15B	48677	9F
48363	18A	48428	9D	48507	18A	48612	12A	48678	14A
48364	17C	48429	9F	48508	41D	48613	9F	48679	9D
48365	2A	48430	84F	48509	8A	48614	16A	48680	2E
48366	5C	48431	81A	48510	17A	48615	18A	48681	18A

48682	9F
48683	8E
48684	6C
48685	18A
48686	2B
48687	5C
48688	1E
48689	55C
48690	15B
48691	6C
48692	8C
48693	8E
48694	17B
48695	9F
48696	16A
48697	6C
48698	18A
48699	15A
48700	21A
48701	16B
48702	55B
48703	55B
48704	15B
48705	5C
48706	87F
48707	86C
48708	12A
48709	8D
48710	55D
48711	8C
48712	9D
48713	21B
48714	8C
48715	8B
48716	26A
48717	8E
48718	21D
48719	21D
48720	26A
48721	55B
48722	8C
48723	2B
48724	89A
48725	21B
48726	21B
48727	9D
48728	17B
48729	5B
48730	87F
48731	9F
48732	87F
48733	21B
48734	21B
48735	87F
48736	2E
48737	82F
48738	89A
48739	89A
48740	9D
48741	9E
48742	8A
48743	5B
48744	9B
48745	26A
48746	8B
48747	8C
48748	16A
48749	6B
48750	18B
48751	2B
48752	21D
48753	2B
48754	2B
48755	5C
48756	12A
48757	2E
48758	12A
48759	15B
48760	87F
48761	87F
48762	5C
48763	16A
48764	8E
48765	41D
48766	21B
48767	21B
48768	89A
48769	21B
48770	14A
48771	6G
48772	41D
48773	66A
48774	66A
48775	66A

LNWR G2A Class 0-8-0 7F

48895	8F
48898	1E
48930	21B
48964	21B
49002	8F
49008	8F
49025	8F
49034	26F
49037	8A
49045	21B
49049	8F
49070	21C
49078	21B
49079	2B
49081	21B
49087	26F
49093	1E
49094	1E
49099	21B
49104	8F
49106	21B
49114	8A
49122	8F
49125	21B
49126	21B
49129	8F
49130	8A
49134	26F
49139	8F
49141	8F
49142	8A
49144	8A
49147	26F
49154	8F
49155	8A
49173	8A
49199	26F
49216	21B
49224	8A
49240	21C
49246	1E
49262	9D
49267	8F
49277	9D
49281	9D
49287	1E
49293	2B
49314	2B
49323	26F
49328	21B
49335	26F
49344	8F
49350	2B
49352	8A
49361	21B
49373	2B
49375	8A
49377	2B
49381	8F
49382	26F
49391	9D
49394	8A

LNWR G2 Class 0-8-0 7F

49402	8F
49403	9D
49404	8A
49406	9D
49407	5B
49408	8F
49415	8A
49416	8A
49425	2B
49426	26F
49428	24L
49430	21B
49431	2B
49432	8A
49434	8A
49437	8A
49438	8F
49439	2B
49440	2B
49446	9D
49447	8F
49448	8A
49449	24L
49451	8F
49452	21C
49454	5B

Fowler 0-8-0 7F

49508	26B

Aspinall 0-4-0ST 0F

51204	26B
51206	27A
51207	26B
51218	82E
51222	50D
51232	27A
51237	26B
51241	50D
51244	50D
51253	27A

Aspinall Rebuilt 0-6-0ST 2F

51408	26B
51412	CW
51446	CW

Aspinall 0-6-0 3F

52093	CW
52119	6K
52121	56F
52218	CW
52248	26E
52275	26E
52311	27B
52312	CW
52345	26C
52413	56A
52438	6K
52441	CW
52456	26E
52461	56A
52515	56F
52523	26C

Fowler 2-8-0 7F

53803	82F
53804	82F
53806	82F
53807	82F
53808	82F
53809	82F
53810	82F

Pickersgill 4-4-0 3P

54463	60A
54465	66B
54466	60B
54482	60B
54486	63A
54495	60C
54500	63A
54502	68B

McIntosh 439 Class 0-4-4T 2P

55173	63C
55189	66E
55204	63C
55217	63C
55225	67A
55234	68D
55260	63C
55269	60A

Drummond 0-4-0ST 0F

56029	65E
56031	66B
56039	65D

McIntosh 0-6-0T 2F

56159	66A

McIntosh 0-6-0T 3F

56232	67D
56278	66B
56282	67D
56302	68B
56312	68B
56313	66B
56325	66B
56336	66C
56347	63A

Drummond 0-6-0 2F

57237	66B
57240	65B
57242	66C
57249	67B
57251	65B
57252	65J
57253	65B
57254	67D
57258	65B
57259	65D
57261	65B
57265	65F
57266	67D
57267	66B
57269	65B
57270	66B
57274	67D
57275	66A
57278	66B
57284	67B
57291	66B
57295	67B
57296	65D
57299	66B
57300	67B
57302	68B
57309	67D
57311	65B
57314	65D
57326	66B
57328	66B
57329	68B
57331	67B
57336	65D
57338	65F
57340	68C
57341	65D
57345	63A
57347	66A
57348	67D
57355	67D
57357	67D
57359	67B
57360	66A
57362	68B

LNWR 'G2A' class 7F 0-8-0 No 49281 wends its way past Derby station in July 1961 on its way back to its home base at Buxton. Built at Crewe Works in February 1918 as a 'G1' class, it was converted to a 'G2A' in December 1938, which involved the fitting of a higher pressure Belpaire boiler. No 49281 was one of the 1962 withdrawals and was scrapped at Crewe Works. *G. W. Sharpe*

LNWR 'G2' class 7F 0-8-0 No 49407 awaits work at its home shed Crewe South on a Sunday in April 1962. Built in November 1921 this was a development of the 'G1' class, again with a higher pressure boiler. No 49407 moved to Wolverhampton Bushbury in November 1962, Bescot in July 1963, back to Crewe South five months later, and finally, in March 1964, returned to Bescot. It remained in service until withdrawn during the week ended 5 December 1964, along with 'G2A' No 48895. This left only two ex-LNWR engines in service, Nos 49361 and 49430, both being withdrawn from Bescot during the week ended 26 December 1964. After storage at Bescot, all four went to Cashmore's at Great Bridge for scrap. *R. H. G. Simpson*

Aspinall L&Y Class 21 0-4-0ST No 51237 is at Manchester Agecroft shed in August 1962. Built at Horwich Works and dating from March 1906, No 51237 remained at Agecroft until withdrawn during the week ended 25 May 1963, leaving only two others, No 51232 and No 51253 in service. Both were withdrawn within the next two months. All three were cut up at Horwich Works. *G. W. Sharpe*

Crewe Works used ex-L&Y Aspinall rebuilt 2F 0-6-0STs as part of its shunting fleet until August 1962, when the last was withdrawn. This is No 51446 taking a rest from its works shunting duties in August 1961. Crewe Works had been its home since before nationalisation and withdrawal came in March 1962, leaving three in service, in service stock at Horwich Works. Behind No 51446 is LMS 4F 0-6-0 No 44363, which joined the works shunters in January 1959, withdrawal coming during the week ended 2 November 1963. *R. H. G. Simpson*

Another class to be removed from the railway scene in 1962 was the Aspinall-designed L&Y 3F 0-6-0s. This is No 52515, the pride of Sowerby Bridge depot, partnered with LMS 4F 0-6-0 No 44408, a Normanton engine, at Darlington on Saturday 29 September 1962 on an enthusiasts' special which ran from Sowerby Bridge to York, travelling outward via Wakefield Kirkgate and Doncaster and back via Darlington and Leeds City. Built at Horwich Works in November 1906, and numbered 898 with the L&Y, No 52515 was the last on the active list. Originally built with superheated round-top firebox boiler, in August 1929 it was converted to a round-top saturated boiler. Not secured for preservation, it returned to its birthplace for scrapping. *G. W. Sharpe*

Fowler-designed 7F 2-8-0 No 53810 is at Bath Green Park shed in September 1962. Intended for the Somerset & Dorset line, No 53810 was one of the later batch of five built by Robert Stephenson & Co in August 1925 and spent its entire working life on the S&D, withdrawal coming in December 1963. Cashmore's at Newport carried out the scrapping. *P. H. Groom*

The remaining eight Pickersgill ex-Caledonian Railway Class 72 3P 4-4-0s were withdrawn during 1962, including No 54500 seen here in store at Forfar shed, just after withdrawal in March. Dating from December 1922 and built by the North British Locomotive Co, it spent its entire British Railways days allocated to Perth. In May 1963 it went to Arnott Young's at Old Kilpatrick for scrap. *G. W. Sharpe*

The McIntosh '439' class 2P 0-4-4T was also removed from the railway scene during 1962. No 55189, with stovepipe chimney and dating from November 1907, was one of the last three to go. Here it is seen at Carstairs in October 1961 on carriage shunting duties. Carstairs was its last allocation after transfer from Glasgow Polmadie in October 1960, and after storage at Edinburgh Dalry Road shed it was rescued for preservation and is now at the Bo'ness & Kinneil Railway. *G. W. Sharpe*

Another of the last survivors of the '439' class 2P 0-4-4Ts was No 55260. This was one of the post-Grouping batch built in May 1925. At nationalisation No 55260 was based at Hurlford, moving to Motherwell in December 1950 and then to Beattock in May 1952. Here it stayed until January 1961 when it moved to Perth, then to Oban two months later, and back to Perth in July 1962. This is No 55260 at Perth station on Sunday 17 June 1962 after arrival from Alyth Junction as part or the RCTS/SLS 10-day tour of Scotland. No 55260 had worked the train, including the two Caledonian Railway coaches seen here, through Coupar Angus, up the branch to Blairgowrie and back, and then on to Perth. No 55260 was placed in store at Perth shed from August 1962 until September 1963 when it went to Arnott Young's at Carmyle for scrap. *G. W. Sharpe*

Only 14 of the original 34 Caledonian Railway 0-4-0STs came into British Railways stock, and the last three were withdrawn in 1962. Here we have No 56031, dating from July 1900, in store at Motherwell shed in August 1962 after withdrawal. Next month it went to Glasgow Cowlairs Works for scrapping. *Author's collection*

The last of the ex-Caledonian Railway McIntosh 0-6-0T class managed to survive into 1962, with nine examples all being withdrawn during the year. The final three went in December, including No 56302, still with original chimney, here at Dumfries shed in August 1962. Dating from May 1905, its last journey was to the Motherwell Machinery & Scrap Co at Wishaw for cutting up in December 1963, following storage at Dumfries goods yard from October 1962. *P. H. Groom*

Another engine withdrawn in 1962 was No 57345, here in store at Forfar shed in March 1962. This was a Drummond design of 0-6-0, with No 57345 emerging from Glasgow St Rollox Works in April 1892. Its British Railways career started at Aberdeen Ferryhill, transferring to Perth during the week ended 6 May 1950. Here it remained until withdrawn. Placed in store at Forfar in February 1962, it left in October 1962 for dismantling at Arnott Young's yard at Old Kilpatrick. *G. W. Sharpe*

McIntosh Caledonian Railway '812' class 3F 0-6-0 No 57627 is at Glasgow Corkerhill shed in May 1963. Built at Glasgow St Rollox Works in November 1899, it was allocated to Ardrossan for the whole of its British Railways days. It was withdrawn on 7 November 1963, with classmate No 57581 also at Ardrossan, leaving only Nos 57568 and 57600 on the active list, (both were withdrawn that same month on the 29th), 57568 from Motherwell and 57600 from Dumfries. No 57627 was sold to Arnott Young, West of Scotland Shipbreaking Co at Troon for scrap. *G. W. Sharpe*

57365	66A
57369	66A
57370	66B
57375	68C
57378	68B
57383	67B
57384	66B
57385	66E
57386	66E
57398	66B
57417	66A
57445	68C
57447	66C

McIntosh 812 Class 0-6-0 3F

57550	64C
57555	66A
57562	67B
57565	64C
57566	67D
57568	68D
57569	67C
57571	66A
57572	67B
57577	67B
57581	66A
57587	63C
57590	67D
57592	65D
57594	67D
57596	67C
57597	66A
57600	68B
57601	68B
57602	68B
57603	66A
57604	66E
57607	65D
57608	66E
57611	67C
57612	65F
57613	66E
57614	67C
57615	67C
57617	65B
57618	66E
57620	66A
57621	68B
57622	66A
57625	66A
57626	66E
57627	67D

McIntosh 652 Class 0-6-0 3F

57630	66C
57631	65B
57634	64C
57635	63C
57642	65J
57643	67B
57644	67C
57645	64C

Pickersgill 294 Class 0-6-0 3F

57652	65D
57654	64C
57655	66E
57658	67C
57661	68B
57666	66B
57667	66A
57668	66B
57670	66E
57671	66A
57672	66A
57673	67D
57674	66A
57679	65J
57681	66B
57682	66A
57684	66A
57686	65B
57688	66B
57689	66A
57690	66D
57691	65F

Johnson 0-6-0 2F

58120	12E
58123	21B
58124	21C
58128	21C
58138	18A
58143	18A
58148	21C
58160	12E
58166	15D
58177	12E
58182	12E
58185	21B
58214	15D
58218	21B
58228	18A

McIntosh Caledonian Railway '652' class 3F 0-6-0 No 57635 is seen in store at Forfar shed in March 1962 just after official withdrawal. Built at Glasgow St Rollox Works in June 1908, at nationalisation No 57635 was allocated to Carstairs, moving to Oban in June 1960 and remaining until withdrawn, although in reality it had been in storage at Forfar since December 1961. It remained rusting away until March 1963, when it left for cutting up at its birthplace, Glasgow St Rollox. *G. W. Sharpe*

Pickersgill-designed Caledonian Railway '294' class 3F 0-6-0 No 57671 is at Motherwell shed in June 1962 just after transfer from Glasgow Polmadie. The shed staff had not even bothered to fit a 66B shedplate. No doubt in poor condition, it was withdrawn the next month. Built at Glasgow St Rollox Works in January 1919, after withdrawal it was stored at Motherwell until September 1962 when it was sent to Inverurie Works for scrapping. *G. W. Sharpe*

Johnson Midland Railway 2F 0-6-0 No 58218 is at Rugby on pilot duties on Saturday 4 June 1960. This was one of 12 of the class withdrawn during 1962, leaving only three (Nos 58143, 58148 and 58182, all at Coalville) to remain in service at the beginning of 1963. No 58218 dated from February 1883 and had transferred from its Rugby home to its final shed, Bescot, during the week ended 25 February 1961. It had been in storage at Bescot from April 1962 until September, when it was sent to Cashmore's at Great Bridge for scrapping. *L. Hanson*

Putting up a fine display climbing away from Wood Green Tunnel in June 1962 on the 4.05pm King's Cross to York is Gresley 'A4' 4-6-2 No 60003 *Andrew K. McCosh*. Built at Doncaster Works, No 60003 entered traffic on 12 August 1937 and was one of five to be withdrawn in 1962, returning to Doncaster for cutting up. *P. H. Groom*

A4 Class 4-6-2 8P6F

60001*	52A
60002*	52A
60003*	34A
60004*	64B
60005*	52A
60006*	34A
60007*	34A
60008*	34A
60009*	64B
60010*	34A
60011*	64B
60012*	64B
60013*	34A
60014*	34A
60015*	34A
60016*	52A
60017*	34A
60018*	52A
60019*	52A
60020*	52A
60021*	34A
60022*	34A
60023*	52A
60024*	64B
60025*	34A
60026*	34A
60027*	64B
60028*	34A
60029*	34A
60030*	34A
60031*	64B
60032*	34A
60033*	34A
60034*	34A

A3 Class 4-6-2 7P6F

60036*	56B
60037*	64A
60038*	55A
60039*	34A
60040*	52A
60041*	64A
60042*	52A
60043*	64A
60044*	34A
60045*	52A
60046*	34F
60047*	34F
60048*	34F
60049*	34F
60050*	34F
60051*	52A
60052*	52A
60053*	52A
60054*	34F
60056*	34F
60057*	64A
60058*	51A
60059*	34A
60060*	52A
60061*	34A
60062*	34E
60063*	34A
60065*	34F
60066*	34A
60067*	34A
60068*	12C
60069*	56B
60070*	56B
60071*	52A
60072*	52B
60073*	52B
60074*	55H
60075*	52A
60076*	52A
60077*	56B
60078*	52A
60080*	56B
60081*	55H
60082*	52B
60083*	52B
60084*	55H
60085*	52B
60086*	55H
60087*	64A
60088*	52B
60089*	64A
60090*	64A
60091*	51A
60092*	56B
60093*	12C
60094*	64A
60096*	64A
60097*	64A
60098*	64B
60099*	64B
60100*	64B
60101*	64B
60103*	34A
60105*	34F
60106*	34F
60107*	34A
60108*	34E
60109*	34A
60110*	34A
60111*	34F
60112*	34F

A1 Class 4-6-2 8P6F

60113*	36A
60114*	36A
60115*	56C
60116*	52B
60117*	56C
60118*	56C
60119*	36A
60120*	56C
60121*	50A
60122*	36A
60123*	56C
60124*	50A
60125*	36A
60126*	50A
60127*	52B
60128*	36A
60129*	52B
60130*	56C
60131*	56C
60132*	52B
60133*	56C
60134*	56C
60135*	56C
60136*	36A
60137*	52B
60138*	50A

Gresley 'A3' 4-6-2 No 60046 *Diamond Jubilee* looks extremely smart at King's Cross shed in April 1962. Originally built as an 'A1' class in 1924, it entered traffic on 9 August. Rebuilding at Doncaster to Class A3 took place in August 1941. When this photograph was taken, No 60046 was a Grantham engine, moving to Peterborough New England on 9 September 1962 and back to Grantham on 21 April 1963 from where it was withdrawn on 16 June 1963 and despatched in August to Doncaster Works for scrapping. *P. H. Groom*

'A3' 4-6-2 No 60097 *Humorist* is at Edinburgh St Margarets shed in August 1962. This was a unique member of the class as it had a double chimney, Kylchap blastpipe and full smoke deflectors. It had been allocated to St Margarets on 13 December 1961 after transfer from Haymarket and was sent to Doncaster Works for repair in July 1963, but instead was withdrawn on 24 August. *P. H. Groom*

'A1/1' class 4-6-2 No 60113 *Great Northern* is at King's Cross shed in August 1962, with only three months left before withdrawal. Rebuilt by Thompson from a Gresley 'A1' in September 1945, it was not a complete success and spent most of its working life on the ex-Great Northern main line. After withdrawal, No 60113 was cut up at Doncaster. *P. H. Groom*

60139*	36A
60140*	50A
60141*	56C
60142*	52B
60143*	52B
60144*	36A
60145*	56C
60146*	50A
60147*	52B
60148*	56C
60149*	36A
60150*	50A
60151*	52B
60152*	64B
60153*	50A
60154*	50A
60155*	52B
60156*	36A
60157*	36A
60158*	36A
60159*	64B
60160*	64B
60161*	64B
60162*	64B

A2 Class 4-6-2 8P7F

60500*	34E
60511*	52D
60512*	50A
60513*	34E
60514*	34E
60515*	50A
60516*	50A
60517*	52D
60518*	50A
60519*	64A
60520*	36A
60521*	52D
60522*	50A
60523*	36A
60524*	50A
60525*	61B
60526*	50A
60527*	61B
60528*	62B
60529*	64A
60530*	64A
60531*	61B
60532*	62B
60533*	36A
60534*	64A
60535*	64A
60536*	64A
60537*	64A
60538*	52D
60539*	52D

V2 Class 2-6-2 7P6F

60800*	34A
60801	52D
60802	52B
60803	34E
60804	62B
60805	52B
60806	51L
60807	52B
60808	51L
60809*	51A
60810	50A
60811	52B
60812	52B
60813	64A
60814	34A
60815	15E
60816	64A
60817	34E
60818	64A
60819	64A
60820	34E
60821	34E
60822	62B
60823	63A
60824	64A
60825	64A
60826	36A
60827	64A
60828	50A
60829	34E
60830	34E
60831	50A
60832	34E
60833	52B
60834	62B
60835*	52B
60836	64A
60837	50A
60838	62B
60839	50A
60840	64A
60841	34E
60842	50A
60843	52D
60844	62B
60845	34E
60846	51L
60847*	50A
60848	50A
60849	36A
60850	36A
60851	61B
60852	36A
60853	34E
60854	34A
60855	50A
60856	50A
60857	36A
60858	34E
60859	51L
60860*	52B
60861	56A
60862	34A
60863	15E
60864	50A
60865	52D
60866	34E
60867	34E
60868	52B
60869	34E
60870	36A
60871	34A
60872*	36A
60873*	64A
60874	34E
60875	36A
60876	50A
60877	50A
60878	50A
60879	50A
60880	34E
60881	34E
60882	64A
60883	64A
60884	56A
60885	51L
60886	52B
60887	50A
60888	61B
60889	36A
60890	15E
60891	52B
60892	64A
60893	34E
60894	64A
60895	50A
60896	36A
60897	36A
60898	61B
60899	36A
60900	64A
60901	51L
60902	34A
60903	34A
60904	52B
60905	36A
60906	34E
60907	50A
60908	36A
60909	36A
60910	52B
60911	50A
60912	34E
60913	52D
60914	34E
60915	51L
60916	51L
60917	36A
60918	50A
60919	61B
60920	64A
60921	36A
60922	52B
60923	52A
60924	34E
60925	50A
60926	52D
60927	64A
60928	36A
60929	52D
60930	36A
60931	64A
60932	52B
60933	64A
60934	52D
60935	36A
60936	36A
60937	64A
60938	34E
60939	50A
60940	52B
60941	50A
60942	52A
60943	36A
60944	52B
60945	52B
60946	51L
60947	52D
60948	34E
60949	52D
60950	34A
60951	64A
60952	52A
60953	64A
60954	50A
60955	61B
60956	34E
60957	64B
60958	64A
60959	64A
60960	51L
60961	50A
60962	52B
60963	50A
60964*	52A
60965	64A
60966	34E
60967	50A
60968	50A
60969	64A
60970	63A
60971	64A
60972	61B
60973	63A
60974	50A
60975	50A
60976	52B
60977	50A
60978	52B
60979	52A
60980	64A
60981	50A
60982	50A
60983	34A

B1 Class 4-6-0 5MT

61000*	40E
61001*	36A
61002*	50A
61003*	36A
61004*	41A
61005*	31A
61006*	40A
61007*	64A
61008*	26B
61009*	40A
61010*	50B
61011*	2F
61012*	50B
61013*	56B
61014*	52H
61015*	56A
61016*	56C
61017*	56A
61018*	50A
61019*	52C
61020*	50A
61021*	50A
61022*	52H
61023*	56B
61024*	56A
61025*	52C
61026*	40A
61027*	41A
61028*	2F
61029*	64A
61030*	55H
61031*	50A
61032*	51A
61033*	41A
61034*	51L
61035*	52C
61036*	36A
61037*	51A
61038*	52G
61039*	50A
61040*	56A
61041	41A
61042	40A
61043	32A
61044	41A
61045	32A
61046	31A
61047	41A
61048	31A
61049	50A
61050	41A
61051	41A
61052	31B
61053	50A
61054	32A
61055	36A
61056	41A
61058	40A
61059	31B
61060	40A
61061	51C
61062	50A
61063	15E
61064	12C
61065	50B
61066	31B
61067	65C
61068	50A
61069	50A
61070	34E
61071	50A
61072	62C
61073	34E
61074	34E
61075	34E
61076	64B
61077	15E
61078	2F
61079	40B
61080	50B
61081	64B

'A1' class 4-6-2 No 60139 *Sea Eagle* climbs away from London on Holloway Bank on an express for York in April 1962. Built at Darlington Works, No 60139 was an A. H. Peppercorn design and entered traffic on 23 December 1948, going new to King's Cross shed. July 1951 saw the locomotive at Leeds Copley Hill, then it went to Grantham in December 1955, back to King's Cross in April 1957 and finally to Doncaster in April 1959. Withdrawal came on 7 June 1964 and scrapping was carried out at Cox & Danks' yard at Wadsley Bridge. *P. H. Groom*

'A2/3' Class 4-6-2 No 60500 *Edward Thompson* is on a mineral working at Hatfield on Thursday 15 November 1962. This was the 2,000th engine built at Doncaster Works, entering traffic at Gateshead shed on 24 May 1946. It was a Thompson design, and was named after its designer in view of his impending retirement and replacement by A. H. Peppercorn as Chief Mechanical Engineer. The engine's final home was Peterborough New England, being transferred there from King's Cross on 4 June 1950. It was withdrawn on 16 June 1963, and then returned to Doncaster Works for cutting up. *G. W. Sharpe*

One of the 'A2/3' class withdrawn during 1962 was No 60519 *Honeyway*, seen here at Edinburgh Haymarket shed in May 1961, where it had been allocated when it entered traffic on 1 February 1947. No 60519 moved across the city to St Margarets shed on 16 October 1961, and south to York on 2 December 1962, and was withdrawn 16 days later. Cutting up was carried out at Doncaster Works. *G. W. Sharpe*

'A2' class 4-6-2 No 60534 *Irish Elegance* is at Edinburgh St Margaret's manual coal stage in August 1962. Built under Peppercorn at Doncaster Works, No 60534, entered traffic on 23 April 1948, going to York. On 27 November 1949 transfer to Edinburgh Haymarket and on 13 November 1961 to St Margarets was authorised, from where withdrawal was actioned at the end of 1962. It had been in storage at Bathgate shed from October 1962 and was there until June 1964 when sold to G. H. Campbell at Airdrie for scrap. *P. H. Groom*

'V2' class 2-6-2 No 60835 *The Green Howard, Alexandra, Princess of Wales's Own Yorkshire Regiment* is at Darlington shed in March 1962 after its last general overhaul. Built at Darlington, it entered traffic at York shed on 23 September 1938. It was named the next day at a ceremony at Richmond station to mark the 250th anniversary of the Green Howard Regiment. When this photograph was taken, No 60835 was a Heaton-based engine after moving there from Tweedmouth on 12 April 1953. It had a 10-year stay at 52B, moving to Gateshead on 16 June 1963 and to Aberdeen Ferryhill 14 days later. On 19 July 1964 it moved to Edinburgh St Margarets, from where withdrawal was actioned on 19 October 1965, and it was then sold for scrap to G. H. Campbell at Airdrie. *Pictorail*

'V2' class 2-6-2 No 60862 is at its home shed King's Cross in January 1962, still in ex-works condition after its last Darlington Works visit in September/October 1961 when, during a general overhaul, a double chimney, Kylchap double blastpipe and speedometer were fitted. The outside steam pipes had been fitted at another 'general' at Darlington in February 1957. Darlington had built this engine and released it to traffic to Manchester Gorton shed on 13 June 1939. It had been based at King's Cross since 19 March 1950 and moved to Peterborough New England on 21 April 1963, being withdrawn the same year on 16 June. Stored at New England until October, it then went to Doncaster Works for scrap. *P. H. Groom*

'V2' class 2-6-2 No 60924 is at Sunbeck Level Crossing on the Gilling branch on 18 August 1962 on the Saturdays-only 10.50am Scarborough to Newcastle. Some summer Saturday trains were sent over this route to avoid congestion around York, bringing the unusual sight of express locomotives and their trains to this single-track line. The last one ran on 8 September 1962. To gain access to the branch from the Scarborough line meant a reversal at Malton and at Sessay Wood Junction, north of York, and just south of Pilmoor was where the East Coast main line was joined. Sessay Wood Junction closed on 19 March 1963, after which any trains to and from Scarborough would be routed via York. No 60924 had been built at Darlington Works and entered traffic on 22 November 1941 allocated to King's Cross. Transfer to Peterborough New England was actioned on 21 November 1942 and to Doncaster on 29 April 1962, from where withdrawal took place on 22 September 1963. Doncaster Works scrapped No 60924 the following November. *M. Mitchell*

'V2' class 2-6-2 No 60981 runs past Ripon in June 1962 on a van train, a fast working for which these engines were ideally suited. Built at Darlington Works, No 60981 entered traffic on 20 April 1944 and was allocated to York. Darlington added the engine to its allocation on 19 July 1953, and then it returned to York on 27 September 1953 through to withdrawal on 15 April 1963, with a return to Darlington Works for cutting up. *G. W. Sharpe*

61082	40B	61148	62A	61213	36E	61278	62B	61343	62A
61083	41D	61149	30A	61214	56C	61279	36A	61344	65C
61084	50A	61150	41A	61215*	50B	61280	32A	61345	64A
61086	50A	61151	41A	61216	52C	61281	40E	61346	61B
61087	36A	61152	41A	61217	12C	61282	34E	61347	61B
61088	40E	61153	41A	61218	51L	61283	30A	61348	40A
61089	40A	61154	41A	61219	64B	61284	40A	61349	64A
61090	41A	61155	41A	61220	51L	61285	40E	61350	61B
61091	34E	61156	30A	61221*	64B	61286	31A	61351	64A
61092	40E	61157	36A	61222	12C	61287	31A	61352	63B
61093	41D	61158	36A	61223	40A	61288	50A	61353	51A
61094	41A	61159	40B	61224	51A	61289	50B	61354	64A
61095	32A	61160	40A	61225	36E	61290	12C	61355	65A
61096	31B	61161	56A	61226	30A	61291	50A	61356	64A
61097	34E	61162	41A	61227	40E	61292	62B	61357	64A
61098	40B	61163	40E	61228	41A	61293	62B	61358	62A
61099	64A	61164	41A	61229	50A	61294	64A	61359	64A
61100	56C	61165	41F	61230	56F	61295	56B	61360	36A
61101	62C	61166	41A	61231	36E	61296	56A	61361	40E
61102	62B	61167	41F	61232	40E	61297	56B	61362	30A
61103	62A	61168	40B	61233	31B	61298	26B	61363	31A
61104	41A	61169	41A	61234	41A	61299	40E	61364	34A
61105	41A	61170	36A	61235	40B	61300	31A	61365	36A
61106	2F	61171	31B	61236	31B	61301	31A	61366	40B
61107	36A	61172	62B	61237*	52G	61302	34E	61367	34F
61108	64A	61173	51L	61238*	52H	61303	51L	61368	2F
61109	41A	61174	34E	61239	12C	61304	51A	61369	26B
61110	56B	61175	40E	61240*	50A	61305	50B	61370	41D
61111	41A	61176	51A	61241*	52C	61306	50B	61371	31A
61112	41A	61177	40E	61242*	64A	61307	64A	61372	41A
61113	40A	61178	64B	61243*	65A	61308	64A	61373	41A
61114	40B	61179	34A	61244*	64A	61309	56C	61374	40B
61115	56C	61180	62B	61245*	64B	61310	56B	61375	30A
61116	14D	61181	41A	61246*	64A	61311	30A	61376	15E
61117	65C	61182	31B	61247*	40E	61312	41A	61377	41J
61118	62A	61183	41A	61248*	40B	61313	41A	61378	30A
61119	30A	61184	64A	61249*	41A	61314	36A	61379*	40B
61120	36E	61185	40B	61250*	36A	61315	41A	61380	15E
61121	36A	61186	2F	61251*	34F	61316	41F	61381	15E
61122	36A	61187	15E	61252	31B	61317	40B	61382	51A
61123	56B	61188	40E	61253	30A	61318	40B	61383	56F
61124	36A	61189*	56F	61254	32A	61319	50A	61384	40A
61125	36A	61190	40B	61255	51L	61320	56C	61385	56A
61126	36E	61191	64A	61256	50B	61321	51A	61386	56F
61127	36A	61192	15E	61257	51L	61322	52C	61387	56F
61128	36A	61193	36A	61258	40A	61323	31B	61388	50A
61129	56C	61194	41F	61259	51L	61324	64C	61389	34F
61130	40B	61195	40B	61260	64A	61325	40B	61390	40E
61131	56A	61196	36A	61261	65A	61326	36A	61391	34E
61132	62A	61197	65A	61262	62B	61327	41A	61392	34F
61133	62A	61198	50A	61263	62B	61328	40B	61393	34A
61134	65A	61199	52C	61264	40E	61329	30A	61394	34A
61135	36A	61200	34A	61265	15E	61330	62A	61395	12C
61136	14D	61201	26B	61266	41A	61331	34E	61396	65A
61137	15E	61202	40A	61267	51C	61332	64A	61397	64A
61138	41A	61203	31B	61268	56A	61333	65C	61398	64A
61139	41A	61204	31B	61269	26B	61334	41A	61399	41A
61140	65A	61205	32A	61270	36A	61335	30A	61400	61B
61141	40E	61206	15E	61271	2F	61336	40E	61401	62A
61142	40E	61207	34E	61272	34E	61337	50A	61402	62B
61143	40B	61208	36E	61273	50A	61338	51A	61403	62C
61144	40B	61209	40E	61274	56F	61339	56C	61404	65C
61145	36A	61210	34E	61275	51C	61340	62B	61405	40A
61146	62A	61211	36E	61276	50A	61341	64A	61406	40B
61147	62A	61212	36E	61277	62B	61342	65A	61407	62C

Thompson 'B1' class 4-6-0 No 61032 *Stembok* is at its home shed, Darlington, on Sunday 13 May 1962. Built at Darlington Works, it entered traffic on 7 August 1947 and was allocated to Stockton-on-Tees, moving to Thornaby on 14 June 1959 when Stockton shed closed. Darlington received No 61032 on 20 September 1959 and Hull Dairycoates on 15 December 1963, from where withdrawal was authorised on 27 November 1966. The nearby Draper's yard cut up No 61032 in March 1967. *L. Hanson*

'B1' 4-6-0 No 61258 is at its home shed Lincoln in April 1962 with self-weighing tender No 4095, with which it had been paired in November 1955, and to which it remained attached until withdrawn on 5 January 1964. Built by the North British Locomotive Co, No 61258 entered traffic at Leeds Neville Hill on 21 November 1947. The first transfer was to Doncaster on 27 January 1952 and the second to Lincoln on 29 June 1952, where it remained until it was withdrawn. It was sent to Doncaster Works and scrapped in April 1964, and was the last 'B1' to be cut up at the works. *Author's collection*

Dundee Tay Bridge is the venue in July 1962 for 'B1' 4-6-0 No 61262 to be taking a rest from its duties. This was an engine that spent its entire working life in Scotland in the '62' shed area. Built by the North British Locomotive Co, it entered traffic at Thornton Junction on 1 December 1947 and was transferred to Dundee on 18 April 1960 and Dunfermline on 28 August 1966, from where withdrawal was actioned on 22 April 1967 when steam was eliminated from Scotland. Stored at Dunfermline from January 1967 until September, No 61262 then made its first and last journey into England for scrapping at Arnott Young's yard at Parkgate. *G. W. Sharpe*

61408 40B
61409 40A

B16 Class 4-6-0 5MT

61417 50A
61418 50A
61420 50A
61421 50A
61434 50A
61435 50A
61437 50A
61438 50A
61439 50A
61444 50A
61448 50A
61449 56D
61453 50A
61454 50A
61455 50A
61457 50A
61461 56D
61463 50A
61464 56D
61467 50A
61468 56D
61472 50A
61475 50A
61476 56D

K2 Class 2-6-0 4MT

61742 34E
61756 34A

K3 Class 2-6-0 5P6F

61800 36A
61801 31B
61804 2F
61805 34E
61807 40A
61809 2F
61810 34E
61811 41J
61812 36A
61813 50B
61816 41A
61817 31B
61818 50B
61819 50B
61820 41D
61821 40E
61822 41D
61825 34E
61826 41H
61827 40E
61829 36A
61830 34E
61831 40E
61832 2F
61834 31B
61835 34E
61837 40E
61839 36A
61840 31B
61841 2F
61843 2F
61845 40A
61846 50B
61847 50B
61848 40A
61853 56B
61854 50B
61856 56B
61857 50B
61859 40A
61861 34E
61862 31B
61864 34E
61867 36A
61868 36A
61869 50B
61870 40E
61871 50B
61872 50B
61873 40E
61875 50B
61877 40E
61880 31B
61883 50B
61884 50B
61886 31B
61887 36A
61889 40E
61890 31B
61893 50B
61895 36A
61896 40E
61897 50B
61899 50B
61905 40B
61906 50B
61907 40E
61908 41F
61910 2F
61912 40A
61913 2F
61914 40E
61915 31B
61917 56B
61918 31B
61922 50B
61923 50B
61926 40A
61929 31B
61930 52H
61932 50B
61934 56B
61935 50B
61939 40E
61940 36A
61942 31B
61943 40E
61944 40B
61945 50B
61946 31B
61947 40E
61948 31B
61949 36A
61950 40B
61951 36A
61952 50B
61953 34E
61954 31B
61956 40B
61957 40E
61958 41F
61960 40B
61962 52H
61963 31B
61965 50B
61966 40E
61969 52H
61970 36A
61972 36A
61973 41H
61974 40B
61976 41A
61977 40E
61980 56B
61981 41F
61982 40E
61984 56B
61985 50B
61986 50B
61987 50B
61989 41H

K1 Class 2-6-0 5P6F

62001 51L
62002 52C
62003 51J
62004 51A
62005 50A
62006 52C
62007 51A
62008 51A
62009 50A
62010 52C
62011 63B
62012 63B
62013 36C
62014 36C
62015 36E
62016 36C
62017 36C
62018 36C
62019 36E
62020 36C
62021 52C
62022 52C
62023 52C
62024 52C
62025 52C
62026 52C
62027 52C
62028 52C
62029 52C
62030 52C
62031 63B
62032 36C
62033 36C
62034 63B
62035 36C
62036 36A
62037 36E
62038 31B
62039 31B
62040 36E
62041 51A
62042 51L
62043 51A
62044 51J
62045 51A
62046 50A
62047 50A
62048 51A
62049 50A
62050 52C
62051 31B
62052 63B
62053 36A
62054 36E
62055 31B
62056 50A
62057 50A
62058 51A
62059 51A
62060 50A
62061 52C
62062 51A
62063 50A
62064 51A
62065 50A
62066 31B
62067 31B
62068 31B
62069 36A
62070 31B

D11 Class 4-4-0 3P2F

62685* 64B

Q6 Class 0-8-0 6F

63340 51F
63341 51L
63342 52K
63343 51L
63344 51L
63345 52K
63346 52K
63347 51L
63348 55H
63349 51L
63350 52H
63351 51F
63352 52C
63353 51F
63354 52K
63355 51L
63356 52C
63357 52K
63358 52H
63359 52K
63360 51L
63361 51L
63362 52C
63363 52C
63364 51L
63365 52K
63366 52C
63367 51L
63368 52K
63369 51L
63370 51L
63371 51L
63373 51L
63374 51L
63375 51L
63376 52C
63377 52H
63378 52C
63379 52K
63380 51L
63381 52C
63382 51L
63383 51C
63384 52H
63385 52C
63386 52C
63387 52C
63388 51L
63389 51L
63390 52C
63391 51C
63392 51C
63393 51L
63394 52C
63395 51A
63396 51L
63397 51C
63398 51F
63399 51L
63400 52C
63401 51L
63402 52C
63403 51F
63404 52K
63405 51L
63406 52K
63407 51F
63408 52C
63409 51L
63410 51C
63411 51L
63412 51C
63413 52C
63414 51C
63415 51C
63416 51L
63417 51L
63418 52K
63419 51C
63420 51L
63421 51C
63422 51C
63423 51A
63424 51L
63425 52H
63426 51L
63427 52K
63428 51L
63429 52C
63430 51L
63431 52C
63432 51L
63433 52K

'B16/3' 4-6-0 No 61439 is at York shed in April 1961. Built at Darlington Works to a Raven design, No 61439 entered traffic on 19 February 1923. During a visit to Darlington Works for a general overhaul in mid-1945, it was rebuilt, under Thompson's directive, with Walschaerts valve gear. Apart from a period at Selby from 30 May to 1 September 1923, No 61439 was based at York and was one of the two class members withdrawn in 1962. Cutting up was carried out at Darlington. *Author's collection*

All the remaining 'K3' class 2-6-0s were withdrawn during 1962, including No 61832, allocated to Woodford Halse, and seen in a crumpled state on Doncaster shed on Sunday 30 April 1961. No doubt the authorities were not pleased as it had left Doncaster Works on 13 April 1961 after a general overhaul. The damage could not have been too drastic as it re-entered the works on 1 May for a casual light repair and returned to traffic on 6 June. Built at Darlington Works, No 61832 had been allocated to Ardsley shed as LNER No 116 on 15 December 1924. Scrapping was carried out at Doncaster Works. *G. W. Sharpe*

'K3' class 2-6-0 No 61905 is at Grimsby Littlefield on a freight working on Thursday 20 April 1961 when allocated to Immingham, where it had been transferred from Nottingham Colwick on 8 August 1948. It returned to Colwick on 14 January 1962 and then moved to Lincoln on 1 July 1962, withdrawal taking place four months later. After storage at Lincoln, it was sold to Cox & Danks, Wadsley Bridge, in March 1963 for scrap. *G. W. Sharpe*

'K1' class 2-6-0 No 62004 is at its home shed, Darlington, on Thursday 20 September 1962. This was a Peppercorn design, with No 62004 being rebuilt by the North British Locomotive Co and entering traffic on 10 June 1949 at Darlington shed. Its only transfer was to West Hartlepool on 6 December 1964, from where it was withdrawn on 16 December 1966 and dispatched to Hughes, Bolckow at Blyth for scrap. *G. W. Sharpe*

'Q6' class 0-8-0 No 63399 is at Tyne Dock shed in December 1962, shortly after transfer from Thornaby on the 2nd. This was a Raven design, with No 63399 being built at Darlington Works and entering traffic at Tyne Dock in December 1918. During its career it was allocated to sheds around the North East, including Blaydon, Newport, Darlington, Hull Dairycoates and North Blyth. Withdrawn from Tyne Dock on 16 March 1964, No 63399 returned to Darlington Works for scrapping. *Pictorail*

Ex-works on Darlington shed on Sunday 13 May 1962 is 'Q6' class 0-8-0 No 63411 awaiting return to Thornaby shed. Its final transfer was to Tyne Dock on 2 December 1962, from where No 63411 was withdrawn on 6 April 1965. Built by Armstrong Whitworth in December 1919, the end came for No 63411 at Cohen's scrapyard at Cargo Fleet in June 1965. *L. Hanson*

63434 52C
63435 51L
63436 55H
63437 52C
63438 51C
63439 52K
63440 51C
63441 52C
63442 51L
63443 51F
63444 52C
63445 51L
63446 51F
63447 51L
63448 52K
63449 55H
63450 51L
63451 51L
63452 51L
63453 52C
63454 51C
63455 52K
63456 52K
63458 52C
63459 51F

Q7 Class 0-8-0 8F
63460 52H
63461 52H
63462 52H
63463 52H
63464 52H
63465 52H
63466 52H
63467 52H
63468 52H
63469 52H
63470 52H
63471 52H
63472 52H
63473 52H
63474 52H

O1 Class 2-8-0 8F
63571 41H

O4 Class 2-8-0 7F
63574 41A
63575 9G
63576 36C
63577 41J

O1 Class 2-8-0 8F
63578 16D
63579 16D

O4 Class 2-8-0 7F
63584 56B
63585 40E
63586 36E
63587 40E
63588 56A

O1 Class 2-8-0 8F
63589 40E
63590 41H
63591 16D
63592 40E

O4 Class 2-8-0 7F
63593 36A

O1 Class 2-8-0 8F
63594 40E
63596 41H

O4 Class 2-8-0 7F
63598 9G
63599 41A
63600 9G
63601 36C
63602 36E
63603 9G
63604 41A
63605 56B
63606 36C
63607 40B
63609 41A

O1 Class 2-8-0 8F
63610 16D

O4 Class 2-8-0 7F
63611 41F
63612 41H
63613 36A
63615 40B
63616 40E
63617 36C
63618 36A

O1 Class 2-8-0 8F
63619 41H

O4 Class 2-8-0 7F
63621 41A
63622 41J
63623 41F
63624 41A
63628 36C

O1 Class 2-8-0 8F
63630 41H

O4 Class 2-8-0 7F
63631 9G
63632 36E
63633 56B
63634 40B
63635 41J
63636 41J
63637 36E
63639 40E
63641 9G
63644 40E
63645 41A

O1 Class 2-8-0 8F
63646 41H

O4 Class 2-8-0 7F
63647 36E
63648 41F

O1 Class 2-8-0 8F
63650 41H

O4 Class 2-8-0 7F
63651 40B

O1 Class 2-8-0 8F
63652 41H

O4 Class 2-8-0 7F
63653 36C
63655 36E
63656 41H
63657 40E
63658 41A
63659 41F
63661 41F

O1 Class 2-8-0 8F
63663 41H

O4 Class 2-8-0 7F
63664 41J
63665 36E
63666 36C

O1 Class 2-8-0 8F
63670 41H

O4 Class 2-8-0 7F
63671 36C
63672 36E
63674 40E
63675 40E

O1 Class 2-8-0 8F
63676 16D

O4 Class 2-8-0 7F
63677 36A

O1 Class 2-8-0 8F
63678 41H

O4 Class 2-8-0 7F
63679 41J
63681 9G
63683 41J
63684 41F
63685 41A
63686 9G

O1 Class 2-8-0 8F
63687 31B

O4 Class 2-8-0 7F
63688 36E

O1 Class 2-8-0 8F
63689 16D

O4 Class 2-8-0 7F
63690 36C
63691 41J
63692 40B
63693 36A
63695 41A
63697 41J
63698 36A
63701 41F
63702 36E
63703 41J
63704 36E
63705 41H
63706 41H
63707 40B
63708 40B

O1 Class 2-8-0 8F
63711 16D
63712 52H

O4 Class 2-8-0 7F
63713 9G
63715 41J
63717 41J
63718 36E
63720 41J
63721 9G
63722 41J
63724 56B

O1 Class 2-8-0 8F
63725 31B

O4 Class 2-8-0 7F
63726 36E
63727 36E
63728 36C
63730 36E
63731 41J
63732 41J
63734 41A
63735 41H
63736 36E
63737 41A
63738 40B
63739 41J

O1 Class 2-8-0 8F
63740 16D

O4 Class 2-8-0 7F
63741 36C
63742 41A
63743 9G
63744 36C

O1 Class 2-8-0 8F
63746 31B

O4 Class 2-8-0 7F
63748 36C
63750 40E

O1 Class 2-8-0 8F
63752 16D

O4 Class 2-8-0 7F
63754 40E

O1 Class 2-8-0 8F
63755 52H

O4 Class 2-8-0 7F
63758 40B
63759 40B

O1 Class 2-8-0 8F
63760 52H

O4 Class 2-8-0 7F
63762 41H
63763 41J
63764 36E
63765 41J
63766 9G
63767 9G

O1 Class 2-8-0 8F
63768 40E

O4 Class 2-8-0 7F
63770 40E
63771 36E
63772 41F

O1 Class 2-8-0 8F
63773 41H

O4 Class 2-8-0 7F
63774 41J
63775 9G
63776 41J

O1 Class 2-8-0 8F
63777 16D

O4 Class 2-8-0 7F
63779 36E

O1 Class 2-8-0 8F
63780 31B

O4 Class 2-8-0 7F
63781 36C
63783 41A

O1 Class 2-8-0 8F
63784 41H

O4 Class 2-8-0 7F
63785 36E

O1 Class 2-8-0 8F
63786 31B

O4 Class 2-8-0 7F
63787 41H
63788 36C

All the 15 'Q7' 0-8-0s were withdrawn from Tyne Dock in 1962. This is No 63472 at Darlington shed on 28 February 1962 after its last casual light repair, somewhat surprisingly as it was to be withdrawn nine months later. Built at Darlington Works it entered traffic on 30 April 1924, and returned for cutting up. *Pictorail*

'04/1' class 2-8-0 No 63622 is at Mexborough shed on Saturday 16 July 1960. Built at Gorton Works in May 1914, this was a Robinson Great Central Railway-design with Belpaire boiler, and had been allocated to Mexborough from Barnsley on 3 January 1960. Its relatively clean state in this photograph was due to it leaving Gorton Works on 28 May 1960 after its last heavy intermediate repair. Transferred to Langwith Junction on 3 September 1961, withdrawal came on 1 May 1963, with cutting up carried out at Doncaster Works in June. *Author's collection*

'04/8' class 2-8-0 No 63647 is at Doncaster shed in March 1963, shortly after its transfer from Retford on the 3rd and still awaiting a 36A shedplate to be fitted. Originally built in December 1928, it was rebuilt with a 100A boiler, but retained the original cylinders at Gorton Works during a general overhaul in February 1958. Doncaster was the last allocation for No 63647, withdrawal coming on 6 May 1964. Cox & Danks at Wadsley Bridge carried out the scrapping. *Pictorail*

'04/3' class 2-8-0 No 63666, allocated to Frodingham, is on a freight working at Grimsby Littlefield on Tuesday 14 March 1961. Built in September 1918, this was a ROD (Railway Operating Division) engine until coming into LNER stock and being allocated to Gorton on 22 October 1925. Withdrawn in 1962, it was stored at Frodingham until August 1963 when towed to Doncaster Works for scrapping. *G. W. Sharpe*

'01' class 2-8-0 No 63725 is at Burton Salmon, between Milford Junction and Castleford, on a mineral train in March 1963 while it was allocated to March shed. Originally built in August 1919 by R. Stephenson & Co as an '04' class locomotive, No 63725 was rebuilt at Gorton Works in March 1945 with a 100A boiler, Walschaerts valve gear and new cylinders. From March it moved to Staveley Great Central shed on 24 November 1963 and to the ex-Midland shed at Barrow Hill on 13 June 1965, but it was placed in store on receipt until withdrawn on 11 July. Storage continued until September 1965, when No 63725 was sent to Draper's at Hull and cut up on 4 October. *G. W. Sharpe*

No 63760 was one of the five '01' class 2-8-0s which were allocated to Tyne Dock from September 1951 and fitted with Westinghouse pumps for operating the wagon doors on the Tyne Dock to Consett iron ore trains. All five were withdrawn in 1962. This view of No 63760 is at Tyne Dock shed in June 1962. After withdrawal, No 63760 was stored at Tyne Dock until April 1963 before going to Gorton Works for scrap. *Pictorail*

'01' class 2-8-0 No 63867 brings a train of permanent way cranes through Nottingham Victoria station on Sunday 8 April 1962. No 63867 had been converted from an '04/3' to an '01' at Gorton Works and re-entered traffic on 2 September 1944. It had been reallocated to Annesley from March on 31 January 1949 and remained until withdrawn in 1962. Stored at Annesley from December 1962 until August 1963, it was then sent to Crewe Works for scrapping, as it was part of LMR stock. *M. Mitchell*

01 Class 2-8-0 8F	
63789	16D

04 Class 2-8-0 7F	
63791	36C

01 Class 2-8-0 8F	
63792	16D

04 Class 2-8-0 7F	
63793	36C
63794	9G

01 Class 2-8-0 8F	
63795	41H
63796	16D

04 Class 2-8-0 7F	
63798	36E
63800	41J
63801	41J
63802	36A

01 Class 2-8-0 8F	
63803	31B

04 Class 2-8-0 7F	
63805	9G

01 Class 2-8-0 8F	
63806	16D

04 Class 2-8-0 7F	
63807	36C

01 Class 2-8-0 8F	
63808	16D

04 Class 2-8-0 7F	
63813	41F
63816	40E

01 Class 2-8-0 8F	
63817	16D

04 Class 2-8-0 7F	
63818	36E
63819	40E
63821	41A
63822	41A
63823	56B
63824	36E
63827	41H
63828	41J
63829	41J
63832	36C
63833	41J
63836	36C
63837	40B

01 Class 2-8-0 8F	
63838	16D

04 Class 2-8-0 7F	
63840	41J
63841	41F
63842	41J
63843	41F
63846	41A
63848	9G
63850	41A
63852	41A
63853	41J

01 Class 2-8-0 8F	
63854	16D
63856	52H

04 Class 2-8-0 7F	
63857	56B
63858	36A
63859	40E
63861	41J
63862	9G

01 Class 2-8-0 8F	
63863	40E

04 Class 2-8-0 7F	
63864	56B

01 Class 2-8-0 8F	
63865	16D
63867	16D
63868	31B
63869	16D

04 Class 2-8-0 7F	
63870	41J

01 Class 2-8-0 8F	
63872	31B

04 Class 2-8-0 7F	
63873	40E

01 Class 2-8-0 8F	
63874	52H

04 Class 2-8-0 7F	
63877	41F
63878	40B

'04/7' class 2-8-0 No 63857 is at Pontefract on a very short freight working in March 1962, with only five months to go before withdrawal. Originally built by the North British Locomotive Co in July 1919, No 63857 was rebuilt with a shortened 02-type boiler but retaining the Great Central smokebox at Gorton Works in May 1943. Cutting up was carried out at Gorton Works in October 1962. *G. W. Sharpe*

Gresley-designed '02/4' class 2-8-0 No 63933 is at Grimsby Friargate on a mineral train on Monday 3 April 1961. Added to stock on 3 November 1923, and first allocated to Peterborough New England, this was one of the class fitted with a diagram 100A boiler and a Great Northern-type cab, these changes taking place under Thompson's guidance. This was one of the class withdrawn in 1962 from Grantham shed, where it had been allocated since 28 October 1951. Storage at Grantham from December 1962 to October 1963 followed with sale to the Central Wagon Co at Ince, Wigan, for scrap. *G. W. Sharpe*

'02' class 2-8-0 No 63986, with original cab, is at March shed in May 1962. One of the last three of its class to be built, it left Doncaster Works to take up its duties at Doncaster shed on 7 January 1943. During its working life Colwick, New England, Langwith Junction and Mexborough were the engine's operating bases before it went to Retford on 17 August 1952, where it remained until withdrawn on 7 June 1963. Cutting up was carried out at Doncaster Works two months later. *G. W. Sharpe*

All the seven remaining 'J6' class 0-6-0s were withdrawn in 1962, with this example, No 64277, being one of the last two to go. This is a May 1961 view with the locomotive leaving Leeds City on a West Riding local. Built at Doncaster in August 1922, to a Gresley design, No 64277 had been transferred to Leeds Copley Hill shed from Boston in March 1952 and remained on allocation until withdrawn. Cutting up was carried out at Doncaster Works. *G. W. Sharpe*

Another class to disappear during 1962 was the Robinson Great Central-design 'J11' 0-6-0s, including No 64324 seen here at Retford Great Central shed in April 1962. This engine had come to Retford from Langwith Junction in January 1961. Dating from 1902, after withdrawal No 64324 was scrapped at Gorton Works in May 1963. *G. W. Sharpe*

At the beginning of 1962 only 14 'J35' class 0-6-0s were still in operating stock, and all were withdrawn during the year, including No 64519 seen here at Edinburgh Craigentinny stabling point in March 1961. Built at Glasgow Cowlairs Works and coming into stock in October 1910, No 64519 was first allocated to Glasgow Kipps, moving to Glasgow Eastfield in 1932. Its transfer to Edinburgh St Margarets on 15 February 1943 proved to be the last, as the engine remained on allocation until withdrawn. Stored until May 1963, it then went to Arnott Young at Carmyle for scrapping. *G. W. Sharpe*

01 Class 2-8-0 8F

63879	31B

04 Class 2-8-0 7F

63880	36C
63881	41A
63882	41A
63883	41F
63884	36C
63885	56B

01 Class 2-8-0 8F

63886	16D
63887	31B
63890	31B

04 Class 2-8-0 7F

63893	41J
63895	9G
63897	36C
63898	36C
63899	41H
63900	40E

01 Class 2-8-0 8F

63901	16D

04 Class 2-8-0 7F

63902	41J
63906	36C
63907	41F
63908	36E
63911	41F
63912	41J
63913	41F
63914	36E
63917	36C
63920	56A

02 Class 2-8-0 8F

63922	36A
63923	34F
63924	36E
63925	36E
63926	36E
63927	36E
63928	34F
63929	34F
63930	34F
63931	34F
63932	34F
63933	34F
63934	36E
63935	36A
63936	36E
63937	36E
63938	34F
63939	36E
63940	34F
63941	34F
63942	34F
63943	34F
63945	36E
63946	36E
63948	34F
63949	34F
63951	36E
63955	36E
63956	34F
63960	34F
63961	36E
63962	36A
63963	34F
63964	36E
63965	36E
63966	36E
63967	36A
63968	36A
63969	36E
63971	36E
63972	36E
63973	36E
63974	36A
63975	36E
63976	36E
63977	36A
63978	36A
63979	36E
63980	36E
63981	36A
63982	34F
63983	36E
63984	36A
63985	36A
63986	36E
63987	36E

J6 Class 0-6-0 2P3F

64177	34E
64191	40F
64203	56B
64226	56C
64245	36E
64253	34E
64277	56C

J11 Class 0-6-0 2P3F

64284	40B
64292	41A
64305	40B
64314	41J
64318	40A
64324	36E
64329	41A
64332	36E
64333	41J
64346	40A
64354	36E
64355	40B
64362	40A
64373	41A
64375	9G
64377	41F
64379	41J
64386	40B
64393	41F
64394	41A
64395	36E
64406	41F
64419	41A
64420	9G
64423	36C
64437	9G
64442	41F
64443	41A
64445	41A
64450	36E

J35 Class 0-6-0 3F

64470	65E
64472	65E
64478	62A
64480	62C
64491	62A
64497	64F
64499	12C
64507	65E
64510	64F
64514	65C
64519	64A
64525	62C
64527	64F
64533	64A

J37 Class 0-6-0 5F

64537	65K
64540	65A
64541	65A
64543	62C
64544	65E
64545	62C
64546	62A
64547	64A
64548	65A
64549	62A
64550	62A
64551	65K
64552	64A
64553	64F
64554	64C
64555	64A
64556	62B
64557	64A
64558	65A
64559	65C
64561	64A
64562	64A
64563	65C
64564	62A
64566	64A
64568	62C
64569	64C
64570	65K
64571	65K
64572	64A
64573	65C
64574	65E
64575	62B
64576	64A
64577	64A
64578	65A
64579	65E
64580	65A
64581	65A
64582	64A
64583	64F
64585	62C
64586	64A
64587	62B
64588	65C
64589	65F
64590	64A
64591	64A
64592	65F
64593	65E
64594	64A
64595	64A
64597	62C
64598	62B
64599	64A
64600	62B
64601	64A
64602	62B
64603	64A
64604	62C
64605	64A
64606	64A
64607	64A
64608	64A
64609	65C
64610	65C
64611	65A
64612	64A
64613	64A
64614	64A
64615	62B
64616	62A
64617	62C
64618	62A
64619	62B
64620	62B
64621	65C
64622	65A
64623	65A
64624	64A
64625	64A
64626	65C
64627	62B
64628	65E
64629	62A
64630	62C
64631	62B
64632	65A
64633	65A
64634	64F
64635	62A
64636	65K
64637	64A
64638	65A
64639	65A

J19 Class 0-6-0 3P5F

64657	30A
64664	30A
64671	32A
64673	30A

J20 Class 0-6-0 5F

64687	31B
64690	31B
64691	31B
64696	31A
64699	31B

J39 Class 0-6-0 4P5F

64701	52G
64703	52G
64704	52G
64705	56B
64706	51L
64709	50B
64711	52D
64713	52G
64718	9G
64719	51F
64727	9G
64730	51L
64739	16D
64740	9G
64742	2F
64744	9G
64747	2F
64749	56B
64754	56B
64756	51F
64757	51L
64758	51L
64760	56B
64786	62B
64790	62A
64791	56F
64792	62A
64794	62A
64795	64A
64796	56B
64798	16D
64801	56F
64806	52B
64809	2F
64811	56B
64812	52G
64813	52D
64814	52F
64817	56F
64818	51F
64819	50B
64820	56B
64821	51L
64822	62B
64833	52G
64835	51F
64836	56B
64840	56B
64842	52B
64843	52G
64844	52D
64846	52G
64847	52G
64848	51F
64849	51C
64850	50F
64851	52G
64852	52B
64853	52G
64854	52G

A typical line-up of power at Glasgow Eastfield that was rapidly going to disappear, this view in August 1960 shows 'J37' class 0-6-0 No 64581 sharing the yard with sister locomotive No 64632 and 'J36' class 0-6-0 No 65296, all Eastfield-based engines. No 64581 was a 1962 withdrawal, No 64632 was withdrawn on 6 December 1965 after moving to Thornton Junction, and No 65296 was another 1962 casualty. Nos 64581 and 65296 were cut up at Inverurie Works and No 64632 at McWilliam's yard at Shettleston. *Pictorail*

Only four 'J19' class 0-6-0s survived into 1962, including No 64673 seen here at London Stratford shed in June 1962. All were withdrawn by the end of the year. This was an A. J. Hill design for the Great Eastern Railway (GER), with this engine being built at Stratford Works and entering traffic in October 1920. At nationalisation No 64673 was based at March shed, moving to South Lynn during the week ended 4 June 1949. From here the engine moved to Cambridge during the week ended 13 January 1951, to Bury St Edmunds in December 1952, and back to Cambridge the following month. In June 1959 a move to Kings Lynn was made, returning to Cambridge in February 1960 and finally moving to Stratford nine months later. After withdrawal, No 64673 was scrapped at Stratford Works. *P. H. Groom*

The 'J20' class was another A. J. Hill design for the GER, and at the beginning of 1962 only five remained in service. By the end of September they had all been withdrawn, including No 64691 seen here in store at March shed in July 1962. Also built at Stratford Works, No 64691 entered service in December 1922. At nationalisation Stratford was its depot before it moved to March during January 1954, where it remained until withdrawn. Storage continued at March until August 1963 when No 64691 was despatched to Doncaster Works for scrapping. *G. W. Sharpe*

Gresley-designed 'J39' class 0-6-0 No 64851 is at Sunderland shed in August 1961, just after transfer from Tyne Dock. All the remaining 'J39s' were withdrawn in 1962, including No 64851. Built at Darlington Works, it entered traffic on 17 March 1934 and was first allocated to Newport, and spent its entire career working from North Eastern area sheds. After withdrawal it was sent to Darlington Works for scrapping. *Pictorail*

64855	52B
64856	52B
64857	51L
64858	52G
64859	51F
64860	52A
64861	55H
64863	55H
64864	52B
64865	52A
64866	52B
64867	50F
64868	52D
64869	52F
64870	51L
64871	52B
64872	56F
64875	9G
64877	12C
64879	56B
64880	9G
64884	12C
64886	56F
64888	12C
64895	12C
64897	52D
64899	12C
64903	56F
64907	56F
64910	52B
64911	56B
64915	52B
64917	52D
64918	56B
64919	56F
64921	52B
64922	55H
64923	52B
64924	52D
64925	52D
64926	52B
64927	51F
64929	52D
64933	55H
64934	55H
64935	55H
64936	52A
64938	52A
64939	52B
64940	50B
64941	52D
64942	52G
64943	50B
64944	55H
64945	52B
64946	64A
64947	55H
64949	52D
64950	62B
64955	9G
64963	62C
64969	51F
64971	50B
64975	65D
64978	52A
64979	51F
64982	51F
64986	62A

J21 Class 0-6-0 2F

65033	52F

J36 Class 0-6-0 2F

65210	65E
65211	65C
65214	65F
65216*	65E
65217*	65F
65218	65A
65222*	65F
65224*	64A
65228	65A
65230	65C
65234	64G
65237	12C
65241	65E
65243*	64B
65246	65C
65251	64F
65253*	62C
65257	65K
65258	64B
65260	65E
65261	64F
65265	64F
65266	65E
65267	64F
65268*	64F
65273	65C
65275	64G
65277	64F
65280	65K
65282	64F
65285	65E
65287	65E
65288	64A
65290	64F
65293	12C
65296	65A
65297	65D
65300	63B
65303	65B
65304	65J
65305	64F
65306	65F
65307	62C
65309	64F
65310	65J
65311*	65K
65312	12C
65313	63B
65315	65A
65316	64G
65318	64F
65319	62B
65320	65C
65321	12C
65323	62C
65325	65E
65327	64A
65329	64A
65330	64G
65331	64G
65334	64A
65335	65D

65338 62C
65341 64F
65344 64A
65345 62A
65346 64F

J15 Class 0-6-0 1P2F

65361 30A
65420 31B
65445 30A
65453 30A
65457 31A
65460 30A
65462 30A
65464 30A
65465 30A
65469 31A
65476 30A

J17 Class 0-6-0 2P4F

65521 32A
65532 31A
65541 31B
65560 31B
65567 32A
65576 31B
65577 31B
65578 31B
65581 32A
65582 31A
65583 32A
65586 32A

J25 Class 0-6-0 3F

65645 52A
65663 52B
65670 52H
65693 52H
65695 52H
65720 51L
65726 52A
65728 52A

J26 Class 0-6-0 3F

65731 51F
65735 51F
65743 51L
65747 51L
65751 51L
65755 51L
65756 51L
65757 51L
65761 51L
65763 51L
65768 51L
65772 51L
65773 51L
65776 51L

J27 Class 0-6-0 5F

65786 52F
65787 51L
65788 51L
65789 52F
65790 51L
65791 52E
65792 52F
65794 52F
65795 52E
65796 52E
65797 52F
65799 52F
65800 52F
65801 52F
65802 52E
65804 52F
65805 51C
65807 52E
65808 52F
65809 52E
65810 52F
65811 52F
65812 52E
65813 52E
65814 52E
65815 52F
65817 52G
65818 51C
65819 52F
65820 51C
65821 52E
65822 52F
65823 52G
65825 52E
65828 52F
65830 51C
65831 52E
65832 52G
65833 52G
65834 52F
65835 52G
65837 52E
65838 52F
65839 52E
65841 52G
65842 52E
65844 50F
65845 52F
65846 51C
65849 50F
65850 52E
65851 52F
65852 52E
65853 51L
65854 52G
65855 51L
65857 52F
65858 52E
65859 51L
65860 51A
65861 52F
65862 52F
65863 52F
65864 52F
65865 51L
65867 52F
65869 52G
65870 51L
65871 52G
65872 52G
65873 52G
65874 52G
65875 52F
65876 52F
65877 52E
65878 52G
65879 52F
65880 52F
65881 52F
65882 52F
65883 52G
65884 51L
65885 52G
65887 52G
65888 50F
65889 52F
65890 50A
65891 52F
65892 52G
65893 52F
65894 50A

J38 Class 0-6-0 6F

65900 62A
65901 62A
65902 62A
65903 62C
65904 62A
65905 62A
65906 62C
65907 62A
65908 62A
65909 65K
65910 62A
65911 62A
65912 64A
65913 62A
65914 64A
65915 64A
65916 62A
65917 65K
65918 64A
65919 64A
65920 64A
65921 62A
65922 64A
65923 62C
65924 62C
65925 62A
65926 62C
65927 64A
65928 62C
65929 64A
65930 62C
65931 62A
65932 62A
65933 62C
65934 64A

V3 Class 2-6-2T 4MT

67600 65A

V1 Class 2-6-2T 3MT

67601 65A
67602 65A
67603 65A

V3 Class 2-6-2T 4MT

67604 65A
67605 64A
67606 64A
67607 65C
67608 65A
67609 65E
67611 65C
67613 67B
67614 67B
67615 64B
67616 67B
67617 64A
67618 65E
67619 65C
67620 64B
67621 65C

V1 Class 2-6-2T 3MT

67622 65C

V3 Class 2-6-2T 4MT

67623 67B
67625 65C
67626 65C
67628 65A

V1 Class 2-6-2T 3MT

67629 65C
67630 65C
67631 65C

V3 Class 2-6-2T 4MT

67632 65C
67633 65C
67634 52C
67635 51L
67636 52C

V1 Class 2-6-2T 3MT

67637 52B

V3 Class 2-6-2T 4MT

67638 50B

V1 Class 2-6-2T 3MT

67639 52A

V3 Class 2-6-2T 4MT

67640 51L

V1 Class 2-6-2T 3MT

67641 52B

V3 Class 2-6-2T 4MT

67642 52B
67643 65C
67644 65A
67645 52B
67646 52B
67647 52B
67648 67B

V1 Class 2-6-2T 3MT

67649 64A

V3 Class 2-6-2T 4MT

67651 52B
67652 52B
67653 52C
67654 52B

V1 Class 2-6-2T 3MT

67655 65C

V3 Class 2-6-2T 4MT

67656 52B
67657 52A
67658 52B

V1 Class 2-6-2T 3MT

67659 64A

V3 Class 2-6-2T 4MT

67660 64A
67661 67B
67662 65C
67663 50B

V1 Class 2-6-2T 3MT

67664 65A

V3 Class 2-6-2T 4MT

67666 64A
67667 65A
67668 64A
67672 62C

V1 Class 2-6-2T 3MT

67673 52B

V3 Class 2-6-2T 4MT

67674 64A
67675 65A
67676 67B
67677 50B
67678 65C
67679 67B

V1 Class 2-6-2T 3MT

67680 65A

V3 Class 2-6-2T 4MT

67682 51A
67683 52B
67684 50B
67685 52B
67686 50B
67687 52A
67688 52A
67689 52A
67690 52B
67691 52B

L1 Class 2-6-4T 4MT

67703 30A
67710 9G
67715 32A

The last survivor of the 'J21' class 0-6-0s, No 65033 managed to last into 1962 and was withdrawn in April. This is the engine at South Blyth in September 1961. Built at Gateshead Works in March 1889 to a design by T. W. Worsdell, during its British Railways days, No 65033 operated from Darlington, Blaydon, Heaton and South Blyth. After storage at South Blyth from April until August 1962, it then went to Darlington Works for further storage for a number of years before being preserved and becoming part of the Railway Museum at Beamish, County Durham. *G. W. Sharpe*

'J36' class 0-6-0 No 65218 is dumped alongside the old disused coaling stage at Glasgow Eastfield shed in August 1962, here paired with a tender cab. Placed in store the previous month, No 65218 was officially withdrawn in October 1962 and sent to Inverurie Works for cutting up in January 1963. This was an M. Holmes design for the North British Railway and No 65218 had been built at Cowlairs Works and entered traffic in April 1890 as No 9632. Its first allocation was Thornton Junction and here it remained until 28 June 1960, when it was transferred to Eastfield. *G. W. Sharpe*

The damaged state of 'J36' No 65237 at Carlisle Canal shed in September 1962 led to its withdrawal the following month. The 'J36s' at Carlisle were still very active at this time and were a familiar sight on transfer trips between the Carlisle yards. It is presumed that the damage was a result of a collision on one of these workings. No 65237 had been built by Neilson Reid & Co Ltd in October 1891 and entered service at Glasgow Eastfield shed. Time was also spent at Fort William and Glasgow Kipps sheds before it went to Carlisle Canal on 29 December 1958. After withdrawal, No 65237 was cut up at Inverurie Works. *Pictorail*

'J15' class 0-6-0 No 65460 is at London Stratford shed in 1961, after transfer from Norwich in December 1960. It was another class to be removed from the railway scene in 1962, with No 65460 one of the last to go. This was a design drawn up by T. W. Worsdell for the Great Eastern Railway, before Worsdell moved to the North Eastern Railway in 1885 as Chief Mechanical Engineer. No 65460 was built at Stratford Works in February 1912. At nationalisation it was at Norwich shed, moving to Lowestoft during the week ended 1 October 1955, before returning to Norwich in September 1960, and then going to Stratford. After withdrawal, storage at Stratford until November 1962 was followed by sale to Cashmore's at Great Bridge for scrap.
R. H. G. Simpson

All the 12 remaining 'J17' class 0-6-0s were withdrawn during 1962, including No 65541 seen here on Cambridge shed on Sunday 24 April 1960. Its transfer to March shed in November 1960 was its last, and withdrawal on 16 September 1962, along with Nos 65576 and 65582, both March engines, saw the class extinct. No 65541 lived on, in a way, as it was used as a stationary boiler until January 1964 when it went to Doncaster Works for scrap.
G. W. Sharpe

'J17' class 0-6-0 No 65567 is at Thetford on Saturday 31 March 1962 with 'Britannia' class 4-6-2 No 70003 *John Bunyan* alongside. The engines were part of the RCTS Great Eastern Commemorative Steam Rail Tour. Leaving London Liverpool Street at 9.10am, with 292 passengers on board the six-coach train, the first part was hauled by No 70003 through to Norwich. Here No 65567, with its red coupling rods and the only steam engine on Norwich's allocation, took over for a run to Thetford via Dereham and Swaffham. At Thetford, as can be seen in this photograph, No 70003 took over for the return run to London. No 65567 transferred to March shed immediately after this tour and following withdrawal and storage at various locations was preserved. It is now at the National Railway Museum with its old Great Eastern Railway number 1217. *G. W. Sharpe*

'J25' class 0-6-0 No 65693 is at Tyne Dock shed in March 1961, just after transfer from Hull Dairycoates, still with a 50B shedplate. This was a Wilson Worsdell design for the North Eastern Railway, with No 65693 dating from April 1900. All the remaining 'J25s' were withdrawn during 1962, with No 65693 going in April. It had been placed in store at Tyne Dock the previous month and remained there until early 1963, when it went to Darlington Works for scrap. *Pictorail*

The 'J26' class was another Worsdell design and all 14 survivors were condemned in 1962. This is No 65743 dumped at Thornaby shed in June 1962. It had been built at Darlington Works in October 1904 and had been transferred to Thornaby from Newport shed when this shed closed on 1 June 1958. After withdrawal, No 65743 returned to Darlington for scrapping. *G. W. Sharpe*

The roofless through road shed at Percy Main in August 1961 sees one of its stud of 'J27' class 0-6-0s on view, No 65802. This was the only type of steam locomotive allocated there for a number of years in the BR period, which was somewhat unique with around 22 locomotives on strength. No 65802 was built in June 1908 and was withdrawn on 7 August 1966 from North Blyth and cut up at the nearby Hughes, Bolckow yard. *G. W. Sharpe*

At home at Edinburgh St Margarets shed in July 1962 is Gresley-designed 'J38' class 0-6-0 No 65922. As No 1426, this engine was built at Darlington Works and entered traffic at Dundee Tay Bridge shed on 26 March 1926. Transfer to Dunfermline on 12 December 1943 was followed by a move to St Margarets on 10 November 1954 and finally to Thornton Junction on 14 September 1964. Withdrawal was authorised on 19 October 1966 and after storage, the Motherwell Machinery & Scrap Co at Wishaw scrapped No 65922 in February 1967. *Pictorail*

The remaining 'V1' class 2-6-2Ts were also all withdrawn during 1962. This is Gateshead-allocated No 67637 preparing to leave Carlisle Citadel station with a local to Newcastle on Saturday 25 July 1959. A Gresley design, No 67637 was added to stock as No 479 on 16 May 1935 from Doncaster Works and allocated to Blaydon shed. Gateshead had acquired the engine from Sunderland on 25 January 1959, and it moved to Heaton shed on 11 June 1961, from where it was withdrawn in May 1962. It was sent to Darlington Works for cutting up in February 1963, after storage at Heaton. *G. W. Sharpe*

'V3' class 2-6-2T No 67662 is at Glasgow Parkhead shed in store in May 1962, still clean after its last general overhaul at Darlington Works. Built at Doncaster, it entered traffic as a 'V1' class on 3 July 1938 at Parkhead shed. Conversion to a 'V3', with higher pressure boiler, was carried out at Darlington Works whilst undergoing a general overhaul in January 1955. No 67662 spent nearly the whole of its time at Parkhead, coming out of store on 8 December 1962 and being transferred first to Heaton and then three weeks later to Gateshead. These may well have been 'paper only' moves as No 67662 was withdrawn on 14 January 1963. It reached Gateshead, as it is recorded as being in store there from January until March 1962, when it was sent to Darlington Works for scrapping. *G. W. Sharpe*

Thompson-designed 'L1' class 2-6-4T No 67800 is at King's Cross shed in April 1962. The first of the class entered traffic on 29 May 1945, having been built at Doncaster Works. Building then continued at Darlington Works, with the second of the class entering traffic on 22 January 1948. Later examples, Nos 67731 to 67765, were built by the North British Locomotive Co, and Nos 67766 to 67800 by Robert Stephenson & Hawthorn Ltd. No 67800 left the works on 15 September 1950 and went into service at King's Cross. Later reallocations were Grantham on 7 October 1956, King's Cross on 21 September 1958 and Nottingham Colwick on 8 April 1962. Withdrawal started in 1960, with No 67702 going from Stratford shed on 31 October. Sixty-four survived into 1962, but all had gone by the end of the year with No 67800 being one of the last batch to go. Darlington Works carried out the cutting up in March 1963. *P. H. Groom*

67716 30A
67720 30A
67721 56F
67723 30A
67724 30A
67727 9G
67729 30A
67730 32A
67731 30A
67733 9G
67734 30A
67735 30A
67737 30A
67741 40E
67742 56B
67743 40E
67744 40E
67745 40E
67746 40E
67747 40E
67749 40E
67751 40E
67752 34F
67753 40E
67754 56F
67755 56B
67756 40E
67757 34F
67759 56F
67761 34F
67763 56B
67764 56F
67765 56B
67766 56B
67767 40E
67770 34A
67771 2F
67773 34F
67774 34F
67776 34F
67777 56B
67778 34E
67779 34A
67780 36A
67781 2F
67783 40E
67784 36A
67785 34F
67786 34A
67787 36A
67788 40E
67789 2F
67791 34F
67792 40E
67793 34A
67795 34E
67796 34F
67797 34A
67798 34F
67799 40E
67800 34A

J94 Class 0-6-0ST 4F

68006 17C
68007 51A
68008 56B
68009 40E
68010 51A
68011 56B
68012 9G
68013 17C
68014 51A
68015 56B
68016 52H
68017 51A
68018 40F
68019 52H
68020 41J
68021 51C
68023 51L
68024 51A
68025 51A
68029 52H
68030 17C
68031 52H
68032 51C
68034 17C
68035 51A
68036 51C
68037 51A
68038 52H
68039 51L
68040 51A
68041 51C
68042 50B
68043 51A
68044 51C
68045 56B
68046 50A
68047 51A
68048 52H
68049 56B
68050 51A
68051 51C
68052 51A
68053 51C
68054 52H
68055 51C
68056 51C
68057 51C
68058 51C
68059 52H
68060 51A
68061 50A
68062 56B
68063 6F
68064 9G
68065 6F
68066 6F
68067 36E
68068 9G
68069 41J
68070 40F
68071 51A
68074 40E
68075 36E
68077 40F
68078 41J
68079 9G

Y9 Class 0-4-0ST 0F

68095 64A
68101 62C
68104 65E
68117 65E

J88 Class 0-6-0T 0F

68335 64B
68336 65D
68342 64A
68345 65E
68346 62C
68350 65B
68353 62A

J83 Class 0-6-0T 2F

68442 65E
68445 65E
68448 64A
68453 64A
68454 64A
68458 67C
68470 64A
68472 64A
68477 64A
68479 65A
68481 64B

J69 Class 0-6-0T 2F

68499 30A
68542 30A
68549 30A
68556 30A
68565 30A
68566 30A
68600 30A
68609 30A
68621 30A
68626 30A
68635 30A

J72 Class 0-6-0T 2F

68695 52A
68707 51C
68709 66C
68723 52A
68733 66C
68736 52A
68750 66C
68754 51L

J50 Class 0-6-0T 4F

68892 56C
68900 56B
68904 56A
68908 56F
68910 56A
68917 36A
68922 56F
68925 56C

A cold Saturday, 3 March 1962, finds 'L1' class 2-6-4T No 67767 at Nottingham Victoria with the 12.55pm Nottingham to Grantham local. 'B1' 4-6-0 No 61192 is over on the right. No 67767 was another 'L1' withdrawn in December 1962 from Colwick shed and was cut up at Doncaster Works in March 1963. *M. Mitchell*

68926	36A
68928	36A
68934	56B
68935	56B
68937	56B
68939	56A
68961	34E
68963	56F
68964	56F
68965	56B
68971	34E
68972	36A
68976	34E
68977	56F
68982	40E
68983	36A
68984	56C
68986	36A
68987	36A
68988	56C
68989	34E

J72 Class 0-6-0T 2F

69001	52A
69002	51L
69003	51C
69004	51L
69005	52A
69006	51L
69007	51L
69008	52B
69009	50B
69010	50B
69011	50B
69013	66B
69014	64A
69016	51L
69017	51L
69018	51A
69019	51L
69020	50B
69021	51C
69022	51C
69023	52C
69024	52B
69025	52H
69026	52B
69027	52A
69028	52B

N10 Class 0-6-2T 3F

69097	52A
69101	52A
69109	52A

N15 Class 0-6-2T 3MT

69126	65D
69128	64A
69131	65A
69135	64A
69137	65K
69138	64A
69150	64A
69155	12C
69156	64F
69163	65A
69178	66C
69181	65A
69188	65A
69191	65A
69196	66C
69204	62A
69211	64B
69212	65A
69216	64F
69218	65A
69224	64A

N2 Class 0-6-2T 3P2F

69504	34E
69512	34E
69520	34E
69523	34A
69529	34E
69535	34A
69538	34A
69546	34E
69568	34A
69575	34E
69579	34E
69583	34E
69593	34A

N7 Class 0-6-2T 3MT

69621	30A
69632	30A
69640	30A
69646	30A
69653	30A
69671	30A
69692	30A
69697	30A
69725	30A

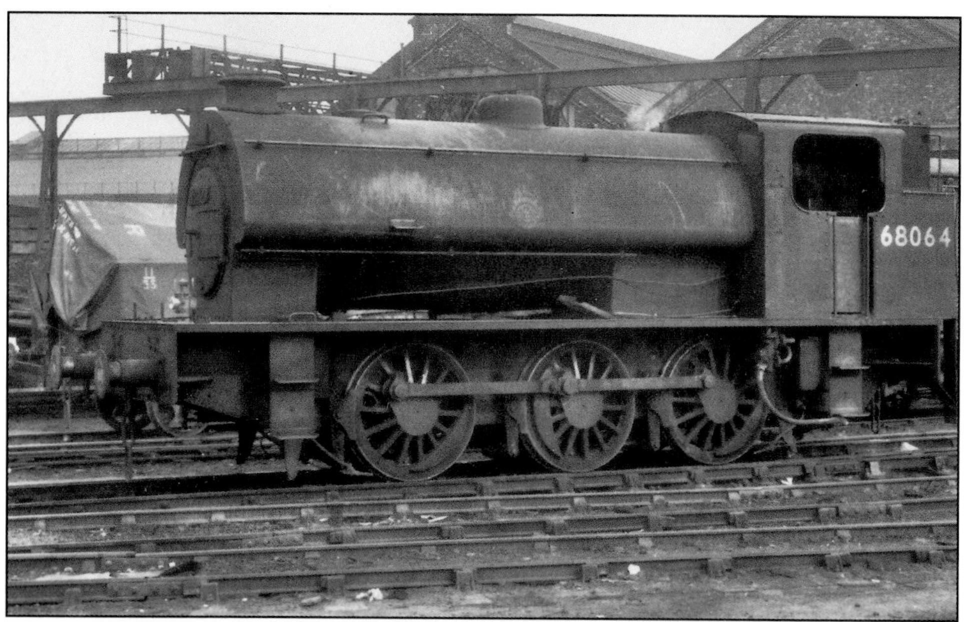

'J94' class 0-6-0ST No 68064 is at Manchester Gorton Works in May 1960 on shunting duty. This was one of 21 class members withdrawn in 1962. The 75 engines of the class, designed by Hunslet to the specification of Riddles, were purchased from the Ministry of Supply in 1946 and designated the 'J94' class by the LNER. When taken into stock of the LNER in June, No 68064 was allocated to Manchester Gorton shed and spent its time either at Gorton or Trafford Park. After withdrawal, it was cut up at Darlington Works. *Pictorail*

The last survivor of the 'Y9' 0-4-0ST class, No 68095, is at Edinburgh St Margarets shed in August 1962, in store on the opposite side of the main line to the running shed. Built in December 1887 at Cowlairs Works and first allocated to Glasgow Kipps, this little engine came to St Margarets from Polmont on 25 February 1946. The four survivors of the class were all withdrawn in 1962, with No 68095 going into store at Bathgate until March 1965, when it was purchased for preservation at Lytham Museum. *G. W. Sharpe*

Another 'Y9' 0-4-0ST that lasted into 1962, No 68101, is here seen out of use at Dunfermline shed in August 1960 with 'J88' class 0-6-0T No 68346 behind. Both were withdrawn on 8 October 1962. No 68101 is coupled to a four-wheel wooden-bodied wagon used as a coal carrier to supplement the meagre coal capacity of these engines. A simple three-link coupling with safety chains was the means of attachment for this engine. No 68101 dated from June 1889 and went new to Glasgow Kipps. The only other transfer was to Dunfermline on 4 August 1932. After withdrawal No 68101 continued in storage until February 1963, when it was sent to Inverurie Works for scrap. *G. W. Sharpe*

The last 'J88' class 0-6-0T No 68345 to be withdrawn in 1962 stands at Glasgow Kipps shed in August 1962. Built at Cowlairs Works in July 1912, it was one of a once 35-strong class to a design by W. P. Reid for the North British Railway. This example is somewhat unique in being fitted with a stovepipe chimney. It had come to Kipps shed in March 1961 from Glasgow St Rollox and was placed in store in July 1962, where it remained until June 1963 when it was despatched to Cowlairs Works for scrapping. *P. H. Groom*

'J83' class 0-6-0T No 68477 is at Edinburgh St Margarets shed on Friday 13 April 1962, with classmate No 68453 behind. Eleven 'J83s' survived into 1962, and all had gone by the end of the year, with No 68477 the last in service. An M. Holmes design for the North British Railway, No 68477 was built by Sharp, Stewart & Co and entered traffic in May 1901. It was used as a stationary boiler at St Margarets until September 1963, when it was sent to Bathgate for storage, and it was sold to the Motherwell Machinery & Scrap Co at Wishaw in June 1964 for scrap. *G. W. Sharpe*

'J69' class 0-6-0T No 68565, with No 68600 behind, is at Stratford shed in March 1962. This was yet another class to be confined to the scrapheap in 1962, with all 11 survivors gone by 16 September, plus the two allocated to department stock. All were based at Stratford. No 68565 had been built at Stratford Works in December 1895 to a design by J. Holden for the GER and had been transferred to Stratford from Lowestoft shed in November 1959. After withdrawal, scrapping was carried out at Stratford. *R. H. G. Simpson*

The station pilot engines at Newcastle were painted in lined green in the 1960s and carried the totems for British Railways and the North Eastern Railway. This is one of them, 'J72' class 0-6-0T No 68723, at Newcastle station on Friday 23 August 1963. Dating from April 1922, this was one of the batch built by Armstrong, Whitworth & Co to a design dating back to 1898. No 68723 did not have much longer to go in active service as it was withdrawn from Gateshead shed on 23 September 1963 and cut up at Darlington Works soon after. *G. W. Sharpe*

One of the 'J50' class 0-6-0Ts withdrawn in 1962, No 68939, is here seen on shunting duties at Batley in April 1962. This was a Gresley design, with No 68939 coming into service in June 1924. Wakefield was its last shed, it having been transferred there from Ardsley in February 1959. After withdrawal it returned to its birthplace, Doncaster Works, for scrapping. *G. W. Sharpe*

Surprisingly, British Railways built a further batch of 28 'J72' class 0-6-0Ts at Darlington Works from October 1949 to May 1951 and this is one of them, No 69019, at West Hartlepool shed in April 1962, just after transfer from Thornaby shed. Ten of this batch were withdrawn during 1962, but No 69019 carried on into 1963, being withdrawn on 9 December, still on allocation at West Hartlepool. It was placed in store and sold to Cohen's at Cargo Fleet for scrap in August 1964. *Pictorail*

Three 'N10' class 0-6-2Ts survived into 1962, all being withdrawn in April, including No 69101, seen on shunting duties at Bowes Bridge in 1960. Dating from December 1902, No 69101 was a Worsdell design for the North Eastern Railway (NER) and had been sub-shedded at Bowes Bridge since April 1959, when transferred to the parent shed at Gateshead from Tyne Dock. After withdrawal, Darlington Works carried out the scrapping. *G. W. Sharpe*

The survivors of the 'N15' class 0-6-2Ts were also all withdrawn in 1962, including No 69128 seen here at Aberdeen Ferryhill shed in March 1961, before transfer to Edinburgh St Margarets three months later. Built by the North British Locomotive Co to a design by W. P. Reid, No 69128 took to the rails in June 1910. After withdrawal, the engine took up stationary boiler duty at St Margarets until November 1964, when it was towed to the Motherwell Machinery & Scrap Co at Wishaw for dismantling. *Pictorail*

The 'N2' class 0-6-2Ts were once a familiar sight on suburban workings in and out of King's Cross, but by the end of September 1962 they had all been withdrawn, with the last 13 working from Peterborough New England. No 69512 was one of them, seen here shortly before withdrawal at New England shed, awaiting dispatch to Doncaster Works for cutting up. *G. W. Sharpe*

Another class to go from the London scene was the 'N7' 0-6-2Ts, with only nine managing to survive into 1962. The last ones were withdrawn in September, including No 69692 here at Stratford shed in October 1962 awaiting cutting up at Stratford Works, which took place in January 1963. *P. H. Groom*

Standard 'Britannia' 4-6-2 No 70007 *Coeur-De-Lion* is at Lincoln shed in April 1962 fitted with handhold smoke deflectors. Entering traffic on 25 April 1951, its first allocation was Stratford, moving to Norwich a month later where it was used on the GE (Great Eastern) lines express service from London Liverpool Street. Surplus to requirements when the Class 40 diesels took over, No 70007 moved to March in November 1961 and again, when displaced by diesels, to Carlisle Kingmoor during the week ended 7 December 1963. Here it remained until withdrawn during the week ended 19 June 1965 and after storage at Crewe South shed it went back to where it had been built, Crewe Works, for cutting up. *Pictorail*

Standard 'Britannia' Class 4-6-2 7P6F

70000*	31B
70001*	31B
70002*	31B
70003*	31B
70004*	1A
70005*	31B
70006*	31B
70007*	31B
70008*	31B
70009*	31B
70010*	31B
70011*	31B
70012*	31B
70013*	31B
70014*	14D
70015*	14D
70016*	12C
70017*	21D
70018*	12C
70019*	12A
70020*	12A
70021*	1A
70022*	12A
70023*	12A
70024*	21D
70025*	21D
70026*	21D
70027*	21D
70028*	21D
70029*	21D
70030*	31B
70031*	21D
70032*	1A
70033*	1A
70034*	31B
70035*	40B
70036*	40B
70037*	40B
70038*	40B
70039*	40B
70040*	40B
70041*	40B
70042*	1A
70043*	21D
70044*	55A
70045*	14D
70046*	1A
70047	1A
70048*	14D
70049*	14D
70050*	66A
70051*	66A
70052*	66A
70053*	55A
70054*	55A

Standard 4-6-2 8P

71000*	5A

Standard 'Clan' Class 4-6-2 6P5F

72000*	66A
72001*	66A
72002*	66A
72003*	66A
72004*	66A
72005*	12A
72006*	12A
72007*	12A
72008*	12A
72009*	12A

Standard 4-6-0 5MT

73000	41D
73001	82C
73002	41D
73003	82E
73004	1A
73005	63A
73006	63A
73007	63A
73008	63A
73009	63A
73010	14D
73011	6J
73012	82C
73013	1A
73014	1A
73015	82E
73016	41D
73017	71G
73018	71G
73019	82F
73020	71G
73021	87F
73022	71G
73023	87F
73024	89A
73025	89A
73026	89A
73027	82C
73028	82E
73029	71G
73030	26F
73031	82F
73032	14D
73033	1A
73034	89A
73035	89A
73036	89A
73037	89A
73038	6A
73039	1A
73040	6A
73041	71G
73042	71G
73043	41D
73044	26F
73045	14D
73046	41D
73047	82F
73048	6A
73049	89A
73050	82F
73051	82F
73052	82F
73053	14D
73054	82F

'Britannia' 4-6-2 No 70022 *Tornado*, with a different design of handhold smoke deflectors, is seen at Rugby shed on 19 October 1962, a week after transfer from Birmingham Aston. The arrival of 'Britannias' Nos 70017, 70022, 70023 and 70024 during the week ended 13 October meant that Rugby's 'Jubilees' Nos 45704, 45722 and 45733 were placed in store. The 'Britannias' took over their two station pilot duties as the 'Jubilees' were considered inadequate for main-line work if a diesel failure occurred. No 70022 came into service on 16 August 1951 on the Western Region at Plymouth Laira, moving to Newton Abbot in April 1952 and Cardiff Canton in December 1956. The London Midland Region then acquired the engine in September 1961 when it went to Carlisle Kingmoor. Further transfers took No 70022 to Manchester Longsight in June 1962, and Aston in September 1962. After its time at Rugby it returned to Aston in February 1963, then moved to Carlisle Kingmoor in October 1964, to Upperby a month later and back to Kingmoor at the end of December 1966, from where it was withdrawn during the week ended 23 December 1967. After storage, No 70022 was cut up at Ward's yard at Inverkeithing in April 1968. *G. W. Sharpe*

An immaculate looking 'Britannia', No 70042 *Lord Roberts*, is at its home shed Willesden in April 1962, fitted with handrails to the smoke deflectors. Stratford had received the locomotive new from Crewe Works on 9 April 1953 and its first transfer was to Kentish Town during the week ended 14 June 1958, and then to Trafford Park a month later. From service on the Midland lines, it transferred to Willesden during the week ended 28 December 1960, leaving London for Crewe North during the week ended 23 May 1963 and moving on to Crewe South when North shed closed on 24 May 1965. This was a short stay, for Holyhead acquired the engine during the week ended 3 July 1965 and then came a final transfer to Carlisle Kingmoor during the week ended 5 December 1965. Withdrawn during the week ended 13 May 1967, it was stored at Kingmoor until September when No 70042 was sold to McWilliam's at Shettleston for scrap. *P. H. Groom*

The one and only 'Duke', 4-6-2 No 71000 *Duke of Gloucester*, is seen in store outside Crewe Works paint shop in December 1962 after withdrawal. Built at Crewe, it entered traffic in May 1954 and was allocated to Crewe North for the whole of its working life. Now in preservation, it has worked on the main line again with some remarkable performances to its credit. *Pictorail*

Half the 'Clan' class 4-6-2s were withdrawn at the end of 1962, all allocated to Glasgow Polmadie. The remaining five allocated to Carlisle Kingmoor continued in service, with the last, No 72006, not being withdrawn until the week ended 21 May 1966. This is No 72009 *Clan Stewart* running into Carlisle Citadel station from the north on Saturday 3 August 1963. Built at Crewe Works, No 72009 entered service on 29 March 1952 at Carlisle Kingmoor and was withdrawn from there during the week ended 28 August 1965. Stored until November 1965, it then went to the Motherwell Machinery & Scrap Co at Wishaw for breaking up. *G. W. Sharpe*

Ex-works on Doncaster shed in May 1962 is Shrewsbury-based Standard Class 5MT 4-6-0 No 73034, superbly turned out in lined green. Built at Derby Works, this engine entered traffic on 14 August 1953 and went new to Carlisle Kingmoor. Its stay was short as it was reallocated to Shrewsbury during the week ended 19 September 1953. A move to Wolverhampton Oxley in October 1956 was made, with a return to Shrewsbury in June 1958. The next move was not until May 1966, when No 73034 went to Manchester Agecroft and then finally to Manchester Patricroft in October the same year, from where it was withdrawn during the week ended 16 March 1968 and sent to Cashmore's at Newport two months later for scrapping.
G. W. Sharpe

All the atmosphere of the steam age is captured in this view at Woodford Halse on the Great Central with the fireman of Standard 5MT 4-6-0 No 73069 awaiting the guard's signal to restart a southbound passenger train to Marylebone on 9 August 1962. No 73069 had been built at Derby Works and was first allocated to Derby during the week ended 6 November 1954. Transfer to Leeds Holbeck was actioned in August 1955 and in September 1959 No 73069 came to the Great Central at Leicester shed, then operated from Neasden from June 1960 to June 1962, when it returned to Leicester and then to Woodford Halse shed in February 1963. Cricklewood was its next home in May the same year. Moving to pastures new at Leamington Spa in October 1964, it transferred to Tyseley in June 1965, Bolton in May 1966, Patricroft in April 1968 and finally Carnforth in July. Withdrawal came at the end of steam during the week ended 10 August 1968, giving No 73069 the distinction of being the last of the class in service. Not preserved, it was cut up at Cashmore's, Newport, in March 1969 after storage at Lostock Hall. *G. W. Sharpe*

73055	66A	73078	65A	73101	67A	73124	67A	73147	65B
73056	66A	73079	67A	73102	67A	73125	26F	73148	65B
73057	66A	73080*	71G	73103	67A	73126	26F	73149	65B
73058	66A	73081*	70A	73104	67A	73127	26F	73150	65B
73059	66A	73082*	70A	73105	65A	73128	26F	73151	65B
73060	66A	73083*	70A	73106	63A	73129	26F	73152	65B
73061	66A	73084*	70A	73107	63A	73130	26F	73153	65B
73062	66A	73085*	70A	73108	65A	73131	26F	73154	65B
73063	66A	73086*	70A	73109	65A	73132	26F	73155	41D
73064	66A	73087*	70A	73110*	70A	73133	26F	73156	14D
73065	41D	73088*	70A	73111*	70A	73134	26F	73157	14D
73066	14D	73089*	70A	73112*	70A	73135	17A	73158	14D
73067	6J	73090	89A	73113*	70A	73136	17A	73159	14D
73068	82E	73091	85C	73114*	70A	73137	17A	73160	55E
73069	14D	73092	85C	73115*	70A	73138	17A	73161	55E
73070	6A	73093	85C	73116*	70A	73139	17C	73162	55H
73071	6A	73094	85C	73117*	70A	73140	17A	73163	55G
73072	66A	73095	89A	73118*	70A	73141	17C	73164	55G
73073	6J	73096	89A	73119*	70A	73142	17C	73165	55G
73074	41D	73097	89A	73120	63A	73143	17C	73166	55G
73075	66A	73098	66A	73121	67A	73144	17A	73167	55E
73076	66A	73099	66A	73122	67A	73145	65B	73168	55H
73077	65A	73100	67A	73123	67A	73146	65B	73169	55H

73170 55A
73171 55A

Standard 4-6-0 4MT

75000 81F
75001 81F
75002 82G
75003 84E
75004 82G
75005 85A
75006 84E
75007 81F
75008 81F
75009 82G
75010 6G
75011 6G
75012 6G
75013 6B
75014 6B
75015 27C
75016 27C
75017 27C
75018 27C
75019 27C
75020 89C
75021 81F
75022 81F
75023 82G
75024 84E
75025 85A
75026 89C
75027 82G
75028 6B
75029 84E
75030 1A
75031 1A
75032 6A
75033 6B
75034 6B
75035 6A
75036 6G
75037 1E
75038 1E
75039 6A
75040 15C
75041 15C
75042 15C
75043 15C
75044 15C
75045 27A
75046 27A
75047 27A
75048 27A
75049 27A
75050 6A
75051 6A
75052 1A
75053 6B
75054 6B
75055 16A
75056 16A
75057 15C
75058 15C
75059 15C
75060 15C
75061 15C
75062 16A
75063 16A
75064 16A
75065 71A
75066 71A
75067 71A
75068 71A
75069 73A
75070 75E
75071 82F
75072 82F
75073 82F
75074 73A
75075 75E
75076 70D
75077 70D
75078 70D
75079 70D

Standard 2-6-0 4MT

76000 66B
76001 63B
76002 66B
76003 66B
76004 66B
76005 72B
76006 71A
76007 72B
76008 72B
76009 71A
76010 71A
76011 71A
76012 71A
76013 71A
76014 71A
76015 71B
76016 71A
76017 72B
76018 72B
76019 71B
76020 8G
76021 51F
76022 24J
76023 8G
76024 50A
76025 71B
76026 71B
76027 71A
76028 71A
76029 71A
76030 31B
76031 31B
76032 31B
76033 31B
76034 31B
76035 14D
76036 14D
76037 14D
76038 14D
76039 14D
76040 14D
76041 14D
76042 14D
76043 14D
76044 14D
76045 51F
76046 51F
76047 9E
76048 9F
76049 51F
76050 51F
76051 24J
76052 14D
76053 72B
76054 72B
76055 72B
76056 71B
76057 71B
76058 71B
76059 71A
76060 71A
76061 71A
76062 71A
76063 71A
76064 71A
76065 71A
76066 72B
76067 72B
76068 71A
76069 71A
76070 66B
76071 66B
76072 68B
76073 68B
76074 65F
76075 8G
76076 8G
76077 8G
76078 8G
76079 8G
76080 24D
76081 24D
76082 24D
76083 24D
76084 24D
76085 9F
76086 9E
76087 9F
76088 9E
76089 9E
76090 66B
76091 67A
76092 67A
76093 67A
76094 67A
76095 67A
76096 67A
76097 67A
76098 67A
76099 67A
76100 65D
76101 65D
76102 65D
76103 65F
76104 61B
76105 64C
76106 64C
76107 61B
76108 61B
76109 62C
76110 62C
76111 62C
76112 68C
76113 65B
76114 65B

Standard 2-6-0 3MT

77000 50B
77001 50B
77002 51F
77003 51F
77004 50E
77005 66E
77006 66C
77007 66A
77008 66A
77009 66A
77010 50B
77011 52F
77012 50A
77013 50E
77014 52F
77015 67B
77016 67B
77017 67B
77018 67B
77019 67B

Standard 2-6-0 2MT

78000 89C
78001 85A
78002 89C
78003 89C
78004 86C
78005 89C
78006 89C
78007 89C
78008 85A
78009 85A
78010 51J
78011 51J
78012 51J
78013 16B
78014 51J
78015 51J
78016 51F
78017 8D
78018 6A
78019 8E
78020 16A
78021 16A
78022 36A
78023 36A
78024 36A
78025 36A
78026 41D
78027 41D
78028 16A
78029 16A
78030 5A
78031 6K
78032 6A
78033 6A
78034 6H
78035 8D
78036 24C
78037 24C
78038 8E
78039 8D
78040 27B
78041 27A
78042 27A
78043 27A
78044 27A
78045 61B
78046 64G
78047 64G
78048 64G
78049 64G
78050 66B
78051 66B
78052 60B
78053 61B
78054 61B
78055 8E
78056 6K
78057 8E
78058 6H
78059 6H
78060 27D
78061 27D
78062 27D
78063 27D
78064 27D

Standard 2-6-4T 4MT

80000 67B
80001 66A
80002 66A
80003 66A
80004 68D
80005 67A
80006 66A
80007 66A
80008 67A
80009 67A
80010 75E
80011 75E
80012 75E
80013 75A
80014 75F
80015 75F
80016 75F
80017 75F
80018 75F
80019 75F
80020 67A
80021 67A
80022 66A
80023 66A
80024 67A
80025 67A
80026 66A
80027 66A
80028 67D
80029 67D
80030 67A
80031 75A
80032 75A

One of the named Standard 5MT 4-6-0s, No 73086 *The Green Knight* is at Eastleigh shed in April 1964. The name came from 'N15' 'King Arthur' class 4-6-0 No 30754 which was withdrawn on 24 January 1953 from Basingstoke shed. No 73086 was built at Derby Works, entering traffic in August 1955 and was first allocated to Stewarts Lane shed. Here it remained until June 1959 when transfer to Nine Elms took place. No other transfers were actioned with No 73086 being withdrawn on 2 October 1966 and after storage at Eastleigh it was broken up at Cashmore's, Newport, in February 1967. The name lives on, now attached to preserved Standard 4MT 4-6-0 No 75029 currently based at the North Yorkshire Moors Railway. *G. W. Sharpe*

Manchester Patricroft-allocated Standard 5MT 4-6-0 No 73127, in filthy condition, is sharing Mirfield shed with Hughes/Fowler 6P5F 2-6-0 No 42754 from Manchester Gorton in April 1962. No 73127 was one of the 30 class members fitted with Caprotti valve gear. Built at Derby Works, No 73127 entered traffic in August 1956 at Shrewsbury shed. Transfer to Patricroft was in September 1958, where it remained until withdrawn during the week ended 4 November 1967 until sent to Cashmore's at Newport for scrapping in January 1968. *Pictorail*

Standard 4MT 4-6-0 No 75052 is at Willesden shed in September 1961. Built at Swindon Works, it entered traffic during the week ended 22 December 1956 at Bletchley shed. Willesden added it to its allocation in January 1960 and then No 75052 went to Nuneaton in January 1963. The final allocation was Stoke-on-Trent, from where withdrawal took place during the week ended 12 August 1967 and after storage it went to be cut up at Bird's, Long Marston, in February 1968. *R. H. G. Simpson*

Three Bridges-allocated Standard 4MT 4-6-0 No 75070, paired with a larger tender, is at Birchden Junction on the line to Eridge hauling a local in June 1960. Built at Swindon Works, No 75070 entered traffic at Exmouth Junction shed on 13 October 1955. It was fitted with a double chimney in February 1961. Subsequent moves saw it based at Bath Green Park, Eastleigh, Brighton, Stewarts Lane, Three Bridges, Nine Elms and finally Basingstoke, from where it was withdrawn on 11 September 1966. Stored at Eastleigh until February 1967, it then went to Cashmore's at Newport for scrap. *G. W. Sharpe*

Leicester Central shed is the venue for visiting Woodford Halse-based Standard 4MT 2-6-0 No 76052 on Thursday 22 August 1962. For the record, other engines on shed on this date were Nos 42453, 44847, 44848, 45223, 45277, 60815, 60890, 61169, 61229, 63818, 63867 and 73069. No 76052 had been built at Doncaster Works and entered traffic at York shed on 6 September 1956, moving to Kirkby Stephen shed next month. In May 1960 a move to the Central took No 76052 to Neasden, then to Woodford Halse in July 1962. In October 1963 a move to Birmingham Saltley was made, then to Wolverhampton Oxley in June 1965 and finally to Chester two months later, from where withdrawal was actioned during the week ended 10 December 1966. Stored at Chester until June 1967, the engine then went to Cashmore's at Newport for scrap. *K. C. H. Fairey*

Standard 4MT 2-6-0 No 76054, with a larger tender, is at Southampton Central station on Saturday 4 November 1961. Built at Doncaster Works, it went new to Redhill shed on 26 April 1955, moving to Salisbury in May 1960 and Guildford in June 1964, from where it was withdrawn on 18 October 1964. After storage at Eastleigh, the engine went to Hayes at Bridgend in February 1965 for cutting up. G. W. Sharpe

Standard 3MT 2-6-0 No 77003 is at West Auckland shed on Saturday 8 June 1963. Built at Swindon Works (date to traffic was 25 February 1954), its first allocation was Darlington, with a move to West Auckland six months later. There were no other reallocations until February 1964 when Leeds Stourton added No 77003 to its roster. Here it remained until withdrawn on 7 December 1966. Storage at Normanton shed took place until February 1967, when it was sent to Ward's at Beighton, Sheffield, for cutting up. *G. W. Sharpe*

Standard 2MT 2-6-0 No 78047 is at Hawick shed in August 1960. Built at Darlington Works, this engine had gone new to Hawick on 25 October 1955 and remained on allocation until September 1965, when a transfer was made to Edinburgh St Margarets. In January 1966, Bathgate was No 78047's base; it returned to St Margarets the following August and was withdrawn virtually straight away on 2 September. The Shipbreaking Industries yard at Faslane was where the engine was cut up in January 1967. *Pictorail*

Standard 4MT 2-6-4T No 80150 is at Stewarts Lane shed in July 1961, with Cricklewood-based Stanier 5MT 4-6-0 No 45335 hiding behind. No 80150 had been built at Brighton Works and went new to Brighton shed on 28 December 1956. Its first transfer was to Eastleigh in September 1963, it then went to Feltham in December 1964 for only a month before returning to Eastleigh, from where withdrawal was authorised on 17 October 1965. Barry Docks was where the engine was then sent, which proved to be a lucky move as it was rescued for preservation and can now be seen at the Barry Steam Railway. *G. W. Sharpe*

80033	75A
80034	73F
80035	73F
80036	73F
80037	73J
80038	73J
80039	73J
80040	73J
80041	73J
80042	73J
80043	73J
80044	67A
80045	67A
80046	67A
80047	67A
80048	67A
80049	67A
80050	67A
80051	67A
80052	67A
80053	67A
80054	66A
80055	66A
80056	66A
80057	66A
80058	66A
80059	73J
80060	65J
80061	65J
80062	65J
80063	65J
80064	73J
80065	73J
80066	73J
80067	73A
80068	73A
80069	33B
80070	33B
80071	33B
80072	33B
80073	33B
80074	33B
80075	33B
80076	33B
80077	33B
80078	33B
80079	33B
80080	33B
80081	73A
80082	73B
80083	73B
80084	73B
80085	73J
80086	66A
80087	75E
80088	75E
80089	75E
80090	62B
80091	65B
80092	63A
80093	63A
80094	75E
80095	75F
80096	33B
80097	33B
80098	33B
80099	33B
80100	33B
80101	33B
80102	33B
80103	33B
80104	33B
80105	33B
80106	66A
80107	66A
80108	66A
80109	66A
80110	66A
80111	67B
80112	67B
80113	64G
80114	64G
80115	66A
80116	55H
80117	55H
80118	55H
80119	55H
80120	55H
80121	66A
80122	64C
80123	62B
80124	62B
80125	65J
80126	63A
80127	67A
80128	67B
80129	66A
80130	66A
80131	33B
80132	33B
80133	33C
80134	33B
80135	33B
80136	33B
80137	75F
80138	75A
80139	75F
80140	75F
80141	75F
80142	75F
80143	75A
80144	75A
80145	75A
80146	75A
80147	75A
80148	75A
80149	75A
80150	75A
80151	75A
80152	75A
80153	75A
80154	75A

Standard 2-6-2T 3MT

82000	89C
82001	82G
82002	82G
82003	82E
82004	82F
82005	89C
82006	89C
82007	82B
82008	83B
82009	89C
82010	72A
82011	72A
82012	71A
82013	72A
82014	71A
82015	71A
82016	71A
82017	72A
82018	72A
82019	72A
82020	89C
82021	89C
82022	72A
82023	72A
82024	72A
82025	72A
82026	50E
82027	50E
82028	50F
82029	50F
82030	83B
82031	89C
82032	89A
82033	89C
82034	89C
82035	82E
82036	89A
82037	82E
82038	82B
82039	82E
82040	82E
82041	82F
82042	83B
82043	82E
82044	83B

Standard 2-6-2T 2MT

84000	8B
84001	8B
84002	1E
84003	6K
84004	1E
84005	14E
84006	14D
84007	15A
84008	14D
84009	50B
84010	24F
84011	24F
84012	24F
84013	26C
84014	26C
84015	24G
84016	24F
84017	24F
84018	24F
84019	26C
84020	6G
84021	6G
84022	6G
84023	24J
84024	8B
84025	26C
84026	26C
84027	26C
84028	24G
84029	14E

Austerity 2-8-0 8F

90000	34E
90001	36A
90002	40E
90003	36A
90004	66A
90005	40E
90006	50B
90007	36C
90008	50B
90009	50B
90010	18B
90011	51A
90012	55E
90013	36C
90014	51A
90015	34E
90016	51A
90017	62C
90018	36A
90019	62A
90020	62A
90021	55E
90022	51L
90023	33B
90024	34E
90025	36C
90026	50A
90027	51L
90028	41F
90029	40B
90030	50A
90031	34E
90032	36C
90033	2F
90034	33B
90035	40B
90036	40E
90037	40E
90038	40E
90039	66A
90040	2F
90041	61B
90042	36A
90043	41J
90044	50D
90045	50A
90046	18B
90047	56A
90048	51L
90049	65D
90050	34E
90051	40E
90052	41F
90053	36C
90054	56A
90055	34E
90056	56A
90057	51A
90058	62A
90059	36C
90060	66A
90061	56A
90063	36A
90064	41F
90065	2F
90066	2F
90067	51C
90068	56D
90069	88A
90070	36C
90071	66B
90072	51L
90073	34E
90074	51L
90075	34E
90076	56A
90077	61B
90078	50A
90079	36C
90080	2F
90081	51L
90082	51A
90084	40E
90085	41D
90086	51L
90087	36C
90088	41J
90089	56A
90090	51L
90091	51L
90092	51C
90093	33B
90094	50D
90095	2F
90096	34E
90097	61B
90098	51L
90099	50B
90100	56A
90101	27B
90102	26C
90103	40E
90104	40E
90105	26A
90106	34E
90107	27B
90108	36C
90109	24B
90110	26C
90111	36C
90112	56A
90113	56E
90114	65D
90115	36C
90116	56A
90117	62A
90118	40E
90119	41F
90120	36C
90121	26C
90122	56E
90123	26E

Immaculate Standard 3MT 2-6-2T No 82024 is at Nine Elms shed in May 1963, still with a 72A shedplate despite being transferred from Exmouth Junction six months earlier. Built at Swindon Works, No 82024 went new to Exmouth Junction in October 1954, its only transfer being to Nine Elms. Withdrawn on 7 February 1966, it was stored at Nine Elms until the following April and then scrapped at Cohen's at Morriston. *P. H. Groom*

Crewe Works was the place to see elderly locomotives allocated to shunting duties, with many being the last examples of their class in service. In July 1962 this changed with the allocation of modern steam power in the shape of Standard 2MT 2-6-2Ts Nos 84021, 84022, 84023 and 84024 arriving. This is No 84022 at Crewe Works on Sunday 9 September 1962. Built at Darlington Works, it had gone to Ashford when new on 30 March 1957, moving to Exmouth Junction in May 1961, Llandudno Junction four months later and then Crewe Works, from where it was withdrawn during the week ended 5 September 1964 and cut up at the works. *L. Hanson*

Ex-Works at Darlington shed on Friday 10 May 1963 is 'Austerity' 2-8-0 No 90462, with 'Q6' 0-8-0 No 63431 behind. No 90462 had been built at Vulcan Foundry in May 1944 and numbered 78653 in Ministry of Supply stock. Purchased by the LNER, it was renumbered 3141. At the time this scene was recorded, it was a Thornaby-based engine after transfer from Newport on 1 June 1958. From Thornaby, No 90462 went to Hull Dairycoates on 18 August 1963, from where it was withdrawn on 23 January 1967 and sold to the nearby Draper's yard for scrap. *Pictorail*

90124 56A
90125 88A
90126 56D
90127 55D
90128 65F
90129 34E
90130 34E
90131 40B
90132 51L
90133 36C
90134 65B
90135 56D
90136 41F
90137 2F
90138 24B
90139 41F
90140 26E
90141 26E
90142 26B
90143 24B
90144 36A
90145 41J
90146 34E
90147 6B
90148 85C
90149 88A
90150 36A
90151 34E
90152 18B
90153 41F
90154 34E
90155 51A
90156 36A
90157 12H
90158 34E
90159 24B
90160 50D
90161 36C
90162 41D
90163 26A
90164 27B
90165 34E
90166 36C
90167 88A
90168 62A
90169 34E
90170 8G
90171 24B
90172 51A
90173 8F
90174 81C
90175 40B
90176 18B
90177 62C
90178 8G
90179 87F
90180 34E
90181 24B
90182 62A
90183 26F
90184 56D
90185 34E
90186 50D
90187 24L
90188 86A
90189 36C
90190 41F
90192 6C
90193 65D
90194 26E
90195 41F
90196 33B
90197 26A
90198 66A
90199 65D
90200 56E
90201 86A
90202 41D
90203 41F
90204 27B
90205 26D
90206 26C
90207 87F
90208 36A
90209 41F
90210 56E
90211 41F
90212 8G
90213 50D
90214 18B
90215 34E
90216 27B
90217 50A
90218 2F
90219 27B
90220 41F
90221 40B
90222 26F
90223 34E
90224 36A
90225 86A
90226 26D
90227 6B
90228 50D
90229 66A
90230 56B
90231 24B
90232 36C
90233 56E
90234 66A
90235 36A
90236 56D
90237 2F
90238 18B
90239 34E
90240 51L
90241 24B
90242 8D
90243 55D
90244 33B
90245 27B
90246 34E
90247 55E
90248 26A
90249 55E
90250 41F
90251 18B
90252 41F
90253 34E
90254 55E
90255 36A
90256 33B
90257 8F
90258 24C
90259 40E
90260 50D
90261 84C
90262 50D
90263 40E
90264 24B
90265 50D
90266 24C
90267 26C
90268 85C
90269 34E
90270 34E
90271 26A
90272 50B
90273 51L
90274 24B
90275 41J
90276 41D
90277 24C
90278 27B
90279 36A
90280 40B
90281 56E
90282 27B
90283 27B
90284 18B
90285 40B
90286 36A
90287 40E
90288 36C
90289 26A
90290 41D
90291 26A
90292 26B
90293 36A
90294 40B
90295 24C
90296 36A
90297 24D
90298 33B
90299 2F
90300 56D
90301 41J
90302 41J
90303 40E
90304 34E
90305 36A
90306 26B
90307 26B
90308 55G
90309 51A
90310 56E
90311 41F
90312 87F
90313 84C
90314 24B
90315 84C
90316 24D
90317 8F
90318 55E
90319 67D
90320 66A
90321 56A
90322 56D
90323 86A
90324 26B
90325 55G
90326 56A
90327 27B
90328 26A
90329 56E
90330 41F
90331 26E
90332 55G
90333 56D
90334 55C
90335 24C
90336 55D
90337 55E
90338 26A
90339 56A
90340 36A
90341 56A
90342 56A
90343 27B
90344 51C
90345 55G
90346 2F
90347 55G
90348 56A
90349 34E
90350 62A
90351 56F
90352 50B
90353 56A
90354 26B
90355 81C
90356 81C
90357 55E
90358 41F
90359 26B
90360 56E
90361 56B
90362 55E
90363 56A
90364 26D
90365 2F
90366 26A
90367 24C
90368 41D
90369 6C
90370 56A
90371 26F
90372 26B
90373 51A
90374 24B
90375 24D
90376 26A
90377 51L
90378 50B
90379 56A
90380 56A
90381 27B
90382 56A
90383 40E
90384 41F
90385 56A
90386 66B
90387 66A
90388 26A
90389 26A
90390 26A
90391 41D
90392 6C
90393 40E
90394 40B
90395 55D
90396 56A
90397 56F
90398 26D
90399 26F
90400 41F
90401 41F
90402 26E
90403 2F
90404 56A
90405 56B
90406 51L
90407 55D
90408 26D
90409 51L
90410 41F
90411 41J
90412 56E
90413 26D
90414 41D
90415 56A
90416 27B
90417 56A
90418 41J
90419 26D
90420 24B
90421 41F
90422 36C
90423 8D
90424 50A
90425 36C
90426 51L
90427 50B
90428 34E
90429 56A
90430 51A
90431 41J
90432 40E
90433 2F
90434 51L
90435 51L
90436 65D
90437 40E
90438 40E
90439 34E
90440 65D
90441 62A
90442 36A
90443 40B
90444 62B
90445 51A
90446 51L
90447 36A
90448 2F
90449 41J

90450	50B
90451	51L
90452	51L
90453	36C
90454	34E
90455	61B
90456	36C
90457	56D
90458	50B
90459	51L
90460	40A
90461	51L
90462	51L
90463	67D
90464	8G
90465	51L
90466	81C
90467	50A
90468	66B
90469	36C
90470	56E
90471	41D
90472	62A
90473	40E
90474	2F
90475	50D
90476	36A
90477	36A
90478	50D
90479	51L
90480	36A
90481	51L
90482	50B
90483	84C
90484	36A
90485	84C
90486	2F
90487	55E
90488	55D
90489	65D
90490	34E
90491	41F
90492	40E
90493	65D
90494	36A
90495	41F
90496	36A
90497	56A
90498	36A
90499	41F
90500	51L
90501	36A
90502	34E
90503	51L
90504	2F
90505	67D
90506	36A
90507	8F
90508	41F
90509	8F
90510	40E
90511	55D
90512	36C
90513	62A
90514	34E
90515	62B
90516	2F
90517	51L
90518	50A
90519	41F
90520	2F
90521	41F
90522	36A
90523	26A
90524	2F
90525	26E
90526	41F
90527	27B
90528	36A
90529	87F
90530	26F
90531	50D
90532	6B
90533	26A
90534	62A
90535	27B
90536	66A
90537	36C
90538	36A
90539	65F
90540	36C
90541	24C
90542	62C
90543	56A
90544	86A
90545	40E
90546	26B
90547	62C
90548	26A
90549	67D
90550	36C
90551	36A
90552	27B
90553	62C
90554	40E
90555	26D
90556	24D
90557	24B
90558	26B
90559	36A
90560	62C
90561	26A
90562	55C
90563	2F
90564	26B
90565	81C
90566	6C
90567	41F
90568	26F
90569	36A
90570	26F
90571	50A
90572	88A
90573	88A
90574	8F
90575	62C
90576	27B
90577	40A
90578	50A
90579	88A
90580	41F
90581	56A
90582	41F
90583	40B
90584	24C
90585	84C
90586	50B
90587	41F
90588	55C
90589	26A
90590	41F
90591	55G
90592	24D
90593	51L
90594	40E
90595	24J
90596	66A
90597	36C
90598	36C
90599	27B
90600	62C
90601	36C
90602	36C
90603	51L
90604	56A
90605	55D
90606	6C
90607	56A
90608	41F
90609	50B
90610	55D
90611	55D
90612	41F
90613	34E
90614	62A
90615	56A
90616	66A
90617	55E
90618	34E
90619	55G
90620	56A
90621	55G
90622	56D
90623	50A
90624	55G
90625	56A
90626	26B
90627	50B
90628	66B
90629	40E
90630	81C
90631	56A
90632	26B
90633	56A
90634	40E
90635	56A
90636	36A
90637	55E
90638	2F
90639	56A
90640	66A
90641	26C
90642	56B
90643	27B
90644	56B
90645	55C
90646	36C
90647	36C
90648	36C
90649	55G
90650	55D
90651	56A
90652	55E
90653	33B
90654	56A
90655	56D
90656	56A
90657	41J
90658	24C
90659	34E
90660	34E
90661	55E
90662	34E
90663	50A
90664	55E
90665	34E
90666	55G
90667	8F
90668	41F
90669	26F
90670	50B
90671	26E
90672	2F
90673	55E
90674	40E
90675	24C
90676	87F
90677	50B
90678	56D
90679	56A
90680	55G
90681	24C
90682	55E
90683	36A
90684	55D
90685	81C
90686	8F
90687	27B
90688	50B
90689	24C
90690	66A
90691	84C
90692	56E
90693	81C
90694	55G
90695	50B
90696	36C
90697	2F
90698	56D
90699	55C
90700	41F
90701	2F
90702	8G
90703	34E
90704	50D
90705	66A
90706	24J
90707	56D
90708	26E
90709	36A
90710	56A
90711	56F
90712	27B
90713	24C
90714	36C
90715	26A
90716	18B
90717	34E
90718	26E
90719	41D
90720	24C
90721	56D
90722	55E
90723	56D
90724	27B
90725	26C
90726	55C
90727	62C
90728	55C
90729	26C
90730	34E
90731	56D
90732*	36C

Austerity 2-10-0 8F

90750	66B
90751	66B
90755	65F
90756	66B
90757	65F
90758	66B
90759	65F
90760	66B
90761	66B
90762	66B
90763	12A
90764	66B
90765	65F
90766	65F
90767	66B
90768	66E
90769	65F
90770	66B
90771	66B
90772	66C
90773	65F
90774	65F

Standard 2-10-0 9F

92000	84C
92001	88A
92002	86A
92003	88A
92004	82E
92005	86A
92006	86A
92007	82E
92008	17C
92009	17C
92010	16D
92011	16D
92012	16D
92013	16D
92014	16D
92015	26A

The only named 'Austerity' 2-8-0, No 90732 *Vulcan*, is at Frodingham shed in March 1962, in the filthy condition that was typical of this rugged class. The name was in recognition of the fact that this was the last of the type to be built at the Vulcan Foundry and it came into service in May 1945 as Ministry of Supply No 79312. This was a 1962 withdrawal which was cut up at Gorton Works in December 1962. *Pictorail*

92016	26A	92044	34E	92072	16D	92100	18B	92128	15C
92017	26A	92045	6F	92073	16D	92101	15C	92129	21A
92018	15A	92046	6F	92074	16D	92102	15C	92130	18A
92019	15A	92047	6F	92075	16D	92103	15C	92131	18B
92020	15A	92048	17C	92076	16D	92104	15C	92132	15A
92021	15A	92049	17C	92077	18A	92105	15B	92133	15A
92022	15A	92050	17C	92078	18A	92106	15B	92134	15A
92023	15A	92051	17C	92079	85D	92107	21A	92135	21A
92024	15A	92052	16D	92080	15A	92108	15C	92136	21A
92025	15A	92053	15A	92081	15A	92109	15C	92137	21A
92026	15A	92054	15A	92082	15A	92110	15C	92138	21A
92027	15A	92055	18A	92083	15A	92111	15C	92139	21A
92028	15B	92056	18A	92084	15A	92112	15C	92140	34E
92029	15B	92057	16D	92085	15B	92113	18A	92141	34E
92030	16D	92058	18A	92086	18A	92114	18A	92142	34E
92031	16D	92059	18A	92087	16D	92115	18B	92143	34E
92032	16D	92060	52H	92088	16D	92116	18B	92144	34E
92033	16D	92061	52H	92089	16D	92117	16D	92145	34E
92034	34E	92062	52H	92090	16D	92118	15A	92146	34E
92035	34E	92063	52H	92091	16D	92119	15C	92147	34E
92036	34E	92064	52H	92092	16D	92120	15C	92148	34E
92037	34E	92065	52H	92093	16D	92121	15C	92149	34E
92038	34E	92066	52H	92094	16D	92122	15C	92150	21A
92039	34E	92067	16D	92095	16D	92123	15C	92151	21A
92040	34E	92068	16D	92096	16D	92124	15A	92152	21A
92041	34E	92069	16D	92097	52H	92125	15B	92153	18A
92042	34E	92070	18A	92098	52H	92126	15A	92154	15A
92043	16D	92071	16D	92099	52H	92127	15A	92155	21A

All the remaining 'Austerity' 2-10-0s were withdrawn in 1962, including No 90758 here at Motherwell shed in August 1962. Built at the North British Locomotive Co Ltd in June 1945, it became British Railways stock on 22 June 1950 from storage and was allocated to Motherwell through to withdrawal. Stored at Cowlairs Works from October 1962 to November 1963, it then went to Darlington Works for scrapping *G. W. Sharpe*

Crosti-boilered Standard 9F 2-10-0 No 92029 is at Derby shed on Sunday 9 September 1962. Built at Crewe Works, No 92029 was new to Wellingborough shed during the week ended 9 July 1955. The Crosti boilers were less than successful and No 92029 and the nine others were sent back to Crewe Works for modifications in 1955. No 92029 remained at Wellingborough until transfer to Kettering in December 1960 and then went to Birmingham Saltley in October 1962. November 1963 saw it transferred to Birkenhead, then back to Saltley in April 1964. In June 1966 it was transferred to Wrexham Croes Newydd. A brief spell again at Saltley occurred from August to December 1966 before it returned to Birkenhead, where No 92029 was withdrawn during the week ended 11 November 1967. After storage at Liverpool Speke Junction, it was sent to Campbell's at Airdrie for cutting up in February 1968. *L. Hanson*

Standard 9F 2-10-0 No 92064 is light engine at Newcastle in July 1962. Note the Westinghouse pumps fitted on the side for operating the wagon doors on the Tyne Dock to Consett iron ore trains (see also the photo of No 63760). Built at Crewe Works, No 92064 went new to Tyne Dock shed on 2 December 1955, but was transferred four weeks later to Wellingborough, along with the other six 2-10-0s allocated new to Tyne Dock. This was to cover the shortage of Crosti-boilered 2-10-0s at Wellingborough while they were undergoing the modifications at Crewe. No 92064 returned to Tyne Dock in May 1956, with the others all back by June, and stayed on allocation until withdrawn on 24 November 1966. Thompson's at Stockton-on-Tees conducted the scrapping in April 1967. *G. W. Sharpe*

92156	18A	92175	36A	92194	40B	92213	84C	92232	84C
92157	21A	92176	36A	92195	40B	92214	86A	92233	88A
92158	18A	92177	36A	92196	40B	92215	84C	92234	84C
92159	15A	92178	34E	92197	40B	92216	88A	92235	86A
92160	15B	92179	34E	92198	36A	92217	82B	92236	88A
92161	26A	92180	34E	92199	36A	92218	82B	92237	88A
92162	26A	92181	34E	92200	36A	92219	88A	92238	86A
92163	15B	92182	34E	92201	36A	92220*	88A	92239	71A
92164	15C	92183	34E	92202	40B	92221	82E	92240	81C
92165	21A	92184	34E	92203	81A	92222	86A	92241	88A
92166	21A	92185	34E	92204	81A	92223	86A	92242	86A
92167	21A	92186	34E	92205	71A	92224	81C	92243	86A
92168	36A	92187	34E	92206	71A	92225	86A	92244	88A
92169	36A	92188	34E	92207	81C	92226	81A	92245	88A
92170	36A	92189	36A	92208	88A	92227	88A	92246	88A
92171	36A	92190	36A	92209	86A	92228	84C	92247	81A
92172	36A	92191	36A	92210	82E	92229	86A	92248	82E
92173	36A	92192	36A	92211	71A	92230	86A	92249	86A
92174	36A	92193	40B	92212	86A	92231	71A	92250	86A

A Standard 9F 2-10-0 No 92093 is in full cry on one of the Annesley to Woodford 'windcutter' freights between Whetstone and Ashby Magna on Saturday 24 March 1962. Built at Swindon Works, No 92093 went new to Doncaster shed on 15 January 1957 and was transferred to Annesley during the four weeks ended 23 March 1957. Annesley was its home until June 1965, when it was transferred to Kirkby-in-Ashfield, and during the three-week-period ending on 29 January 1966 left for Carlisle Kingmoor. Here it was withdrawn during the week ended 2 September 1967 and was scrapped at the Motherwell Machinery & Scrap Co at Wishaw in February 1968. *M. Mitchell*

British Railways Diesel Locomotive Allocations at 1 January 1962

Class 44 1Co-Co1

D1*	9A
D2*	1B
D3*	5A
D4*	1B
D5*	1B
D6*	12B
D7*	1B
D8*	5A
D9*	8A
D10*	5A

Class 45 1Co-Co1

D11	55H
D12	55H
D13	55H
D14	55H
D15	55H
D16	55H
D17	55H
D18	55H
D19	55H
D20	55H
D21	55H
D22	52A
D23	55H
D24	52A
D25	55H
D26	55H
D27	55H
D28	52A
D29	55H
D30	52A
D31	55H
D32	55H
D33	82A
D34	82A
D35	82A
D36	82A
D37	82A
D38	82A
D39	82A
D40	82A
D41	82A
D42	82A
D43	14A
D44	14A
D45	14A
D46	14A
D47	14A
D48	14A
D49	14A
D68	14A
D69	14A
D70	14A
D71	14A
D72	14A
D73	14A
D74	14A
D75	14A
D76	14A
D77	14A
D78	14A
D79	17A
D80	17A
D81	17A
D82	17A
D83	17A
D84	17A
D85	17A
D86	17A
D87	17A
D88	17A
D89	17A
D90	17A
D91	12B
D92	17A
D93	17A
D94	17A
D95	17A
D96	17A
D97	17A
D98	17A
D99	17A
D100*	17A
D101	17A
D102	17A
D103	17A
D104	17A
D105	17A
D106	17A
D107	17A
D108	17A
D109	17A
D110	17A
D111	17A
D112	17A
D113	17A
D114	17A
D115	17A
D116	17A
D117	17A
D118	17A
D119	17A
D120	17A
D121	17A
D122	17A
D123	17A
D124	17A
D125	17A
D126	17A
D127	17A
D128	17A
D129	17A
D130	17A
D131	17A
D132	17A
D133	17A
D134	17A
D135	17A
D136	17A
D137	17A

Class 46 1Co-Co1

D138	17A
D139	17A
D140	17A
D141	17A
D142	17A
D143	17A
D144	55H
D145	41A
D146	52A
D147	17A
D148	17A
D149	17A
D150	17A

English Electric Class 40 1Co-Co1

D200	30A
D201	30A
D202	30A
D203	30A
D204	30A
D205	30A
D206	30A
D207	30A
D208	30A
D209	30A
D210*	1B
D211*	1B
D212*	1B
D213	5A
D214*	9A
D215	8A
D216	12B
D217	9A
D218*	9A
D219	8A
D220	9A
D221*	9A
D222	9A
D223*	8A
D224	9A
D225	9A
D226	1B
D227	9A
D228	9A
D229	1B
D230*	12B
D231	8A
D232*	1B
D233*	5A
D234	8A
D235	8A
D236	8A
D237	52A
D238	52A
D239	52A

Class 44 1Co-Co1 No D1 *Scafell Pike* is seen after arrival at Platform 1 at Euston from Manchester in May 1961. Built at Derby Works, it was introduced to traffic in April 1959 and first allocated to Derby shed, then to Camden in April 1960 and Manchester Longsight a month later. Toton acquired No D1 in February 1962 and it remained in use until withdrawn on 30 October 1976, being scrapped at Derby Works.
R. H. G. Simpson

Class 45 1Co-Co1 No D72 is seen at Wellingborough on Saturday 13 May 1961 on an express for St Pancras. Built at Crewe Works, it entered traffic on 19 November 1960 and was allocated to Crewe North, moving to the Midland lines at Derby in January 1961. Withdrawn on 10 September 1984, it was eventually cut up at Vic Berry's yard in Leicester. *L. Hanson*

Class 46 1Co-Co1 No D188 passing Collingham Bridge with the 9.45am Newcastle to Liverpool on the frosty morning of Wednesday 26 December 1962. Built at Derby, it had been released to traffic only a few days before, on 17 December, and allocated to Gateshead. Withdrawal came on 27 November 1983 and D188 was later scrapped at Swindon Works. *M. Mitchell*

Class 40 1Co-Co1 No D200 is at London Stratford shed in 1960. New in March 1958, and built at the English Electric Vulcan Foundry, it remained on the Eastern Region lines out to East Anglia until August 1967, when it moved to the London Midland Region Western lines. Withdrawn on 23 August 1981, but reinstated on 24 April 1983, it worked a number of special railtours alongside more normal duties until final withdrawal on 18 April 1988, following which it was retained for preservation and can be seen at the National Railway Museum. *G. W. Sharpe*

D240	52A
D241	52A
D242	52A
D243	52A
D244	52A
D245	52A
D246	52A
D247	52A
D248	52A
D249	52A
D250	52A
D251	52A
D252	50A
D253	50A
D254	50A
D255	12B
D256	52A
D257	52A
D258	50A
D259	50A
D260	64B
D261	64B
D262	64B
D263	64B
D264	64B
D265	64B
D266	64B
D267	12B
D268	12B
D269	1B
D270	52A
D271	52A
D272	52A
D273	52A
D274	52A
D275	50A
D276	50A
D277	52A
D278	50A
D279	52A
D280	52A
D281	50A
D282	50A
D283	50A
D284	50A
D285	50A
D286	52A
D287	12B
D288	12B
D289	9A
D290	8A
D291	5A
D292	5A
D293	8A
D294	9A
D295	12B
D296	5A
D297	1B
D298	1B
D299	1B
D300	8A
D301	9A
D302	5A
D303	5A
D304	9A
D305	8A
D306	8A
D307	1B
D308	1B
D309	8A
D310	1B
D311	5A
D312	8A
D313	9A
D314	1B
D315	5A
D316	5A
D317	12B
D318	5A
D319	5A
D320	5A
D321	5A
D322	5A
D323	5A
D324	5A
D325	5A
D326	1B
D327	1B
D328	5A
D329	1B
D330	12B
D331	9A
D332	9A
D333	5A
D334	5A
D335	5A
D336	5A
D337	5A
D338	5A
D339	5A
D340	5A
D341	5A
D342	5A
D343	8A
D344	9A
D345	55H
D346	55H
D347	55H
D348	55H
D349	50A
D350	50A
D351	50A
D352	50A
D353	50A
D354	50A
D355	50A
D356	50A
D357	64B
D358	64B
D359	64B
D360	64B
D361	64B
D362	64B
D363	64B
D364	64B
D365	64B
D366	64B
D367	64B
D368	64B
D369	1B
D370	1B
D371	1B

North British Locomotive Co 'Warship' Class Co-Co

D600*	83D
D601*	83D
D602*	83D
D603*	83D
D604*	83D

Class 42 'Warship' C-C

D800*	83D
D801*	83D
D802*	83D
D803*	83D
D804*	83D
D805*	83D
D806*	83D
D807*	83D
D808*	83D
D809*	83D
D810*	83D
D811*	83D
D812*	83D
D813*	83D
D814*	83D
D815*	83D
D816*	83D
D817*	83D
D818*	83D
D819*	83D
D820*	83D
D821*	83D
D822*	83D
D823*	83D
D824*	83A
D825*	83A
D826*	83A
D827*	83A
D828*	83A
D829*	83A
D830*	83A
D831*	83A
D832*	83A

Class 43 'Warship' B-B

D833*	83A
D834*	83A
D835*	83A
D836*	83A
D837*	83A
D838*	83A
D839*	83D
D840*	83D
D841*	83D
D842*	83D
D843*	83D
D844*	83D
D845*	83D
D846*	83D
D847*	83D
D848*	83D
D849*	83D
D850*	83D
D851*	83D
D852*	83D
D853*	83D
D854*	83D
D855*	83D
D856*	83D
D857*	83D
D858*	83D

Class 42 'Warship' C-C

D866*	83D
D867*	83D
D868*	83D
D869*	83D
D870*	83D

Class 52 'Western' C-C

D1000*	83D

Class 03 0-6-0 Shunter

D2000	34D
D2001	34D
D2002	34D
D2003	34D
D2004	31A
D2005	31A
D2006	31A
D2007	31A
D2008	31A
D2009	31A
D2010	31B
D2011	31B
D2012	31B
D2013	31B
D2014	31B
D2015	31B
D2016	31B
D2017	31A
D2018	34D
D2019	34D
D2020	40B
D2021	40B
D2022	40B
D2023	40F
D2024	40E
D2025	40F
D2026	40A
D2027	40A
D2028	31A
D2029	34D
D2030	31B
D2031	31B
D2032	32A
D2033	32A
D2034	32A
D2035	32A
D2036	32A
D2037	32A
D2038	32A
D2039	32C
D2040	32B
D2041	32B
D2042	32B
D2043	32B
D2044	52F
D2045	52F
D2046	50A
D2047	52G
D2048	52C
D2049	52C
D2050	52G
D2051	50B
D2052	50B
D2053	50B
D2054	50B
D2055	52C
D2056	52A
D2057	52A
D2058	52A
D2059	52A
D2060	52A
D2061	52A
D2062	50A
D2063	50A
D2064	50B
D2065	50A
D2066	50A
D2067	51L
D2068	51C
D2069	51L
D2070	51C
D2071	56G
D2072	56G
D2073	56G
D2074	56G
D2075	50A
D2076	51C
D2077	51L
D2078	51L
D2079	51A
D2080	51A
D2081	56G
D2082	75A
D2083	73F
D2084	73F
D2085	71A
D2086	82C
D2087	82C
D2088	82C
D2089	56G
D2090	56G
D2091	56G
D2092	52G
D2093	52C
D2094	56G
D2095	56G
D2096	56G
D2097	56G
D2098	56G
D2099	51L
D2100	50B
D2101	50B
D2102	50B
D2103	50A
D2104	52B
D2105	52B
D2106	52C
D2107	51A
D2108	51A

North British Locomotive Company Ltd-built 'Warship' class No D601 *Ark Royal* is at London Old Oak Common depot in 1962. Added to stock in March 1958, it was first allocated to Swindon, moving to Plymouth Laira in May 1958 where it spent the rest of its working days, apart from a short spell at Swansea Landore depot in 1967. Withdrawn on 30 December 1967, it was sent to Barry Docks and remained in store until cut up at Woodham's in June 1980. *R. H. G. Simpson*

Class 42 'Warship' class C-C No D817 *Foxhound* is at Old Oak Common depot in April 1962. Built at Swindon Works, it was added to stock in March 1960 and allocated to Plymouth Laira, moving to Newton Abbot in August 1967, from where it was withdrawn on 3 October 1971. After storage it was scrapped at Swindon Works in March 1972. *P. H. Groom*

The pioneer 'Western' Class 52 C-C No D1000 *Western Enterprise* is inside Swindon Works in December 1961 awaiting entry to traffic. Its first allocation was to Plymouth Laira and during its working days it was also based at Old Oak Common and Swansea Landore. Withdrawal came on 11 February 1974 when back at Laira, and cutting up was carried out at Swindon Works in July 1974. *R. H. G. Simpson*

D2109 51A
D2110 50A
D2111 50A
D2112 50A
D2113 50A
D2114 DG
D2115 DG
D2116 DG
D2117 DG
D2118 DG
D2119 DG
D2120 DG
D2121 DG
D2122 DG
D2123 85A
D2124 DG
D2125 DG
D2126 82C
D2127 83D
D2128 83D
D2129 83E
D2130 83A
D2131 85A
D2132 85A
D2133 83B
D2134 82E
D2135 82E
D2136 85B
D2137 85B
D2138 85B
D2139 85A
D2140 83B
D2141 83B
D2142 83B
D2143 82C
D2144 82C
D2145 82E
D2146 82C
D2147 52A
D2148 52A
D2149 52A
D2150 56G
D2151 50A
D2152 56G
D2153 51A
D2154 51A
D2155 50B
D2156 50B
D2157 50B
D2158 50A
D2159 50A
D2160 50A
D2161 50A
D2162 52A
D2163 52G
D2164 52G
D2165 52C
D2166 52B
D2167 50A
D2168 50B
D2169 50B
D2170 50B
D2171 50B
D2172 50B
D2173 50B
D2174 50B
D2175 83H
D2176 83H
D2177 83H
D2187 82C
D2188 82C
D2189 82C
D2190 DG
D2191 DG
D2192 82C
D2193 82C
D2194 82C
D2195 82C
D2196 82C
D2197 83D
D2198 8A
D2199 8C

Class 04 0-6-0 Shunter

D2200 30F
D2201 31B
D2202 31B
D2203 32A
D2204 51C
D2205 51C
D2206 51C
D2207 40B
D2208 30F
D2209 30F
D2210 32C
D2211 30F
D2212 32D
D2213 6A
D2214 32A
D2215 30A
D2216 30A
D2217 30A
D2218 6A
D2219 32A
D2220 6A
D2221 5B
D2222 32B
D2223 30A
D2224 30A
D2225 30A
D2226 30A
D2227 30A
D2228 30A
D2229 30A
D2230 51C
D2231 51C
D2232 51C
D2233 40B
D2234 40B
D2235 40B
D2236 5B
D2237 31B
D2238 31B
D2239 31B
D2240 31B
D2241 40F
D2242 55H
D2243 55H
D2244 55H
D2245 50A
D2246 55H
D2247 52F
D2248 52F
D2249 52F
D2250 73F
D2251 73C
D2252 71A
D2253 73C
D2254 71A
D2255 83H
D2256 73C
D2257 83H
D2258 83H
D2259 83H
D2260 56G
D2261 56G
D2262 55G
D2263 55G
D2264 56G
D2265 56G
D2266 55D
D2267 55A
D2268 50A
D2269 50A
D2270 50A
D2271 55A
D2272 55A
D2273 55A
D2274 71B
D2275 71B
D2276 73F
D2277 73E
D2278 75C
D2279 75C
D2280 75C
D2281 75A
D2282 75A
D2283 73C
D2284 73C
D2285 73F
D2286 75A
D2287 73F
D2288 71A
D2289 71A
D2290 70C
D2291 71A
D2292 71G
D2293 73F
D2294 75C
D2295 70C
D2296 40F
D2297 40A
D2298 40A
D2299 40A
D2300 40E
D2301 41J
D2302 40E
D2303 40A
D2304 51A
D2305 51A
D2306 51A
D2307 51A
D2308 51A
D2309 56G
D2310 52G
D2311 52H
D2312 52H
D2313 52H
D2314 52H
D2315 52H
D2316 51A
D2317 51A
D2318 51A
D2319 51A
D2320 51L
D2321 52C
D2322 52B
D2323 55E
D2324 55E
D2325 52A
D2326 52H
D2327 52H
D2328 52H
D2329 52G
D2330 52A
D2331 51C
D2332 52B
D2333 52A
D2334 52B
D2335 52C
D2336 51A
D2337 51A
D2338 51A
D2339 52B

Class 03 0-6-0 Shunter

D2372 8D
D2373 8A
D2374 6C
D2375 6C
D2376 6C
D2377 17A
D2378 17A
D2379 17A
D2380 17A
D2381 17A
D2382 17A
D2383 17A
D2384 17A
D2385 8C
D2386 21E
D2387 21E
D2388 6C
D2389 9G
D2390 9G
D2391 9G
D2392 9G
D2393 8A
D2394 8D
D2395 21C
D2396 21E
D2397 75C
D2398 73C
D2399 73F

Class 05 0-6-0 Shunter

D2400 40B
D2401 40F
D2402 40F
D2403 40B
D2404 40A
D2405 40A
D2406 40A
D2407 40A
D2408 40A
D2409 40F

Class 06 0-4-0 Shunter

D2410 60A
D2411 60A
D2412 60A
D2413 60A
D2414 61A
D2415 61A
D2416 61A
D2417 61A
D2418 61A
D2419 61A
D2420 61A
D2421 61A
D2422 61A
D2423 60A
D2424 61A
D2425 66D
D2426 66D
D2427 66D
D2428 66D
D2429 66D
D2430 66B
D2431 66A
D2432 66A
D2433 66A
D2434 67C
D2435 67C
D2436 67C
D2437 67C
D2438 67C
D2439 67A
D2440 67A
D2441 67A
D2442 67A
D2443 67A
D2444 67A

Hudswell Clarke/Gardner 0-6-0 Shunter

D2500 6C
D2501 6C
D2502 6C
D2503 6C
D2504 6C
D2505 6C
D2506 6C
D2507 6C
D2508 6C
D2509 6C
D2510 6C
D2511 12E
D2512 12E
D2513 12E
D2514 12E
D2515 12E
D2516 12E
D2517 12E

Class 03 0-6-0 diesel shunter No D2192 is at Swindon on shunting duties in May 1962. Built at Swindon Works, it was allocated to Swindon shed when new in May 1961 and, apart for a time at Swansea Danygraig from August to October 1961, remained a Swindon engine. Withdrawn on 25 January 1969, it was purchased for preservation and can be seen at the Paignton & Dartmouth Railway, today bearing the name 'Ardent'. *G. W. Sharpe*

Class 04 0-6-0 diesel shunter No D2202 is seen at March shed in March 1961 with its wheels and motion covered and a front shield fitted for work on the Wisbech & Upwell tramway. Built by the Drewry Car Co as the main contractor at the Vulcan Foundry at Newton-le-Willows, No D2202 entered service as No 11102 in June 1952 and was allocated to March through to withdrawal on 10 February 1968. Cohen's at Kettering carried out the scrapping in June 1968. *R. H. G. Simpson*

One of the Class 04s built by Robert Stephenson & Hawthorn, No D2289 is seen at Eastleigh shed in 1962. New in May 1960, it was first allocated to Eastleigh and transferred to Norwood Junction in May 1965, Brighton in August 1966, back to Norwood Junction a month later and then returned to Eastleigh in December 1967. Withdrawn in September 1971, No D2289 was exported for service in Italy. *G. W. Sharpe*

Andrew Barclay Class 05 0-6-0 diesel shunter No D2409 is at Doncaster Works in April 1962. Introduced to traffic on 4 March 1957, it was first allocated to Lincoln as No 11186. Transferred to Boston in December 1957, then to Nottingham Colwick in January 1964 and finally to Staveley Barrow Hill in July 1965, it was withdrawn on 28 December 1968. C. F. Booth at Rotherham carried out the scrapping, but not until March 1970. *G. W. Sharpe*

Hudswell Clarke 0-6-0 diesel shunter No D2502 awaits repair at Birkenhead shed in July 1963. It was allocated new to Birkenhead as No 11118 on 28 January 1956 and moved to Carnforth in January 1967 and Barrow three months later, from where it was withdrawn on 7 October 1967. After storage, No D2502 was sold to C. F. Booth at Rotherham for scrap in March 1968. *Pictorail*

Hunslet Engine Co Class 05 0-6-0 diesel shunter No D2600 is at Selby shed in August 1960. New on 13 July 1960, it was first allocated to York then moved to Goole in September 1960, from where it was withdrawn on 30 December 1967. It was then sold for further service to Duport Steel for work at its plant at Briton Ferry. *P. H. Groom*

D2518	1C
D2519	5B

Class 05 0-6-0 Shunter

D2550	30F
D2551	30F
D2552	30F
D2553	32A
D2554	30F
D2555	32C
D2556	32B
D2557	32B
D2558	32A
D2559	32A
D2560	32B
D2561	32B
D2562	32A
D2563	32A
D2564	32B
D2565	32A
D2566	32A
D2567	32A
D2568	32C
D2569	32A
D2570	32C
D2571	32D
D2572	32B
D2573	32C
D2574	68C
D2575	68C
D2576	62A
D2577	62A
D2578	62A
D2579	62A
D2580	62A
D2581	62A
D2582	62A
D2583	62A
D2584	62A
D2585	62A
D2586	56B
D2587	56A
D2588	56A
D2589	56A
D2590	56A
D2591	56A
D2592	56A
D2593	56A
D2594	52A
D2595	56B
D2596	56B
D2597	56B
D2598	50D
D2599	50D
D2600	50D
D2601	50D
D2602	50D
D2603	56B
D2604	56B
D2605	56B
D2606	56B
D2607	56B
D2608	56B
D2609	50D
D2610	50D
D2611	50D
D2613	50D
D2614	50D
D2615	52D
D2616	50D
D2617	51A
D2618	51A

North British Locomotive Co/Paxman 0-4-0 Shunter

D2700	50D
D2701	50D
D2702	50D
D2703	65K
D2704	62C
D2705	64A
D2706	64A
D2707	62C

North British Locomotive Co/MAN 0-4-0 Shunter

D2708	62B
D2709	62B
D2710	62B
D2711	62B
D2712	62B
D2713	62B
D2714	62B
D2715	62B
D2716	62B
D2717	62C
D2718	62C
D2719	64F
D2720	64A
D2721	64A
D2722	64A
D2723	61B
D2724	64A
D2725	64A
D2726	64A
D2727	64A
D2728	64A
D2729	64A
D2730	64A
D2731	64A
D2732	64A
D2733	65G
D2734	65G
D2735	65G
D2736	65G
D2737	65G
D2738	65G
D2739	65J
D2740	65J
D2741	65J
D2742	65J
D2743	62C
D2744	62C
D2745	64A
D2746	64A
D2747	64A
D2748	64A
D2749	64A
D2750	64A
D2751	64B
D2752	64B
D2753	64B
D2754	64C
D2755	64C
D2756	65A
D2757	65A
D2758	65A
D2759	65A
D2760	65A
D2761	65A
D2762	65A
D2763	65A
D2764	65A
D2765	65A
D2766	65A
D2767	65A
D2768	65C
D2769	65E
D2770	65E
D2771	65E
D2772	65B
D2773	65B
D2774	65F
D2775	65F
D2776	65K
D2777	65K
D2778	65K
D2779	64A
D2780	65A

Class 02 0-4-0 Shunter

D2850	27A
D2851	27A
D2852	27A
D2853	27A
D2854	27A
D2855	27A
D2856	27A
D2857	27A
D2858	26A
D2859	17B
D2860	24F
D2861	24F
D2862	24F
D2863	24F
D2864	8B
D2865	8B
D2866	27A
D2867	27A
D2868	27A
D2869	27A

North British Locomotive Co/MAN 0-4-0 Shunter

D2900	1D
D2901	1D
D2902	1D
D2903	1D
D2904	1D
D2905	1D
D2906	1D
D2907	1D
D2908	2A
D2909	2A
D2910	2A
D2911	2A
D2912	2A
D2913	2A

Hunslet/Gardner 0-4-0 Shunter

D2950	32B
D2951	32B
D2952	32B

Class 01 0-4-0 Shunter

D2953	30A
D2954	30A
D2955	30A
D2956	30A

Ruston & Hornsby 0-4-0 Shunter

D2957	30A
D2958	30A

Brush/Petter 0-4-0 Shunter

D2999	30A

Class 08 0-6-0 Shunter

D3000	82A
D3001	82A
D3002	82A
D3003	82A
D3004	84F
D3005	67C
D3006	67C
D3007	67B
D3008	67B
D3009	67B
D3010	71A
D3011	71A
D3012	71A
D3013	71A
D3014	75C
D3015	1B
D3016	1A
D3017	1B
D3018	1A
D3019	8C
D3020	21D
D3021	21F
D3022	14A
D3023	14A
D3024	14A
D3025	84F
D3026	84B
D3027	84B
D3028	84B
D3029	84F
D3030	81A
D3031	81A
D3032	81A
D3033	81A
D3034	84B
D3035	84B
D3036	84B
D3037	84B
D3038	84B
D3039	84B
D3040	70B
D3041	70B
D3042	70B
D3043	73F
D3044	73F
D3045	73F
D3046	75C
D3047	75C
D3048	75C
D3049	75C
D3050	1A
D3051	1A
D3052	1A
D3053	2A
D3054	2A
D3055	2A
D3056	15A
D3057	15A
D3058	15A
D3059	15A
D3060	41F
D3061	41F
D3062	41F
D3063	41F
D3064	41F
D3065	31B
D3066	2F
D3067	2F
D3068	2F
D3069	2F
D3070	50A
D3071	50A
D3072	52A
D3073	52A
D3074	50B
D3075	50B
D3076	52A
D3077	50B
D3078	52H
D3079	50B
D3080	50B
D3081	50B
D3082	21A
D3083	16A
D3084	16A
D3085	16A
D3086	41A
D3087	12B
D3088	21C
D3089	2B
D3090	21C
D3091	21F
D3092	73F
D3093	75A
D3094	75A
D3095	73C
D3096	75C
D3097	73C
D3098	73C
D3099	73C
D3100	70B

North British Locomotive Co Paxman-engined 0-4-0 diesel shunter No D2706 is at Edinburgh St Margarets in August 1962. Allocated new to St Margarets as No 11706 on 29 December 1955, it remained at 64A until February 1967, when maintenance responsibilities were transferred to Leith Central. On 4 March 1967 it was withdrawn and sold to the Slag Reduction Co at Ickles, South Yorkshire, for scrap. *P. H. Groom*

One of the later batch of North British Locomotive Co-built 0-4-0 diesel shunters with MAN engines, No D2720 is seen at Edinburgh St Margarets in July 1962. New at St Margarets on 24 June 1958, it remained on allocation until Leith Central took it into care in February 1967. Withdrawn on 3 August 1967, it was sold to J. N. Connell at Coatbridge for scrap and cut up in July 1971. *R. H. G. Simpson*

North British Locomotive Co diesel-hydraulic 0-4-0 shunter No D2907 is at Devons Road shed, London, in June 1961. Allocated new to Devons Road on 16 August 1958, it moved to Northampton in November 1963, Rugby in September 1965 and Crewe North in October 1966. Withdrawn on 11 February 1967, it was placed in store at Crewe South and sold to the Slag Reduction Co at Ickles and broken up in September 1967. *G. W. Sharpe*

Hunslet 0-4-0 diesel shunter No D2952 is at Stratford shed in 1960 awaiting attention at the works. An Ipswich-based engine from delivery on 21 January 1955 to withdrawal on 25 December 1966, it was originally numbered 11502. This was another of the shunters sent for scrap at the Slag Reduction Co, cutting up being completed in August 1967. *R. H. G. Simpson*

Andrew Barclay Class 01 0-4-0 diesel shunter is still with its original number 11505 at Stratford shed in April 1961. It was renumbered D2955 in July 1961 and 01002 in June 1974. New to traffic on 19 February 1956, and allocated to Stratford, this engine and sister locomotive D2954 (01001) finished their working days separated from the main railway system at Holyhead Breakwater. Still in British Railways ownership, both engines were used at the Silica Works of William Wild & Sons. Withdrawal for 01001 came on 14 September 1979 and 01002 on 15 March 1981. Both were cut up on site by a local contractor. *R. H. G. Simpson*

Ruston & Hornsby 0-4-0 diesel shunter No D2957 is at Stratford shed in February 1960. First allocated to Immingham shed as No 11507 on 6 March 1956, it moved to Stratford in January 1957. Here it stayed until August 1966 when it was reallocated to Goole, from where it was withdrawn on 12 March 1967. It was another candidate for the scrapyard at Ickles, being cut up in August 1967. *R. H. G. Simpson*

0-4-0 diesel shunter No D2999 is at Stratford shed in May 1962. This was a demonstrator locomotive built for Brush Traction at Gorton by Beyer Peacock in 1958. It was used on loan at Mile End goods yard and purchased by British Railways in September 1960. Throughout, it was based at Stratford and was withdrawn on 15 October 1967 and sold to C. F. Booth at Rotherham for scrap. It was not finally cut up until October 1970. *R. H. G. Simpson*

D3101	73F
D3102	86E
D3103	86E
D3104	86E
D3105	84C
D3106	84C
D3107	84C
D3108	84C
D3109	84C
D3110	84C
D3111	89A
D3112	84F
D3113	84F
D3114	81A
D3115	84F
D3116	84F

BR/Crossley 0-6-0 Shunter

D3117	18A
D3118	18A
D3119	18A
D3120	18A
D3121	18A
D3122	18A
D3123	9D
D3124	18A
D3125	18A
D3126	18A

Class 08 0-6-0 Shunter

D3127	41A
D3128	34D
D3129	41A
D3130	31B
D3131	41A
D3132	65F
D3133	65F
D3134	65F
D3135	65F
D3136	65F

Class 10 BR/Blackstone 0-6-0 Shunter

D3137	51L
D3138	51L
D3139	51L
D3140	51L
D3141	51L
D3142	51L
D3143	51L
D3144	51L
D3145	51L
D3146	51L
D3147	51L
D3148	51L
D3149	51L
D3150	51L
D3151	51L

BR/Blackstone 0-6-0 Shunter

D3152	40B
D3153	40B
D3154	40B
D3155	40B
D3156	40B
D3157	40B
D3158	40B
D3159	40B
D3160	40B
D3161	40B
D3162	40B
D3163	40B
D3164	40B
D3165	40B
D3166	40B

Class 08 0-6-0 Shunter

D3167	21A
D3168	21A
D3169	2A
D3170	12B
D3171	12C
D3172	24C
D3173	1A
D3174	1A
D3175	5B
D3176	6A
D3177	1A
D3178	1A
D3179	14A
D3180	14A
D3181	14A
D3182	82A
D3183	82A
D3184	82A
D3185	82A
D3186	82A
D3187	82A
D3188	86E
D3189	86E
D3190	86E
D3191	84B
D3192	84F
D3193	89A
D3194	89A
D3195	81D
D3196	81C
D3197	66A
D3198	66A
D3199	66A
D3200	66A
D3201	66A
D3202	66B
D3203	66B
D3204	66B
D3205	66B
D3206	66B
D3207	65A
D3208	65A
D3209	65A
D3210	65A
D3211	65A
D3212	65C
D3213	65C
D3214	65C
D3215	65B
D3216	65B
D3217	75A
D3218	75A
D3219	75A
D3220	75A
D3221	75A
D3222	75C
D3223	75C
D3224	75C
D3225	75C
D3226	75C
D3227	51A
D3228	51A
D3229	51A
D3230	50B
D3231	50B
D3232	50B
D3233	50B
D3234	50B
D3235	50A
D3236	50B
D3237	50A
D3238	50A
D3239	50A
D3240	50A
D3241	52G
D3242	52G
D3243	52B
D3244	52B
D3245	5B
D3246	16A
D3247	16A
D3248	21A
D3249	14A
D3250	21A
D3251	41A
D3252	41A
D3253	41A
D3254	41A
D3255	82A
D3256	82A
D3257	82A
D3258	CED
D3259	CED
D3260	CED
D3261	CED
D3262	CED
D3263	CED
D3264	CED
D3265	CED
D3266	CED
D3267	CED
D3268	81D
D3269	81D
D3270	75C
D3271	70C
D3272	70C
D3273	70C
D3274	70C
D3275	62A
D3276	65F
D3277	65C
D3278	65B
D3279	65B
D3280	65B
D3281	65F
D3282	66B
D3283	66B
D3284	66B
D3285	66B
D3286	66B
D3287	66D
D3288	41A
D3289	41A
D3290	16A
D3291	5B
D3292	5B
D3293	41A
D3294	55B
D3295	55B
D3296	55B
D3297	55B
D3298	30F
D3299	30F
D3300	30A
D3301	30A

D3302	30F
D3303	30A
D3304	14A
D3305	14A
D3306	14A
D3307	34G
D3308	34G
D3309	34G
D3310	34G
D3311	34G
D3312	34G
D3313	50A
D3314	50A
D3315	50A
D3316	52B
D3317	52B
D3318	50A
D3319	50A
D3320	50A
D3321	52B
D3322	52H
D3323	50B
D3324	52A
D3325	41A
D3326	41A
D3327	31B
D3328	31B
D3329	41F
D3330	41A
D3331	34G
D3332	34G
D3333	41F
D3334	34G
D3335	41A
D3336	41A
D3337	62A
D3338	62A
D3339	62A
D3340	62A
D3341	62A
D3342	62C
D3343	62C
D3344	62C
D3345	62C
D3346	62C
D3347	62B
D3348	66B
D3349	66B
D3350	66B
D3351	66B
D3352	87F
D3353	87F
D3354	87F
D3355	87F
D3356	87A
D3357	87F
D3358	87F
D3359	87F
D3360	87F
D3361	DG
D3362	CED
D3363	CED
D3364	CED
D3365	CED
D3366	CED
D3367	5B
D3368	24C
D3369	24C
D3370	8C
D3371	24C
D3372	26A
D3373	26A
D3374	24C
D3375	55G
D3376	55D
D3377	55D
D3378	55D
D3379	55D
D3380	55E
D3381	55E
D3382	66B
D3383	66A
D3384	66B
D3385	66B
D3386	65B
D3387	65B
D3388	65A
D3389	65A
D3390	65A
D3391	65A
D3392	65A
D3393	65A
D3394	65E
D3395	65E
D3396	65A
D3397	CED
D3398	CED
D3399	CED
D3400	CED
D3401	CED
D3402	CED
D3403	CED
D3404	CED
D3405	CED
D3406	81A
D3407	CED
D3408	65B
D3409	65E
D3410	65C
D3411	65G
D3412	65G
D3413	65D
D3414	65D
D3415	65D
D3416	65E
D3417	65B
D3418	65A
D3419	CED
D3420	CED
D3421	CED
D3422	CED
D3423	CED
D3424	CED
D3425	CED
D3426	CED
D3427	CED
D3428	CED
D3429	DG
D3430	DG
D3431	DG
D3432	87B
D3433	87B
D3434	87B
D3435	87B
D3436	87B
D3437	87B
D3438	87B

Class 10 BR/Blackstone 0-6-0 Shunter

D3439	36A
D3440	34E
D3441	34E
D3442	40F
D3443	36A
D3444	36A
D3445	34E
D3446	34E
D3447	34E
D3448	34E
D3449	34E
D3450	34E
D3451	34E
D3452	34E
D3453	34E

Class 08 0-6-0 Shunter

D3454	55B
D3455	52A
D3456	51A
D3457	55F
D3458	55D
D3459	70B
D3460	73C
D3461	75C
D3462	73C
D3463	73C
D3464	75C
D3465	75C
D3466	73F
D3467	73F
D3468	73C
D3469	75C
D3470	73F
D3471	73C
D3472	73C

Class 10 BR/Blackstone 0-6-0 Shunter

D3473	36A
D3474	36A
D3475	40B
D3476	41A
D3477	40B
D3478	40B
D3479	36A
D3480	36A
D3481	36A
D3482	36A
D3483	36A
D3484	36A
D3485	34E
D3486	34E
D3487	34E
D3488	34E
D3489	40F
D3490	40F
D3491	31B
D3492	31B
D3493	31B
D3494	31B
D3495	30F
D3496	30F
D3497	30A
D3498	30A
D3499	30A
D3500	30A
D3501	30A
D3502	30A

Class 08 0-6-0 Shunter

D3503	82A
D3504	82A
D3505	82A
D3506	82A
D3507	82A
D3508	82A
D3509	83F
D3510	83F
D3511	83A
D3512	81C
D3513	83A
D3514	83G
D3515	83A
D3516	83D
D3517	83A
D3518	84E
D3519	83A
D3520	83D
D3521	83C
D3522	83C
D3523	83D
D3524	83D
D3525	83D
D3526	83D
D3527	CED
D3528	66B
D3529	66A
D3530	65E
D3531	65E
D3532	65C
D3533	65E
D3534	65A
D3535	63A
D3536	65J
D3537	65J
D3538	65J
D3539	65J
D3540	62C
D3541	63A
D3542	63A
D3543	63A
D3544	63A
D3545	63A
D3546	61A
D3547	61A
D3548	61A
D3549	61A
D3550	61A
D3551	61A
D3552	61A
D3553	61A
D3554	64F
D3555	64F
D3556	65K
D3557	65K
D3558	64A
D3559	65K
D3560	64C
D3561	64C
D3562	65C
D3563	67C
D3564	67C
D3565	12A
D3566	12A
D3567	12A
D3568	17B
D3569	17B
D3570	17B
D3571	17B
D3572	17B
D3573	14A
D3574	41A
D3575	41A
D3576	21A
D3577	21A
D3578	8A
D3579	8A
D3580	12F
D3581	24C
D3582	21A
D3583	5B
D3584	5B
D3585	17B
D3586	17B
D3587	17B
D3588	26A
D3589	26A
D3590	26A
D3591	26A
D3592	26A
D3593	CED
D3594	CED
D3595	CED
D3596	CED
D3597	81A
D3598	81A
D3599	81A
D3600	81A
D3601	81A
D3602	81A
D3603	CED
D3604	81A
D3605	CED
D3606	CED
D3607	CED
D3608	30A
D3609	30A
D3610	31A
D3611	31A

Class 10 BR/Blackstone 0-6-0 Shunter

D3612	36E
D3613	36E
D3614	36E

D3615	36E
D3616	36E
D3617	36E
D3618	36E
D3619	36E
D3620	36E
D3621	36A
D3622	36A
D3623	36A
D3624	40E
D3625	40E
D3626	40E
D3627	40E
D3628	40E
D3629	34E
D3630	34E
D3631	30A
D3632	30A
D3633	30A
D3634	30A
D3635	30A
D3636	30A
D3637	36A
D3638	36C
D3639	36C
D3640	36C
D3641	36C
D3642	36C
D3643	36C
D3644	36C
D3645	36C
D3646	36C
D3647	36C
D3648	36A
D3649	36A
D3650	36A
D3651	36A

Class 08 0-6-0 Shunter

D3652	55C
D3653	55C
D3654	55B
D3655	55B
D3656	55F
D3657	55F
D3658	55F
D3659	41A
D3660	41A
D3661	41A
D3662	41A
D3663	41A
D3664	41A

Class 09 0-6-0 Shunter

D3665	71A
D3666	71A
D3667	71A
D3668	75C
D3669	75C
D3670	73E
D3671	73E

Class 08 0-6-0 Shunter

D3672	51C
D3673	52C
D3674	52C
D3675	50B
D3676	50B
D3677	51A
D3678	52C
D3679	52F
D3680	30F
D3681	30A
D3682	30A
D3683	30A
D3684	30A
D3685	41A
D3686	41A
D3687	34G
D3688	34D
D3689	34D
D3690	34D
D3691	34D
D3692	34G
D3693	34G
D3694	41A
D3695	41A
D3696	41A
D3697	41F
D3698	41A
D3699	41A
D3700	41A
D3701	41A
D3702	41A
D3703	41A
D3704	34G
D3705	34G
D3706	34G
D3707	41A
D3708	34D
D3709	34D
D3710	34G
D3711	34G
D3712	34G
D3713	34G
D3714	34G
D3715	34G
D3716	34G
D3717	34G
D3718	34G

Class 09 0-6-0 Shunter

D3719	73E
D3720	75C
D3721	73E

Class 08 0-6-0 Shunter

D3722	34G
D3723	34G
D3724	34G
D3725	34G
D3726	41F
D3727	41A
D3728	64A
D3729	64A
D3730	64A
D3731	64A
D3732	64C
D3733	64C
D3734	64A
D3735	60A
D3736	64A
D3737	64C
D3738	64B
D3739	64B
D3740	64A
D3741	64A
D3742	64A
D3743	DG
D3744	DG
D3745	86A
D3746	86A
D3747	CED
D3748	86A
D3749	CED
D3750	82A
D3751	82A
D3752	84B
D3753	81C
D3754	81C
D3755	84B
D3756	81C
D3757	84B
D3758	DG
D3759	81C
D3760	DG
D3761	81C
D3762	81C
D3763	5B
D3764	6A
D3765	9A
D3766	9A
D3767	9A
D3768	9A
D3769	9A
D3770	9A
D3771	9B
D3772	9B
D3773	17B
D3774	21D
D3775	21D
D3776	15A
D3777	15A
D3778	15A
D3779	26A
D3780	21F
D3781	21F
D3782	24B
D3783	24B
D3784	26A
D3785	15E
D3786	15C
D3787	15C
D3788	15C
D3789	15C
D3790	15C
D3791	15C
D3792	18C
D3793	8D
D3794	8D
D3795	1A
D3796	8B
D3797	8B
D3798	5B
D3799	5B
D3800	5D
D3801	5D
D3802	5B
D3803	82A
D3804	82C
D3805	82A
D3806	82A
D3807	86A
D3808	86A
D3809	86A
D3810	86A
D3811	86A
D3812	86A
D3813	86A
D3814	86A
D3815	86A
D3816	86A
D3817	86A
D3818	86A
D3819	86A
D3820	86A
D3821	86A
D3822	86A
D3823	86A
D3824	86A
D3825	DG
D3826	DG
D3827	DG
D3828	DG
D3829	DG
D3830	DG
D3831	81D
D3832	6B
D3833	6B
D3834	8B
D3835	8B
D3836	8F
D3837	8F
D3838	21D
D3839	21E
D3840	21E
D3841	21E
D3842	26A
D3843	26A
D3844	26A
D3845	26A
D3846	24C
D3847	1B
D3848	1B
D3849	1B
D3850	1B
D3851	8B
D3852	9F
D3853	9F
D3854	9F
D3855	8C
D3856	8C
D3857	8C
D3858	27E
D3859	16A
D3860	16A
D3861	16A
D3862	17A
D3863	17A
D3864	17A
D3865	21A
D3866	5D
D3867	21C
D3868	26A
D3869	14A
D3870	8C
D3871	21C
D3872	50A
D3873	51L
D3874	50A
D3875	51L
D3876	51L
D3877	64C
D3878	64A
D3879	64A
D3880	64A
D3881	64A
D3882	64A
D3883	64A
D3884	64A
D3885	64A
D3886	64A
D3887	64A
D3888	64A
D3889	64A
D3890	64A
D3891	64A
D3892	64A
D3893	64A
D3894	65A
D3895	65A
D3896	65A
D3897	65A
D3898	65B
D3899	65B
D3900	65B
D3901	65B
D3902	65E
D3903	65B
D3904	65B
D3905	66A
D3906	66A
D3907	66A
D3908	66A
D3909	66A
D3910	66A
D3911	66A
D3912	66A
D3913	66A
D3914	66A
D3915	66A
D3916	66A
D3917	66A
D3918	66A
D3919	66A
D3920	66D
D3921	66D
D3922	67A
D3923	67A
D3924	67A
D3925	67A
D3926	67D
D3927	67D
D3928	67D
D3929	67D

Class 08 0-6-0 shunter No D3808 is at Newport Ebbw Junction shed in August 1960. Built at Horwich Works, it was first allocated to Bristol St Philips Marsh on 16 January 1959, moving to Newport Ebbw Junction the next month. Renumbered 08641 in April 1974, the engine is still in service, at present owned by First Group and allocated to Plymouth Laira for maintenance. *R. H. G. Simpson*

Class 10 0-6-0 diesel shunter No D4075 was built by Darlington Works and fitted with a Blackstone six-cylinder Type ER6T engine. This is a March 1963 scene with the locomotive at Peterborough New England shed, where it had gone new on 30 September 1961. Its only transfer was to Lincoln in October 1968, from where it was withdrawn on 11 June 1972 and sent to Cohen's at Kettering in March 1973 for scrap. *R. H. G Simpson*

D3930	61A	D3951	84E	D3972	81F	D3993	85B	D4014	83A
D3931	61A	D3952	84E	D3973	84E	D3994	85B	D4015	82A
D3932	61A	D3953	81D	D3974	84E	D3995	84F	D4016	82D
D3933	61A	D3954	81A	D3975	84E	D3996	84F	D4017	82A
D3934	61A	D3955	81C	D3976	84B	D3997	84G	D4018	82A
D3935	61A	D3956	84E	D3977	84B	D3998	82D	D4019	82A
D3936	61A	D3957	84E	D3978	84B	D3999	82A	D4020	82A
D3937	55D	D3958	84E	D3979	84B	D4000	81A	D4021	82D
D3938	52A	D3959	81F	D3980	84F	D4001	86A	D4022	82A
D3939	52K	D3960	81F	D3981	84F	D4002	86A	D4023	82D
D3940	50A	D3961	81C	D3982	84F	D4003	81A	D4024	82A
D3941	55D	D3962	81A	D3983	84E	D4004	81A	D4025	82A
D3942	52B	D3963	81F	D3984	84E	D4005	83E	D4026	82A
D3943	52B	D3964	81F	D3985	84E	D4006	81A	D4027	82C
D3944	50B	D3965	84E	D3986	85B	D4007	83E	D4028	41A
D3945	50B	D3966	84E	D3987	85B	D4008	83E	D4029	41A
D3946	50A	D3967	81F	D3988	84F	D4009	83E	D4030	41A
D3947	81A	D3968	84E	D3989	85B	D4010	83D	D4031	41A
D3948	81D	D3969	84E	D3990	85B	D4011	86A	D4032	41A
D3949	81C	D3970	89A	D3991	85B	D4012	86A	D4033	41A
D3950	84E	D3971	81F	D3992	85B	D4013	83E	D4034	41A

D4035	41A
D4036	41A
D4037	41A
D4038	41A
D4039	41A
D4040	41A
D4041	41A
D4042	41A
D4043	41A
D4044	41A
D4045	41A
D4046	41A
D4047	41A
D4048	41A

Class 10 BR/Blackstone 0-6-0 Shunter

D4049	41A
D4050	41A
D4051	41A
D4052	41A
D4053	41A
D4054	41A
D4055	41A
D4056	41A
D4057	41A
D4058	41A
D4059	41A
D4060	41A
D4061	41A
D4062	41A
D4063	41A
D4064	41A
D4065	41A
D4066	41A
D4067	41A
D4068	41A
D4069	41A
D4070	41A
D4071	41A
D4072	41A
D4073	41A
D4074	41A
D4075	34E
D4076	34E
D4077	34E
D4078	34G
D4079	36A
D4080	36A

Class 08 0-6-0 Shunter

D4095	60A
D4096	60A
D4097	63B
D4098	63A

Class 09 0-6-0 Shunter

D4099	73C
D4100	73F
D4101	73F
D4102	75C
D4103	75C
D4104	75C
D4105	6A
D4106	12A
D4107	12B
D4108	5D
D4109	5D
D4110	5D
D4111	2B
D4112	2B

Class 24 Bo-Bo

D5000	73C
D5001	73C
D5002	73C
D5003	73C
D5004	73C
D5005	73C
D5006	73C
D5007	73C
D5008	73C
D5009	73C
D5010	73C
D5011	73C
D5012	73C
D5013	73C
D5014	73C
D5015	1B
D5016	1B
D5017	73C
D5018	1B
D5019	1B
D5020	1A
D5021	1A
D5022	1B
D5023	1C
D5024	1A
D5025	1A
D5026	1B
D5027	1A
D5028	1A
D5029	1A
D5030	1A
D5031	1C
D5032	1A
D5033	1A
D5034	1A
D5035	1C
D5036	32B
D5037	32B
D5038	32B
D5039	32B
D5040	32B
D5041	32B
D5042	32B
D5043	32B
D5044	32B
D5045	32B
D5046	32B
D5047	32B
D5048	32B
D5049	32B
D5050	34G
D5051	34G
D5052	34G
D5053	34G
D5054	34G
D5055	34G
D5056	34G
D5057	34G
D5058	34G
D5059	34G
D5060	34G
D5061	34G
D5062	34G
D5063	34G
D5064	34G
D5065	34G
D5066	34G
D5067	34G
D5068	34G
D5069	34G
D5070	34G
D5071	34G
D5072	34G
D5073	1A
D5074	1C
D5075	1A
D5076	1A
D5077	1A
D5078	1A
D5079	1A
D5080	1A
D5081	1C
D5082	1A
D5083	1A
D5084	14A
D5085	14A
D5086	14A
D5087	14A
D5088	14A
D5089	14A
D5090	14A
D5091	14A
D5092	14A
D5093	14A
D5094	34G
D5095	34G
D5096	52A
D5097	52A
D5098	52A
D5099	52A
D5100	52A
D5101	52A
D5102	52A
D5103	52A
D5104	52A
D5105	52A
D5106	52A
D5107	52A
D5108	52A
D5109	52A
D5110	52A
D5111	52A
D5112	51L
D5113	51L
D5114	60A
D5115	60A
D5116	60A
D5117	60A
D5118	60A
D5119	60A
D5120	60A
D5121	60A
D5122	60A
D5123	60A
D5124	60A
D5125	60A
D5126	60A
D5127	60A
D5128	60A
D5129	60A
D5130	60A
D5131	60A
D5132	60A
D5133	1A
D5134	9A
D5135	9A
D5136	9A
D5137	9A
D5138	9A
D5139	9A
D5140	9A
D5141	9A
D5142	9A
D5143	1A
D5144	1A
D5145	1A
D5146	1A
D5147	52A
D5148	52A
D5149	52A
D5150	52A

Class 25 Bo-Bo

D5151	51L
D5152	51L
D5153	51L
D5154	51L
D5155	51L
D5156	52A
D5157	52A
D5158	51L
D5159	51L
D5160	51L
D5161	51L
D5162	51L
D5163	51L
D5164	51L
D5165	51L
D5166	51L
D5167	51L
D5168	51L
D5169	51L
D5170	51L

Class 26 BRC& W Bo-Bo

D5300	64B
D5301	64B
D5302	64B
D5303	64B
D5304	64B
D5305	64B
D5306	64B
D5307	64B
D5308	64B
D5309	64B
D5310	64B
D5311	64B
D5312	64B
D5313	64B
D5314	64B
D5315	64B
D5316	64B
D5317	64B
D5318	64B
D5319	64B
D5320	60A
D5321	60A
D5322	60A
D5323	60A
D5324	60A
D5325	60A
D5326	60A
D5327	60A
D5328	60A
D5329	60A
D5330	60A
D5331	60A
D5332	60A
D5333	60A
D5334	60A
D5335	60A
D5336	60A
D5337	60A
D5338	60A
D5339	60A
D5340	60A
D5341	60A
D5342	60A
D5343	60A
D5344	60A
D5345	60A
D5346	60A

Class 27 BRC&W Bo-Bo

D5347	65A
D5348	65A
D5349	65A
D5350	65A
D5351	65A
D5352	65A
D5353	65A
D5354	65A
D5355	65A
D5356	65A
D5357	65A
D5358	65A
D5359	65A
D5360	65A
D5361	65A
D5362	65A
D5363	65A
D5364	65A
D5365	65A

Class 31 Brush A1A-A1A

D5500	32A
D5501	30A
D5502	30A
D5503	30A
D5504	30A
D5505	30A
D5506	30A

Class 24 Bo-Bo No D5054 is north of Finsbury Park on a northbound local composed of two quad-art sets in May 1962. Built at Crewe Works, it entered traffic at March shed on 18 December 1959 and transferred to Finsbury Park in January 1961. In October 1966 No D5054 was reallocated to Glasgow Eastfield, then to Carlisle Kingmoor in March 1968 and to Manchester Longsight the next month. It became part of the Crewe area diesel pool in September 1968 and was withdrawn on 17 July 1976, by then numbered 24054. Storage at Crewe Basford Hall followed for a month and then it was taken into departmental stock as TDB968008, where it was used until 1982. Sold for preservation, it is now at the East Lancs Railway at Bury. *P. H. Groom*

Class 26 Bo-Bo No D5320 is seen at Helmsdale in November 1962 on a freight working. New in April 1959, it worked from Edinburgh Haymarket until June 1960, when it was transferred to Inverness. Subsequent transfers were between these two depots until it was stored at various locations. It was withdrawn as No 26028 at the beginning of October 1991, and later scrapped. *R. H. G. Simpson*

Class 27 No D5378 was a new addition to stock in 1962 and is at Thornaby shed just after delivery in March. It was transferred to the Midlands in January 1966, to the Nottingham Division, and to Glasgow Eastfield in November 1969, from where it was withdrawn on 6 May 1978 numbered 27031. Cutting up was undertaken at Glasgow Works. *Pictorail*

D5507	30A
D5508	31B
D5509	30A
D5510	30A
D5511	30A
D5512	30A
D5513	30A
D5514	30A
D5515	30A
D5516	30A
D5517	30A
D5518	30A
D5519	30A
D5520	32B
D5521	32B
D5522	32B
D5523	32B
D5524	32B
D5525	31B
D5526	32B
D5527	32B
D5528	32B
D5529	32B
D5530	32B
D5531	32B
D5532	32A
D5533	32A
D5534	32A
D5535	32A
D5536	32A
D5537	32B
D5538	32B
D5539	32B
D5540	32B
D5541	32B
D5542	32B
D5543	32B
D5544	32B
D5545	31B
D5546	31B
D5547	31B
D5548	32B
D5549	32B
D5550	32B
D5551	32B
D5552	32B
D5553	32B
D5554	32B
D5555	32A
D5556	32A
D5557	32A
D5558	32A
D5559	32A
D5560	32A
D5561	32A
D5562	32A
D5563	31B
D5564	31B
D5565	32A
D5566	32A
D5567	32A
D5568	31B
D5569	31B
D5570	31B
D5571	31B
D5572	31B
D5573	31B
D5574	32A
D5575	32A
D5576	32A
D5577	32A
D5578	31B
D5579	31B
D5580	31B
D5581	32B
D5582	31B
D5583	31B
D5584	31B
D5585	30A
D5586	30A
D5587	30A
D5588	30A
D5589	30A
D5590	30A
D5591	30A
D5592	30A
D5593	30A
D5594	30A
D5595	30A
D5596	30A
D5597	30A
D5598	30A
D5599	30A
D5600	31B
D5601	34G
D5602	34G
D5603	34G
D5604	34G
D5605	34G
D5606	34G
D5607	34G
D5608	34G
D5609	34G
D5610	34G
D5611	34G
D5612	34G
D5613	34G
D5614	34G
D5615	34G
D5616	30A
D5617	30A
D5618	30A
D5619	30A
D5620	31B
D5621	31B
D5622	30A
D5623	30A
D5624	30A
D5625	30A
D5626	30A
D5627	30A
D5628	31B
D5629	31B
D5630	32A
D5631	32A
D5632	30A
D5633	30A
D5634	30A
D5635	30A
D5636	30A
D5637	30A
D5638	31B
D5639	34G
D5640	34G
D5641	34G
D5642	34G
D5643	34G
D5644	34G
D5645	34G
D5646	34G
D5647	34G
D5648	34G
D5649	34G
D5650	34G
D5651	34G
D5652	34G
D5653	34G
D5654	34G
D5655	41A
D5656	41A
D5657	41A
D5658	31B
D5659	31B
D5660	31B
D5661	31B
D5662	31B
D5663	31B
D5664	31B
D5665	31B
D5666	31B
D5667	31B
D5668	31B
D5669	31B
D5670	31B
D5671	34G
D5672	34G
D5673	34G
D5674	34G
D5675	34G
D5676	34G
D5677	34G
D5678	34G
D5679	34G
D5680	41A
D5681	41A
D5682	41A
D5683	41A
D5684	41A
D5685	41A
D5686	41A
D5687	41A
D5688	41A
D5689	41A
D5690	41A
D5691	41A
D5692	41A
D5693	41A
D5694	30A
D5695	30A
D5696	30A
D5697	30A
D5698	30A
D5699	30A

Class 28 Metropolitan-Vickers Co-Bo

D5700	17A
D5701	17A
D5702	17A
D5703	17A
D5704	17A
D5705	17A
D5706	17A
D5707	17A
D5708	17A
D5709	17A
D5710	17A
D5711	17A
D5712	17A
D5713	17A
D5714	17A
D5715	17A
D5716	17A
D5717	17A
D5718	17A
D5719	12E

Class 31 Brush A1A-A1A

D5800	31B
D5801	30A
D5802	31B
D5803	31B
D5804	31B
D5805	41A
D5806	41A
D5807	41A
D5808	41A
D5809	41A
D5810	41A
D5811	41A
D5812	41A
D5813	41A
D5814	41A
D5815	41A
D5816	41A
D5817	41A
D5818	41A
D5819	41A
D5820	41A
D5821	41A
D5822	41A
D5823	41A
D5824	41A
D5825	41A
D5826	41A
D5827	41A
D5828	41A

Class 23 English Electric Bo-Bo

D5900	34G
D5901	34G
D5902	34G
D5903	34G
D5904	34G
D5905	34G
D5906	34G
D5907	34G
D5908	34G
D5909	34G

Class 21 North British Locomotive Co Bo-Bo

D6100	65A
D6101	65A
D6102	65A
D6103	65A
D6104	65A
D6105	65A
D6106	65A
D6107	65A
D6108	65A
D6109	65A
D6110	65A
D6111	65A
D6112	65A
D6113	65A
D6114	65A
D6115	65A
D6116	65A
D6117	65A
D6118	65A
D6119	65A
D6120	65A
D6121	65A
D6122	65A
D6123	65A
D6124	65A
D6125	65A
D6126	65A
D6127	65A
D6128	65A
D6129	65A
D6130	65A
D6131	65A
D6132	65A
D6133	65A
D6134	65A
D6135	65A
D6136	65A
D6137	65A
D6138	61A
D6139	61A
D6140	61A
D6141	61A
D6142	61A
D6143	61A
D6144	61A
D6145	61A
D6146	61A
D6147	61A
D6148	61A
D6149	61A
D6150	61A
D6151	61A
D6152	61A
D6153	61A
D6154	61A
D6155	61A
D6156	61A
D6157	61A

Brush Class 31 A1A-A1A No D5504 is at Stratford depot in June 1962. New to traffic on 30 January 1958, its first allocation was Stratford, and it also spent time allocated to March during its years in stock. Withdrawal came when back at Stratford on 5 October 1980 as No 31004, and scrapping was carried out at Swindon Works in June 1981. *R. H. G. Simpson*

One of the last batch of Class 31s to be built, No D5805 later became No 31275. It is here at Nottingham Victoria on Sunday 8 April 1962 on the 2.40pm Manchester Piccadilly to Leicester Central, usually a steam-powered working. New to stock at Sheffield Darnall on 6 July 1961, it was a Sheffield area engine until November 1972, when it was transferred to Thornaby. Subsequent moves saw it at Immingham, Tinsley, Gateshead, Bescot, Carlisle Kingmoor, Toton, Wigan Springs Branch and Crewe diesel depot. At present it is owned by the Harry Needle Railroad Company. *M. Mitchell*

Class 28 Metropolitan-Vickers Co-Bo No D5705 is at Derby shed in April 1959. It was added to stock on 6 December 1958 and allocated to Derby. Two of these engines were used in tandem on the fast overnight freight services, named the 'Condor', from London Hendon to Glasgow and return, inaugurated by the London Midland and Scottish Regions in March 1959. The name 'Condor' was a contraction of 'container door to door' and the train consisted of 27 vacuum-braked and roller-bearing-fitted long-wheelbase flat wagons with a capacity for two containers each. The Class 28 locomotives gave way to other motive power in due course and were placed in store until February 1962, when the entire class was transferred to Cumbria and based at Barrow or Carlisle Upperby. No D5705 was withdrawn on 7 September 1968 and then went into departmental service until 1979. Sold to the Diesel Traction Group, it is now at the East Lancs Railway under the ownership of the Pioner Diesel Group. *P. H. Groom*

Class 23 'Baby Deltic' Bo-Bo No D5902 is at Hornsey shed in August 1959. Until Finsbury Park Diesel Depot opened, diesels were maintained at Hornsey and this view shows the fuelling facilities provided. No D5902 was built at Vulcan Foundry, Newton-le-Willows, by English Electric and entered traffic at Hornsey on 1 May 1959. Moving to Finsbury Park in April 1960, it remained at 34G until withdrawn on 23 November 1969 and, after storage at Stratford for nearly a year, went to Cohen's at Kettering for scrap. *G. W. Sharpe*

Class 21 North British Locomotive Co Bo-Bo No D6119, with a damaged buffer, is at Glasgow St Rollox shed on Sunday 15 April 1962. First allocated to Stratford on 30 June 1959, all those of the class allocated to the Eastern Region were later moved to Scotland, No D6119 going to Glasgow Eastfield in August 1960 where it spent its short career. Re-engined and refurbished in February 1967, and reclassified Class 29, it was withdrawn on 31 December 1971. Following storage, it was cut up at Glasgow Works in August 1972. *G. W. Sharpe*

Another less than successful North British Locomotive Co design was the Class 22 Bo-Bo. Two of the class, Nos D6311 and D6310, are at Plymouth station on a westbound milk train in August 1960. Both were new in January 1960 and based at Plymouth Laira. Later service saw them based at Newton Abbot and Bristol Bath Road. No D6310 lasted the longest, being withdrawn on 27 March 1971 and eventually cut up at Swindon Works in May 1972. No D6311 was withdrawn on 23 September 1968 and was cut up at Cashmore's yard at Newport in May 1969. *G. W. Sharpe*

Class 22 North British Locomotive Co Bo-Bo

D6300	83D
D6301	83D
D6302	83D
D6303	83D
D6304	83D
D6305	83D
D6306	83D
D6307	83D
D6308	83D
D6309	83D
D6310	83D
D6311	83D
D6312	83D
D6313	83D
D6314	83D
D6315	83D
D6316	83D
D6317	83D
D6318	83D
D6319	83D
D6320	83D
D6321	83D
D6322	83D
D6323	83D
D6324	83D
D6325	83D
D6326	83A
D6327	83A
D6328	83A
D6329	83A
D6330	83A
D6331	83A
D6332	83A
D6333	83A
D6334	83A
D6335	83A
D6336	83A

Class 33 BRC&W Bo-Bo

D6500	73C
D6501	73C
D6502	73C
D6503	73C
D6504	73C
D6505	73C
D6506	73C
D6507	73C
D6508	73C
D6509	73C
D6510	73C
D6511	73C
D6512	73C
D6513	73C
D6514	73C
D6515	73C
D6516	73C
D6517	73C
D6518	73C
D6519	73C
D6520	73C
D6521	73C
D6522	73C
D6523	73C
D6524	73C
D6525	73C
D6526	73C
D6527	73C
D6528	73C
D6529	73C
D6530	73C
D6531	73C
D6532	73C
D6533	73C
D6534	73C
D6535	73C
D6536	73C
D6537	73C
D6538	73C
D6539	73C
D6540	73C
D6541	73C
D6542	73C
D6543	73C
D6544	73C
D6545	73C
D6546	73C
D6547	73C
D6548	73C
D6549	73C
D6550	73C
D6551	73C
D6552	73C
D6553	73C
D6554	73C
D6555	73C
D6556	73C
D6557	73C
D6558	73C
D6559	73C
D6560	73C
D6561	73C
D6562	73C
D6563	73C
D6564	73C
D6565	73C
D6566	73C
D6567	73C
D6568	73C
D6569	73C
D6570	73C
D6571	73C
D6572	73C
D6573	73C
D6574	73C
D6575	73C
D6576	73C
D6577	73C
D6578	73C
D6579	73C
D6580	73C
D6581	73C
D6582	73C

Class 37 English Electric Co-Co

D6700	30A
D6701	30A
D6702	30A
D6703	30A
D6704	30A
D6705	30A
D6706	30A
D6707	30A
D6708	30A
D6709	30A
D6710	30A
D6711	30A
D6712	30A
D6713	30A
D6714	30A
D6715	30A
D6716	30A
D6717	30A
D6718	30A
D6719	30A
D6720	30A
D6721	30A
D6722	30A
D6723	30A
D6724	30A
D6725	30A
D6726	30A
D6727	30A
D6728	30A
D6729	30A
D6730	50B
D6731	50B

Class 35 Beyer-Peacock B-B

D7000	82A
D7001	82A
D7002	82D
D7003	82A
D7004	82A
D7005	82D
D7006	82A
D7007	82D
D7008	82A
D7009	82A
D7010	82A
D7011	82A
D7012	82A
D7013	82A
D7014	82A
D7015	82A

Class 20 English Electric Bo-Bo

D8000	1B
D8001	1A
D8002	1A
D8003	1A
D8004	1A
D8005	1A
D8006	1D
D8007	1D
D8008	1D
D8009	1D
D8010	1D
D8011	1D
D8012	1D
D8013	1D
D8014	1D
D8015	1D
D8016	1D
D8017	1D
D8018	1D
D8019	1D
D8020	41A
D8021	34G
D8022	34G
D8023	34G
D8024	34G
D8025	34G
D8026	34G
D8027	34G
D8028	61A
D8029	61A
D8030	61A
D8031	61A
D8032	60A
D8033	60A
D8034	61A
D8035	5B
D8036	1A
D8037	1B
D8038	1A
D8039	1B
D8040	1D
D8041	1D
D8042	1D
D8043	1D
D8044	1D
D8045	34G
D8046	34G
D8047	34G
D8048	34G
D8049	34G
D8050	41A
D8051	41A
D8052	41A
D8053	41A
D8054	41A
D8055	41A
D8056	41A
D8057	41A
D8058	41A
D8059	41A
D8060	41A
D8061	41A
D8062	41A
D8063	41A
D8064	41A
D8065	41A
D8066	41A
D8067	41A
D8068	41A
D8069	41A
D8070	65A
D8071	65A
D8072	65A
D8073	65A
D8074	65A
D8075	65A
D8076	65A
D8077	65A
D8078	65A
D8079	65A
D8080	65A
D8081	65A
D8082	65A
D8083	65A
D8084	65A
D8085	65A
D8086	65A
D8087	65A
D8088	65A
D8089	65A
D8090	65A
D8091	65A
D8092	65A
D8093	65A
D8094	65A
D8095	65A
D8096	65A
D8097	65A
D8098	65A
D8099	65A
D8100	65A
D8101	65A
D8102	65A
D8103	65A
D8104	65A
D8105	65A
D8106	65A
D8107	65A
D8108	65A
D8109	65A

Class 15 Clayton/Yorkshire Engine Co Bo-Bo

D8200	32B
D8201	32B
D8202	32B
D8203	32B
D8204	32B
D8205	32B
D8206	32B
D8207	32B
D8208	30A
D8209	30A
D8210	31B
D8211	31B
D8212	31B
D8213	31B
D8214	31B
D8215	31B
D8216	31B
D8217	31B
D8218	31B
D8219	31B
D8220	32B
D8221	32B
D8222	32B
D8223	30A
D8224	30A
D8225	30A
D8226	30A
D8227	30A
D8228	30A
D8229	30A

Class 37 Co-Co No D6717 is at Stratford shed in July 1961 with D6709 behind. New to Stratford on 30 May 1961, it was renumbered 37017 in February 1974 and 37503 in March 1986 and is still in service, now owned by EWS and based at Doncaster for maintenance. *R. H. G. Simpson*

The first Class 35 B-B to be built by Beyer Peacock, No D7000 is at Bristol Bath Road diesel depot in July 1961, with the building work still in progress. Alongside is Class 42 No D810 *Cockade* visiting from Plymouth Laira. No D7000 had been allocated new to Bristol on 16 May 1961 and moved to Old Oak Common in January 1972 from where it was withdrawn on 30 July 1973. After storage, it was cut up at Swindon Works in October 1975. *G. W. Sharpe*

Class 20 Bo-Bo No D8063 at Sheffield Darnall just after delivery in June 1961. It had been released to traffic on the 5th and allocated to Darnall. It remained based in the Sheffield area until April 1968, when it was transferred to Toton for maintenance and spent a time in storage at Leicester in October 1981 before transfer to the Glasgow area. Withdrawn as No 20063 on 19 July 1991, it was then sold for further use in France by CFD Industries. *G. W. Sharpe*

British Thomson-Houston/Clayton Class 15 Bo-Bo No D8234 is at Stratford shed in June 1962 with Class 16 Bo-Bo No D8403 behind. D8234 was allocated new to Stratford on 21 September 1960 and remained working from 30A until withdrawn on 27 March 1971. After storage it was cut up at Crewe Works in November 1971. *R. H. G. Simpson*

North British Locomotive Co Class 16 Bo-Bo No D8402 is undergoing repair at Doncaster Works in January 1964. New to Stratford shed on 16 July 1958, it worked from 30A until withdrawn on 7 July 1968. Cohen's at Kettering carried out the scrapping in November 1969. *Pictorail*

The Class 17 Bo-Bos from Clayton were introduced in 1962. This is No D8505 at Motherwell depot in May 1964. It was withdrawn on 12 October 1968, surplus to requirements when allocated to Carlisle Kingmoor, and after storage was reinstated on 18 May 1969 to Glasgow Polmadie and transferred to Edinburgh Haymarket in July 1969, from where it was finally withdrawn on 6 October 1971. Following storage at Haymarket and Millerhill, it was cut up at Glasgow Works in May 1974. *P. H. Groom*

D8230	30A
D8231	30A
D8232	30A
D8233	30A
D8234	30A
D8235	30A
D8236	30A
D8237	34G
D8238	34G
D8239	34G
D8240	34G
D8241	34G
D8242	34G
D8243	34G

Class 16 North British Locomotive Co Bo-Bo

D8400	30A
D8401	30A
D8402	30A
D8403	30A
D8404	30A
D8405	30A
D8406	30A
D8407	30A
D8408	30A
D8409	30A

Class 55 English Electric 'Deltic' Co-Co

D9000	64B
D9001*	34G
D9002	52A
D9003*	34G
D9004	64B
D9005	52A
D9006	64B
D9007*	34G
D9008	52A
D9009*	34G
D9010	64B
D9011	52A
D9012*	34G
D9013	64B
D9014	52A
D9015*	34G
D9016	64B
D9017	52A
D9018*	34G
D9019	64B

LMS/English Electric Co-Co

10000	1A
10001	1A

SR/BR English Electric 1Co-Co1

10201	1A
10202	1A
10203	1A

LMS/Hawthorn Leslie 0-6-0 Shunter

12001	5B

LMS/English Electric 0-6-0 Shunter

12003	8F
12004	21B
12005	5B
12006	8C
12007	8C
12008	8C
12009	5B
12010	5B
12011	5B
12012	21B
12013	21B
12014	8C
12015	8C
12016	8C
12017	8C
12018	8C
12019	5B
12020	6B
12021	5B
12022	5B
12023	8G
12024	8C
12025	5B
12026	8C
12027	8C
12028	8C
12029	8C
12030	21B
12031	8F
12032	8F

Class 11 LMS/English Electric 0-6-0 Shunter

12033	17A
12034	17A
12035	21A
12036	6A
12037	6A
12038	18A
12039	21A
12040	21A
12041	21A
12042	21A
12043	21A
12044	21A
12045	2A
12046	2A
12047	2A
12048	6A
12049	21A
12050	16A
12051	16A
12052	16A
12053	6A
12054	6A
12055	18A
12056	21F
12057	6A
12058	14A
12059	21A
12060	21A
12061	21A
12062	21A
12063	14A
12064	14A
12065	14A
12066	21A
12067	14A
12068	14A
12069	14A
12070	1A
12071	21E
12072	17A
12073	1E
12074	1E
12075	8B
12076	1A
12077	21A
12078	1A
12079	12A
12080	12A
12081	8C
12082	18A
12083	12A
12084	12C
12085	12C
12086	12C
12087	21C
12088	21D
12089	21D
12090	21D
12091	21B
12092	21E

'Just out of the box' is Class 55 'Deltic' Co-Co No D9018 *Ballymoss* at King's Cross during the month it entered service, December 1961. Allocated to Finsbury Park, it worked from this London base until transfer to York in May 1981. Withdrawn on 13 October 1981, it was broken up at Doncaster Works in January 1982. *R. H. G. Simpson*

Inside Willesden roundhouse in July 1961 is LMS-designed Co-Co No 10001, dating from July 1948. Allocated to Willesden in November 1959, it was withdrawn on 12 March 1966 and placed in store at 1A until January 1968, when it was despatched to Cox & Danks at Acton for scrapping. *R. H. G. Simpson*

Also in Willesden roundhouse in July 1961 is ex-Southern Railway-designed 1Co-Co1 No 10202, dating from October 1951. This locomotive had also been allocated to Willesden in November 1959. It was sent to Derby Works for storage in January 1963 and officially withdrawn later in the year on 7 December. Storage at Derby continued until February 1968 when No 10202 was sent to Cashmore's yard at Great Bridge for scrapping. *R. H. G. Simpson*

One of the 0-6-0 diesel shunters built by the LMS, No 12019 is seen at Crewe South shed in February 1962. Dating from June 1940, and originally numbered 7096, it had been allocated to Crewe South when new, moving to Willesden in July 1942, back to Crewe South in December 1954 and then to Wigan Springs Branch in July 1959. A return to Crewe South was made in January 1961 where No 12019 was employed until January 1967, when it transferred to Rugby. A final reallocation was to Liverpool Speke Junction in April 1967, from where it was withdrawn on 14 October 1967 and sent to the Slag Reduction Co for cutting up. *R. H. G. Simpson*

12093	21C
12094	21C
12095	21B
12096	16A
12097	16A
12098	16A
12099	2B
12100	1A
12101	1A
12102	8G
12103	30A
12104	30A
12105	30A
12106	30A
12107	30A
12108	30A
12109	30A
12110	30A
12111	30A
12112	34G
12113	50B
12114	50B
12115	50B
12116	50B
12117	50B
12118	50B
12119	50B
12120	50B
12121	50B
12122	50B
12123	40B
12124	40B
12125	40B
12126	40B
12127	30A
12128	30A
12129	34G
12130	30A
12131	34G
12132	30A
12133	40B
12134	31A
12135	40B
12136	31B
12137	34G
12138	34G

LNER/English Electric 0-6-0 Shunter

15000	31B
15001	31B
15002	31B
15003	31B
15004	34E

GWR/Hawthorn Leslie/English Electric 0-6-0 Shunter

15100	82C
15101	CED
15102	CED
15103	CED
15104	CED
15105	CED
15106	CED

SR/English Electric 0-6-0 Shunter

15201	75C
15202	73C
15203	75C

Class 12 BR/English Electric 0-6-0 Shunter

15211	75C
15212	75C
15213	75C
15214	71A
15215	75C
15216	73C
15217	73C
15218	73C
15219	73C
15220	73F
15221	73C
15222	73C
15223	73C
15224	73F
15225	73C
15226	73C
15227	73F
15228	73F
15229	73F
15230	82B
15231	71A
15232	71A
15233	71A
15234	71A
15235	71A
15236	71A

LMS-built Class 11 0-6-0 diesel shunter No 12039 is at Birmingham Saltley shed in April 1962. Originally numbered 7126, it went new to Saltley in August 1947 and remained until September 1966 when it became a Crewe Works shunter. In December 1967 it had a short stay of one month at Llandudno Junction before returning to Crewe, this time to the diesel depot, from where it was withdrawn on 19 October 1968. It was stored at Crewe South and Bescot until January 1970, when it was cut up on site at Bescot by Cashmore's. *R. H. G. Simpson*

Ex-LNER 0-6-0 diesel shunter No 15002 is at Doncaster shed in October 1964 after a visit to the works. Built at Doncaster Works, it entered traffic as No 8002 at Stratford on 22 March 1945, moving to March the following June for hump shunting duties in the new Whitemoor yards. Here it remained until January 1966 when a move to Crewe South on the LMR was sanctioned. No 15002 was withdrawn from Crewe on 5 August 1967 and after storage at Crewe, Stafford and Bescot until around August 1968 was sold to King's of Norwich for scrap. *Pictorail*

Built at Swindon Works in May 1948, 0-6-0 diesel shunter No 15102 was first allocated to Old Oak Common and moved to Cardiff East Dock in November 1958, where it is seen in this view in May 1962. A series of moves to other South Wales sheds then took place until April 1966, when it was transferred to Stourbridge Junction and then in April 1967 to Bescot. Withdrawn on 22 July 1967 after storage at Derby, it was sent to the Steelbreaking & Dismantling Co at Chesterfield in September 1968 for scrap. *G. W. Sharpem*

Ex-Southern Railway 0-6-0 diesel shunter No 15202 is at Hither Green shed in April 1958. Originally numbered S2, it dated from September 1937 when it was built at Ashford Works. Its first allocation was Norwood Junction. Hither Green was allocated No 15202 in October 1956 and then it was moved to Ashford in November 1963, from where it was withdrawn on 13 December 1964. Cashmore's at Newport carried out the cutting up in November 1966. *P. H. Groom*

Class 12 0-6-0 diesel shunter No 15234 is on shunting duties at Eastleigh in May 1963. Built at Ashford Works, it was first allocated to Hither Green in December 1951, moving to Eastleigh in March 1955, where it remained until withdrawn on 22 December 1968 and was cut up at Swindon Works in July 1969. *G. W. Sharpe*

British Railways Electric Locomotive Allocations at 1 January 1962

Class 81 BRC&W/BTH Bo-Bo	
E3001	LMW
E3002	LMW
E3003	LMW
E3004	LMW
E3005	LMW
E3006	LMW
E3007	LMW
E3008	LMW
E3009	LMW
E3010	LMW
E3011	LMW
E3012	LMW
E3013	LMW
E3014	LMW
E3015	LMW
E3016	LMW
E3017	LMW
E3018	LMW
E3019	LMW
E3020	LMW
E3021	LMW
E3022	LMW

Class 83 North British Locomotive Co/GEC Bo-Bo	
E3024	LMW
E3025	LMW
E3026	LMW
E3027	LMW
E3028	LMW
E3029	LMW
E3030	LMW
E3031	LMW
E3032	LMW
E3033	LMW
E3034	LMW
E3035	LMW

Class 84 North British Locomotive Co/GEC Bo-Bo	
E3036	LMW
E3037	LMW
E3038	LMW
E3039	LMW
E3040	LMW
E3041	LMW
E3042	LMW
E3043	LMW
E3044	LMW
E3045	LMW

Class 82 Metropolitan-Vickers Bo-Bo	
E3046	LMW
E3047	LMW
E3048	LMW
E3049	LMW
E3050	LMW
E3051	LMW
E3052	LMW
E3054	LMW

Class 85 BR/English Electric Bo-Bo	
E3056	LMW
E3057	LMW
E3058	LMW
E3059	LMW
E3060	LMW
E3061	LMW
E3062	LMW
E3063	LMW
E3064	LMW
E3065	LMW

Class 83 North British Locomotive Co/GEC Bo-Bo	
E3303	LMW
E3304	LMW

Class 71 BR/English Electric Bo-Bo	
E5000	73A
E5001	73A
E5002	73A
E5003	73A
E5004	73A
E5005	73A
E5006	73A
E5007	73A
E5008	73A
E5009	73A
E5010	73A
E5011	73A
E5012	73A
E5013	73A
E5014	73A
E5015	73A
E5016	73A
E5017	73A
E5018	73A
E5019	73A
E5020	73A
E5021	73A
E5022	73A
E5023	73A

Class 70 SR/English Electric Co-Co	
20001	73A
20002	73A
20003	73A

Class 76 LNER/BR Bo-Bo	
26000*	9H
26001	9H
26002	9H
26003	9H
26004	9H
26005	9H
26006	9H
26007	9H
26008	9H
26009	9H
26010	9H
26011	9H
26012	9H
26013	9H
26014	9H
26015	9H
26016	9H
26017	9H
26018	9H
26019	9H
26020	9H
26021	9H
26022	9H
26023	9H
26024	9H
26025	9H
26026	9H
26027	9H
26028	9H
26029	9H
26030	9H
26031	9H
26032	9H
26033	9H
26034	9H
26035	9H
26036	9H
26037	9H
26038	9H
26039	9H
26040	9H
26041	9H
26042	9H
26043	9H
26044	9H
26045	9H
26046*	9H
26047*	9H
26048*	9H
26049*	9H
26050*	9H
26051*	9H
26052*	9H
26053*	9H
26054*	9H
26055*	9H
26056*	9H
26057*	9H

Class ES1 NER Bo-Bo	
26500	52B
26501	52B

Class 77 BR Co-Co	
27000*	9H
27001*	9H
27002*	9H
27003*	9H
27004*	9H
27005*	9H
27006*	9H

Class 83 Bo-Bo No E3030 approaches Manchester Piccadilly in November 1960, a month after entering service. Renumbered 83007 in December 1972, it was withdrawn on 17 July 1983 and scrapped at the Leicester yard of Vic Berry at the end of 1984. *R. H. G. Simpson*

Class 71 Bo-Bo electric No E5012 is seen at St Mary Cray Junction in March 1962 on a mixed freight. Built at Doncaster Works, E5012 entered service on 27 October 1959 at Stewarts Lane, and moved to Ashford for maintenance in August 1966. Withdrawn on 26 November 1977 as 71012, it was cut up at Cashmore's at Newport at the end of October 1978. *G. W. Sharpe*

Class 76 electric Bo-Bo No 26023 is at Crewe Works for repair in 1963. Built at Gorton Works, it entered traffic on 20 September 1951 and spent its days on the Woodhead route. Renumbered 76023 in September 1973, it was withdrawn from Reddish depot on 20 July 1981. Stored until March 1983, it then went to C. F. Booth's yard at Rotherham for scrap. *R. H. G. Simpson*

Class 77 electric Co-Co No 27002 *Aurora* is at Manchester Piccadilly in 1960. Built at Gorton Works, it entered traffic on 18 May 1954 and was withdrawn on 5 October 1968. It was then exported to Holland for use on the Dutch State Railways and renumbered 1506, where it continued in service until 30 August 1984. *R. H. G. Simpson*

British Railways Diesel Multiple-Units Allocations at 1 January 1962

Class 114 Motor Brake Second. Built by BR Derby Works. Two-car Units

No	Shed
E50000	40A
E50001	40A
E50002	40A
E50003	40A
E50004	40A
E50005	40A
E50006	40A
E50007	40A
E50008	40A
E50009	40A
E50010	40A
E50011	40A
E50012	40A
E50013	40A
E50014	41A
E50015	41A
E50016	41A
E50017	41A
E50018	41A
E50019	41A
E50020	41A
E50021	41A
E50022	41A
E50023	41A
E50024	41A
E50025	40A
E50026	41A
E50027	41A
E50028	41A
E50029	41A
E50030	41A
E50031	41A
E50032	40A
E50033	41A
E50034	41A
E50035	41A
E50036	41A
E50037	41A
E50038	40A
E50039	40A
E50040	40A
E50041	40A
E50042	40A
E50043	40A
E50044	40A
E50045	40A
E50046	40A
E50047	40A
E50048	40A
E50049	40A

Class 116 Motor Brake Second. Built by BR Derby Works. Three-car Suburban Units

No	Shed
W50050	84E
W50051	84E
W50052	84E
W50053	84E
W50054	84E
W50055	84E
W50056	84E
W50057	84E
W50058	84E
W50059	84E
W50060	84E
W50061	84E
W50062	84E
W50063	84E
W50064	84E
W50065	84E

Class 116 DMU Nos W50074/W59024/W50116 climbs towards Old Hill Tunnel on the 10.42am Kidderminster to Birmingham Snow Hill on Thursday 30 August 1962. New in August 1957, this unit was not withdrawn until 1987. *M. Mensing*

W50066 84E
W50067 84E
W50068 84E
W50069 84E
W50070 84E
W50071 84E
W50072 84E
W50073 84E
W50074 84E
W50075 84E
W50076 84E
W50077 84E
W50078 84E
W50079 CAT
W50080 CAT
W50081 CAT
W50082 CAT
W50083 CAT
W50084 CAT
W50085 CAT
W50086 CAT
W50087 CAT
W50088 CAT
W50089 CAT
W50090 CAT
W50091 CAT

Class 116 Motor Second. Built by BR Derby Works. Three-car Suburban Units

W50092 84E
W50093 84E
W50094 84E
W50095 84E
W50096 84E
W50097 84E
W50098 84E
W50099 84E
W50100 84E
W50101 84E
W50102 84E
W50103 84E
W50104 84E
W50105 84E
W50106 84E
W50107 84E
W50108 84E
W50109 84E
W50110 84E
W50111 84E
W50112 84E
W50113 84E
W50114 84E
W50115 84E
W50116 84E
W50117 84E
W50118 84E
W50119 84E
W50120 84E
W50121 CAT
W50122 CAT
W50123 CAT
W50124 CAT
W50126 CAT
W50127 CAT
W50128 CAT
W50129 CAT
W50130 CAT
W50131 CAT
W50132 CAT
W50133 CAT

Class 111 Motor Brake Second. Built by Metropolitan-Cammell. Two-car Units

M50134 24F
M50135 9D
M50136 9D
M50137 24F

Class 101 Motor Composite. Built by Metropolitan-Cammell. Four-car Units

E50138 52J
E50139 52J
E50140 52J
E50141 52J
E50142 52J
E50143 52J
E50144 52J
E50145 52J
E50146 52J
E50147 52J
E50148 52J
E50149 52J
E50150 55H
E50151 55H

Class 101 Motor Brake Second. Built by Metropolitan-Cammell. Two-car Units

E50152 56G
E50153 56G
E50154 56G
E50155 56G
E50156 56G
E50157 56G

Class 101 Motor Composite. Built by Metropolitan-Cammell. Two-car Units

E50158 56G
E50159 56G
E50160 56G
E50161 56G
E50162 56G
E50163 56G

Class 101 Motor Brake Second. Built by Metropolitan-Cammell. Two-car Units

E50164 56G
E50165 56G
E50166 56G
E50167 56G

Class 101 Motor Composite. Built by Metropolitan-Cammell. Two-car Units

E50168 56G
E50169 56G
E50170 56G
E50171 56G

Class 101 Motor Composite. Built by Metropolitan-Cammell. Four-car Units

E50172 51A
E50174 51A
E50175 51A
E50176 51A
E50177 51A
E50178 51A
E50179 51A
E50180 51A
E50181 51A
E50182 51A
E50183 51A
E50184 51A
E50185 51A
E50186 51A
E50187 51A
E50188 51A
E50189 51A
E50190 50C
E50191 50C
E50192 51A
E50193 51A
E50194 51A
E50195 51A
E50196 51A
E50197 51A

Class 101 Motor Brake Second. Built by Metropolitan-Cammell. Two-car Units

E50198 52J
E50199 52J
E50200 51A
E50201 52J
E50202 51A
E50203 51A
E50204 52J
E50205 51A
E50206 51A
E50207 52J
E50208 51A
E50209 51A
E50210 52J
E50211 51A
E50212 52J
E50213 52J
E50214 51A
E50215 51A
E50216 52J
E50217 52J
E50218 52J
E50219 52J
E50220 52J
E50221 52J
E50222 52J

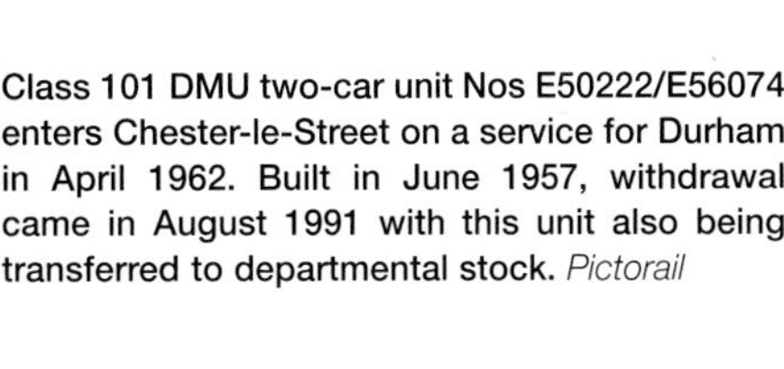
Class 101 DMU two-car unit Nos E50222/E56074 enters Chester-le-Street on a service for Durham in April 1962. Built in June 1957, withdrawal came in August 1991 with this unit also being transferred to departmental stock. *Pictorail*

E50223 52J
E50224 51A
E50225 52J
E50226 52J
E50227 52J
E50228 52J
E50229 52J
E50230 52J
E50231 52J
E50232 52J
E50233 52J

Class 101 Motor Composite. Built by Metropolitan-Cammell. Four-car Units

E50234 55H
E50235 55H
E50236 55H
E50237 55H
E50238 52J
E50239 52J
E50240 55H
E50241 55H
E50242 55H
E50243 55H
E50244 55H
E50245 55H

Class 101 Motor Brake Second. Built by Metropolitan-Cammell. Two-car Units

E50246 52J
E50247 52J
E50248 50C

Class 105 Motor Brake Second. Built by Cravens. Two-car Units

E50249 51A

Class 101 Motor Brake Second. Built by Metropolitan-Cammell. Two-car Units

E50250 51A
E50251 51A
E50252 51A
E50253 51A
E50254 51A
E50255 51A
E50256 51A
E50257 51A
E50258 51A
E50259 51A

Class 101 Motor Composite. Built by Metropolitan-Cammell. Two-car Units

E50260 51A
E50261 51A
E50262 51A
E50263 51A
E50264 51A
E50265 51A
E50266 51A
E50267 51A
E50268 51A
E50269 51A

Class 111 Motor Composite. Built by Metropolitan-Cammell. Three-car Units

E50270 55H
E50271 55H
E50272 55H
E50273 56G
E50274 56G
E50275 56G
E50276 56G
E50277 56G
E50278 56G
E50279 56G

Class 111 Motor Brake Second. Built by Metropolitan-Cammell. Three-car Units

E50280 55H
E50281 55H
E50282 55H
E50283 56G
E50284 56G
E50285 56G
E50286 56G
E50287 56G
E50288 56G
E50289 56G
E50290 51A
E50291 51A
E50292 51A

Class 101 Motor Brake Second. Built by Metropolitan-Cammell. Two-car Units

E50293 51A
E50294 51A
E50295 51A
E50296 52J

Class 101 Motor Brake Second. Built by Metropolitan-Cammell. Three-car Units

M50303 21E
M50304 21E
M50305 21E
M50306 21E
M50307 21E
M50308 21E
M50309 21E
M50310 21E
M50311 21E
M50312 21E
M50313 21E
M50314 21E
M50315 21E
M50316 21E
M50317 21E
M50318 21E
M50319 18A
M50320 21E

Class 101 Motor Composite. Built by Metropolitan-Cammell. Three-car Units

M50321 21E
M50322 21E
M50323 21E
M50324 21E
M50325 21E
M50326 21E
M50327 21E
M50328 21E
M50329 21E
M50330 21E
M50331 21E
M50332 21E
M50333 21E
M50334 21E
M50335 21E
M50336 21E
M50337 18A
M50338 21E

Class 100 Motor Brake Second. Built by Gloucester RC&W Co. Two-car Units

SC50339 64H
SC50340 64H
SC50341 64H
SC50342 64H
SC50343 66C
SC50344 66C
SC50345 64H
SC50346 64H
SC50347 64H
M50348 21F
M50349 21F
M50350 21F
M50351 21F
M50352 21F
M50353 21F
M50354 21F
M50355 21F
M50356 21F
M50357 21F
M50358 21F

Class 106 Motor Brake Second. Built by Cravens. Two-car Units

E50359 50C
E50360 50C
E50361 50C
E50362 50C
E50363 50C
E50364 50C
E50365 50C
E50366 50C
E50367 50C
E50368 50C
E50369 50C
E50370 50C

Class 105 Motor Brake Second. Built by Cravens. Two-car Units

E50371 50C
E50372 50C
E50373 50C
E50374 50C
E50375 50C
E50376 50C
E50377 50C
E50378 50C
E50379 50C
E50380 50C
E50381 50C
E50382 50C
E50383 50C
E50384 50C
E50385 50C
E50386 50C
E50387 50C
E50388 50C
E50389 50C
M50390 18A
M50391 18A
M50392 18A
M50393 18A
M50394 18A

Class 103 Motor Brake Second. Built by Park Royal Vehicles. Two-car Units

M50395 21F
M50396 21F
M50397 21F
M50398 21F
M50399 21F
M50400 21F
M50401 21F
M50402 21F
M50403 21F
M50404 21F
M50405 21F
M50406 21F
M50407 21F
M50408 21F
M50409 21F
M50410 21F
M50411 1C
M50412 1C
M50413 1C
M50414 1C

Class 109 Motor Brake Second. Built by D. Wickham & Co Ltd. Two-car Units

E50416 31A
E50417 31A
E50418 31A

Class 104 Motor Brake Second. Built by Birmingham RC&W Co. Three-car Units

M50420 9D
M50421 9D
M50422 9D
M50423 9A

Class 104 Motor Composite. Built by Birmingham RC&W Co. Three-car Units

M50424 9D
M50425 9D
M50426 9D
M50427 9A

Class 104 Motor Brake Second. Built by Birmingham RC&W Co. Three-car Units

M50428 9D
M50429 9D
M50430 9D
M50431 9D
M50432 9D
M50433 9D
M50434 9D
M50435 9D
M50436 9D
M50437 9D
M50438 9D
M50439 5A
M50440 5A
M50441 18A
M50442 5D
M50443 5D
M50444 5D
M50445 5D
M50446 5D
M50447 5D
M50448 5D
M50449 5D
M50450 5D
M50451 5D
M50452 5D
M50453 5D
M50454 5D
M50455 5D
M50456 5D
M50457 5D
M50458 5D
M50459 5D
M50460 5D
M50461 5D
M50462 9D
M50463 9D
M50464 9D
M50465 5B
M50466 5B
M50467 5B
M50468 5B

A Class 104 DMU three-car unit runs into Cheadle Hulme on a service from Stoke-on-Trent, through Macclesfield, to Manchester in July 1959. Introduced in 1957, many of the type were withdrawn in the latter part of the 1980s and early 1990s. *Author's collection*

M50469 5B
M50470 5B
M50471 5B
M50472 5B
M50473 5B
M50474 5B
M50475 18A
M50476 18A
M50477 18A
M50478 18A
M50479 18A

Class 104 Motor Composite. Built by Birmingham RC&W Co. Three-car Units

M50480 9D
M50481 9D
M50482 9D
M50483 9D
M50484 9D
M50485 9D
M50486 9D
M50487 9D
M50488 9D
M50489 9D
M50490 9D
M50491 5A
M50492 5A
M50493 18A
M50494 5D
M50495 5D
M50496 5D
M50497 5D
M50498 5D
M50499 5D
M50500 5D
M50501 5D
M50502 5D
M50503 5D
M50504 5D
M50505 5D
M50506 5D
M50507 5D
M50508 5D
M50509 5D
M50510 5D
M50511 5D
M50512 5D
M50513 5D
M50514 9D
M50515 9D
M50516 9D
M50517 5B
M50518 5B
M50519 5B
M50520 5B
M50521 5B
M50522 5B
M50523 5B
M50524 5B
M50525 5B
M50526 5B
M50527 18A
M50528 18A
M50529 18A
M50530 18A
M50531 18A

Class 104 Motor Brake Second. Built by Birmingham RC&W Co. Two-car Units

M50532 18A
M50533 18A
M50534 21F
M50535 21F
M50536 5B
M50537 5B
M50538 5B
M50539 21F
M50540 21F
M50541 21F

Class 104 Motor Composite. Built by Birmingham RC&W Co. Four-car Units

E50542 55H
E50543 55H
E50544 55H
E50545 55H
E50546 55H
E50547 55H
E50548 55H
E50549 55H
E50550 50C
E50551 50C
E50552 55H
E50553 50C
E50554 50C
E50555 55H
E50556 52J
E50557 55H
E50558 50C
E50559 50C
E50560 50C
E50561 50C
E50562 50C
E50563 55H
E50564 55H
E50565 55H
E50566 55H
E50567 55H
E50568 55H
E50569 55H
E50570 55H
E50571 50C
E50572 50C
E50573 55H
E50574 50C
E50575 50C
E50576 55H
E50577 52J
E50578 55H
E50579 50C
E50580 50C
E50581 50C
E50582 50C
E50583 50C
E50584 55H
E50585 50C
E50586 50C
E50587 55H
E50588 51A
E50589 55H
E50590 50C
E50591 50C
E50592 55H
E50593 51A

Class 104 Motor Brake Second. Built by Birmingham RC&W Co. Two-car Units

E50594 55H
E50595 50C
E50596 52J
E50597 52J
E50598 51A

Class 108 Motor Brake Second. Built by BR Derby Works. Two- or Three-car Units

E50599	55F
E50600	55F
E50601	55F
E50602	55F
E50603	55F
E50604	55F
E50605	55F
E50606	55F
E50607	55F
E50608	55F
E50609	55F
E50610	55F
E50611	55F
E50612	55F
E50613	55F
E50614	55F
E50615	55F
E50616	55F
E50617	55F
E50618	55F
E50619	55F
E50620	51A
E50621	51A
E50622	51A
E50623	52J
E50624	52J
M50625	6A
M50626	6A
M50627	6A
M50628	8H
M50629	8H

Class 108 Motor Composite. Built by BR Derby Works. Three- or Four-car Units

E50630	52J
E50631	52J
E50632	50C
E50633	50C
E50634	50C
E50635	50C
E50636	52J
E50637	52J
E50638	52J
E50639	52J
E50640	52J
E50641	52J
E50642	52J
E50643	51A
E50644	51A
E50645	51A
E50646	51A

Class 120 Motor Second. Built by BR Swindon Works. Cross-Country Three-car Units

W50647	88A
W50648	88A
W50649	88A
W50650	84E
W50651	84E
W50652	84E
W50653	88A
W50654	84E
W50655	84E
W50656	84E
W50657	88A
W50658	88A
W50659	88A
W50660	88A
W50661	84E
W50662	88A
W50663	88A
W50664	88A
W50665	88A
W50666	88A
W50667	88A
W50668	88A
W50669	88A
W50670	88A
W50671	88A
W50672	88A
W50673	88A
W50674	84E
W50675	88A
W50676	88A
W50677	84E
W50678	84E
W50679	88A
W50680	84E
W50681	88A
W50682	88A
W50683	88A
W50684	88A
W50685	88A
W50686	88A
W50687	82B
W50688	82B
W50689	82B
W50690	82B
W50691	82B
W50692	82B
W50693	82B
W50694	82B
W50695	82B

Class 120 Motor Brake Composite. Built by BR Swindon Works. Cross-Country Three-car Units

W50696	88A
W50697	88A
W50698	88A
W50699	88A
W50700	88A
W50701	84E
W50702	88A
W50703	84E
W50704	84E
W50705	88A
W50706	88A
W50707	88A
W50708	84E
W50709	84E
W50710	84E
W50711	88A
W50712	88A
W50713	84E
W50714	88A
W50715	88A
W50716	88A
W50717	88A
W50718	88A
W50719	88A
W50720	88A
W50721	88A
W50722	88A
W50723	88A
W50724	88A
W50725	84E
W50726	88A
W50727	88A
W50728	84E
W50729	88A
W50730	84E
W50731	84E
W50732	82B
W50733	88A
W50734	88A
W50735	88A
W50736	88A
W50737	82B
W50738	82B
W50739	82B
W50740	82B
W50741	82B
W50742	82B
W50743	82B
W50744	82B

Class 101 Motor Composite. Built by Metropolitan-Cammell. Three-car Units

E50745	51A
E50746	51A
E50747	51A

Class 101 Motor Composite. Built by Metropolitan-Cammell. Four-car Units

E50748	51A
E50749	51A
E50750	51A
E50751	51A

Class 105 Motor Brake Second. Built by Cravens. Three-car Units

M50752	18A
M50753	18A
M50754	18A
M50755	18A
M50756	18A
M50757	18A
M50758	18A
M50759	18A
M50760	18A
M50761	18A
M50762	18A
M50763	18A
M50764	18A
M50765	18A
M50766	18A
M50767	18A
M50768	18A
M50769	18A
M50770	18A

Class 105 Motor Brake Second. Built by Cravens. Two-car Units

M50771	26A
M50772	26A
M50773	26A
M50774	26A
M50775	26A
M50776	26A
M50777	26A
M50778	26A
M50779	26A
M50780	26A
M50781	26A
M50782	26A
M50783	26A
M50784	26A

Class 105 Motor Composite. Built by Cravens. Three-car Units

M50785	18A
M50786	18A
M50787	18A
M50788	18A
M50789	18A
M50790	18A
M50791	18A
M50792	18A
M50793	18A
M50794	18A
M50795	18A
M50796	18A
M50797	18A
M50798	18A
M50799	18A
M50800	18A
M50801	18A
M50802	18A
M50803	18A

Class 105 Motor Composite. Built by Cravens. Two-car Units

M50804	26A
M50805	26A
M50806	26A
M50807	26A
M50809	26A
M50810	26A
M50811	26A
M50812	26A
M50813	26A
M50814	26A
M50815	26A
M50816	26A
M50817	26A

Class 116 Motor Brake Second. Built by BR Derby Works. Three-car Suburban Units

W50818	CAT
W50819	CAT
W50820	CAT
W50821	CAT
W50822	CAT
W50823	CAT
W50824	CAT
W50825	CAT
W50826	CAT
W50827	CAT
W50828	CAT
W50829	CAT
W50830	CAT
W50831	84E
W50832	CAT
W50833	84E
W50834	CAT
W50835	CAT
W50836	CAT
W50837	CAT
W50838	CAT
W50839	CAT
W50840	CAT
W50841	CAT
W50842	CAT
W50843	CAT
W50844	CAT
W50845	CAT
W50846	CAT
W50847	CAT
W50848	CAT
W50849	CAT
W50850	CAT
W50851	CAT
W50852	CAT
W50853	CAT
W50854	CAT
W50855	CAT
W50856	CAT
W50857	CAT
W50858	CAT
W50859	82B
W50860	82B
W50861	82B
W50862	CAT
W50863	CAT
W50864	CAT
W50865	CAT
W50866	CAT
W50867	CAT
W50868	CAT
W50869	CAT
W50870	CAT

A Class 120 DMU three-car Cross-Country set, dating from 1958, has just arrived at Bristol Temple Meads in April 1961. Many of these units were later transferred to the LMR and based at Derby Etches Park for services in the Midlands. Withdrawal of these units commenced in the 1980s. *H. D. Ramsey/Initial Photographics*

A Class 105 Cravens DMU three-car unit runs into the staggered platforms at Wigston South on a Leicester to Rugby working in July 1961, with only five months to go before the line was closed. Introduced in 1957/8, withdrawal of the class commenced in 1980. *Author's collection*

Class 116 Motor Second. Built by BR Derby Works. Three-car Suburban Units

W50871	CAT
W50872	CAT
W50873	CAT
W50874	CAT
W50875	CAT
W50876	CAT
W50877	CAT
W50878	CAT
W50879	CAT
W50880	CAT
W50881	CAT
W50882	CAT
W50883	CAT
W50884	84E
W50885	CAT
W50886	84E
W50887	CAT
W50888	CAT
W50889	CAT
W50890	CAT
W50891	CAT
W50892	CAT
W50893	CAT
W50894	CAT
W50895	CAT
W50896	CAT
W50897	CAT
W50898	CAT
W50899	CAT
W50900	CAT
W50901	CAT
W50902	CAT
W50903	CAT
W50904	CAT
W50905	CAT
W50906	CAT
W50907	CAT
W50908	CAT
W50909	CAT
W50910	CAT
W50911	CAT
W50912	82B
W50913	82B
W50914	82B
W50915	CAT
W50916	CAT
W50917	CAT
W50918	CAT
W50919	CAT
W50920	CAT
W50921	CAT
W50922	CAT
W50923	CAT

Class 108. Motor Brake Second. Built by BR Derby Works. Two-car Units

M50924	6A
M50925	6A
M50926	6A
M50927	6A
M50928	6A
M50929	6A
M50930	6A
M50931	6A
M50932	6A
M50933	6A
M50934	6A
M50935	6A

Class 126 Motor Second. Built by BR Swindon Works. Six-car Inter-City Units

SC50936	67C

Class 108 Motor Brake Second. Built by BR Derby Works. Two-car Units

M50938	1E
M50939	1E
M50940	1E
M50941	1E
M50942	1E
M50943	1E
M50944	1E
M50945	1E
M50946	1E
M50947	8H
M50948	9E
M50949	9E
M50950	9E
M50951	9H
M50952	9E
M50953	9E
M50954	9E
M50955	9E
M50956	9E
M50957	9E
M50958	9E
M50959	9H
M50960	9E
M50961	9E
M50962	9D
M50963	9D
M50964	24F
M50965	6A
M50966	6A
M50967	6A
M50968	6A
M50969	18A
M50970	6A
M50971	6A
M50972	6A
M50973	8H
M50974	8H
M50975	8H
M50976	8H
M50977	8H
M50978	6A
M50979	18A
M50980	18A
M50981	18A
M50982	5D
M50983	18A
M50984	18A
M50985	6A
M50986	18A
M50987	6A

Class 125 Motor Second. Built by BR Derby Works. Three-car Suburban Units

E50988	30A
E50989	30A
E50990	30A
E50991	30A
E50992	30A
E50993	30A
E50994	30A
E50995	30A
E50996	30A
E50997	30A
E50998	30A
E50999	30A
E51000	30A
E51001	30A
E51002	30A
E51003	30A
E51004	30A
E51005	30A
E51006	30A
E51007	30A

Class 126 Motor Second. Built by BR Swindon Works. Six-car Inter-City Units

SC51008	67C
SC51009	67C
SC51010	67C
SC51011	67C
SC51012	67C
SC51013	67C
SC51014	67C
SC51015	67C
SC51016	67C
SC51017	67C
SC51018	67C
SC51019	67C
SC51020	67C
SC51021	67C
SC51022	67C
SC51023	67C
SC51024	67C
SC51025	67C
SC51026	67C
SC51027	67C
SC51028	67C
SC51029	67C

Class 126 Motor Brake Second Built by BR Swindon Works. Six-car Inter-City Units

SC51030	67C
SC51031	67C
SC51032	67C
SC51033	67C
SC51034	67C
SC51035	67C
SC51036	67C
SC51037	67C
SC51038	67C
SC51039	67C
SC51040	67C
SC51041	67C
SC51042	67C
SC51043	67C
SC51044	67C
SC51045	67C
SC51046	67C
SC51047	67C
SC51048	67C
SC51049	67C
SC51050	67C
SC51051	67C

Class 119 Motor Brake Composite. Built by Gloucester RC&W Co. Three-car Cross-Country Units

W51052	82B
W51053	82B
W51054	88A
W51055	88A
W51056	88A
W51057	88A
W51058	88A
W51059	88A
W51060	82B
W51061	82B
W51062	82B
W51063	82B
W51064	82B
W51065	82B
W51066	82B
W51067	82B
W51068	82B
W51069	82B
W51070	82B
W51071	84E
W51072	84E
W51073	88A
W51074	88A
W51075	88A
W51076	84E
W51077	82B
W51078	88A
W51079	88A

Class 119 Motor Second. Built by Gloucester RC&W Co. Three-car Cross-Country Units

W51080	82B
W51081	82B
W51082	88A
W51083	88A
W51084	88A
W51085	88A
W51086	88A
W51087	88A
W51088	82B
W51089	82B
W51090	82B
W51091	82B
W51092	82B
W51093	82B
W51094	82B
W51095	82B
W51096	82B
W51097	82B
W51098	82B
W51099	84E
W51100	84E
W51101	88A
W51102	88A
W51103	88A
W51104	84E
W51105	82B
W51106	88A
W51107	88A

Class 100 Motor Brake Second. Built by Gloucester RC&W Co. Two-car Units

SC51108	64H
SC51109	64H
SC51110	64H
SC51111	64H
SC51112	64H
SC51113	66C
SC51114	64H
SC51115	64H
SC51116	64H
SC51117	64H
SC51118	64H
SC51119	66C
SC51120	64H
SC51121	64H
SC51122	64H
SC51123	66C
SC51124	64H
SC51125	64H
SC51126	66C
SC51127	64H

Class 116 Motor Brake Second. Built by BR Derby Works. Three-car Suburban Units

W51128	81D
W51129	82B
W51130	82B
W51131	82B
W51132	CAT
W51133	82B
W51134	82B
W51135	82B
W51136	82B
W51137	82B
W51138	82B
W51139	CAT
W51140	CAT

Class 100 DMU with No SC51115 leading and SC56307 trailing enters Edinburgh Waverley station in August 1960. New in November 1957, withdrawal came in October 1972 with the unit then being used for a number of years as departmental stock. *R. H. G. Simpson*

Class 116 Motor Second. Built by BR Derby Works. Three-car Suburban Units

W51141	81D
W51142	82B
W51143	82B
W51144	82B
W51145	CAT
W51146	82B
W51147	82B
W51148	82B
W51149	82B
W51150	82B
W51151	82B
W51152	CAT
W51153	CAT

Class 125 Motor Brake Second. Built by BR Derby Works. Three-car Suburban Units

E51154	30A
E51155	30A
E51156	30A
E51157	30A
E51158	30A
E51159	30A
E51160	30A
E51161	30A
E51162	30A
E51163	30A
E51164	30A
E51165	30A
E51166	30A
E51167	30A
E51168	30A
E51169	30A
E51170	30A
E51171	30A
E51172	30A
E51173	30A

Class 101 Motor Brake Second. Built by Metropolitan-Cammell. Two-car Units

M51174	21E
M51175	21E
M51176	21E
M51177	21E
M51178	21E
M51179	21E
M51180	21E
M51181	21E
M51182	21E
M51183	21E
M51184	21E
M51185	21E
M51186	21E
M51187	21E
M51188	21E
M51189	21F
M51190	21F
M51191	21F
M51192	21F
M51193	24E
M51194	24E
M51195	24E
M51196	26A
M51197	26A
M51198	24E
M51199	24E
M51200	24E
M51201	24E
M51202	26A
M51203	24F
E51204	55H
E51205	55H
E51206	55F
E51207	55H
E51208	50C
E51209	50C
E51210	55F
E51211	55F
E51212	55F
E51213	55H
E51214	55H
E51215	50C
E51216	50C
E51217	52J
E51218	55H
E51219	51A
E51220	51A
E51221	52J
E51222	55H
E51223	55H
SC51224	64H
SC51225	62B
SC51226	66C
SC51227	66C
SC51228	66C
SC51229	66C
SC51230	66C
SC51231	64H
SC51232	66C
SC51233	66C
SC51234	66C
SC51235	66C
SC51236	66C
SC51237	66C
SC51238	62B
SC51239	62B
SC51240	62B
SC51241	62B
SC51242	62B
SC51243	62B
SC51244	62B
SC51245	62B
SC51246	62B
SC51247	62B
SC51248	64H
SC51249	62B
SC51250	62B
SC51251	62B
SC51252	62B
SC51253	62B

Class 105 Motor Brake Second. Built by Cravens. Two-car Units

E51254	34G
E51255	34G
E51256	34G
E51257	34G
E51258	34G
E51259	34G
E51260	34G
E51261	34G
E51262	34G
E51263	34G
E51264	34G
E51265	34G
E51266	34G
E51267	34G

Class 118 DMU Nos W51313/W59480/W51328 enter Devon at Saltash on a local to Plymouth with the driver preparing to release the single-line token to the signalman in May 1962. This unit was placed in traffic in July 1960 and withdrawn in August 1987. *Pictorail*

Class 105 Cravens DMU two-car unit Nos E51290/E56448 enters King's Cross on a working from Hitchin in May 1962. New in November 1958, the unit was withdrawn in January 1985. *R. H. G. Simpson*

E51268 34G
E51269 40A
E51270 40A
E51271 34G
E51272 34G
E51273 34G
E51274 31A
E51275 31A
E51276 31A
E51277 31A
E51278 31A
E51279 31A
E51280 31A
E51281 31A
E51282 31A
E51283 31A
E51284 31A
E51285 31A
E51286 31A
E51287 31A
E51288 31A
E51289 34G
E51290 34G
E51291 34G
E51292 34G
E51293 34G
E51294 34G
E51295 34G
E51296 34G
E51297 34G
E51298 40A
E51299 40A
E51300 34G
E51301 40A

Class 118 Motor Brake Second. Built by Birmingham RC&W Co. Three-car Suburban Units

W51302 83D
W51303 83D
W51304 83D
W51305 83D
W51306 83D
W51307 83D
W51308 83D
W51309 83D
W51310 83D
W51311 83D
W51312 83D
W51313 83D
W51314 83D
W51315 81D
W51316 81D

Class 118 Motor Second Built by Birmingham RC&W Co. Three-car Suburban Units

W51317 83D
W51318 83D
W51319 83D
W51320 83D
W51321 83D
W51322 83D
W51323 83D
W51324 83D
W51325 83D
W51326 83D
W51327 83D
W51328 83D
W51329 83D
W51330 81D
W51331 81D

Class 117 Motor Brake Second. Built by Pressed Steel Co. Three-car Suburban Units

W51332 81D
W51333 81D
W51334 81C
W51335 81D
W51336 81D
W51337 81D
W51338 81D
W51339 81C
W51340 81C
W51341 81C
W51342 81C
W51343 81D
W51344 81D
W51345 81D
W51346 81C
W51347 81C
W51348 81C
W51349 81C
W51350 81C
W51351 81D
W51352 81D
W51353 81D
W51354 81D
W51355 81D
W51356 81C
W51357 81C
W51358 81D
W51359 81C
W51360 81C
W51361 81C
W51362 81D
W51363 81D
W51364 81C
W51365 81C
W51366 81C
W51367 81D
W51368 81D
W51369 81D
W51370 81D
W51371 81C
W51372 81D
W51373 81C

Class 117 Motor Second. Built by Pressed Steel Co. Three-car Suburban Units

W51374 81D
W51375 81D
W51376 81C
W51377 81D
W51378 81D
W51379 81D
W51380 81D
W51381 81C
W51382 81C
W51383 81C
W51384 81C
W51385 81D
W51386 81D
W51387 81D
W51388 81C
W51389 81C
W51390 81C
W51391 81C
W51392 81C
W51393 81D
W51394 81D
W51395 81D
W51396 81D
W51397 81D
W51398 81C
W51399 81C
W51400 81D
W51401 81C
W51402 81C
W51403 81C
W51404 81D
W51405 81D
W51406 81C
W51407 81C
W51408 81C
W51409 81D
W51410 81D
W51411 81D
W51412 81D
W51413 81C
W51414 81D
W51415 81C

Class 108 Motor Brake Second. Built by BR Derby Works. Two-car Units

M51416 24F
M51417 6A
M51418 6A
M51419 6A
M51420 6A
M51421 6A
M51422 8H
M51423 8H
M51424 6A

Class 101 Motor Brake Second. Built by Metropolitan-Cammell. Two-car Units

E51425 56G
E51426 56G
E51427 56G
E51428 56G
E51429 56G
E51430 56G
E51431 56G
E51432 56G
E51433 56G
E51434 56G

Class 101 Motor Brake Second. Built by Metropolitan-Cammell. Three- and Four-car Units

E51435 52J
E51436 52J
E51437 52J
E51438 52J
E51439 52J
E51440 55H
E51441 52J
E51442 55H
E51443 52J
E51444 51A
SC51445 62B
SC51446 62B
SC51447 62B
SC51448 62B
SC51449 62B
SC51450 62B
SC51451 62B
SC51452 62B
SC51453 62B
SC51454 62B
SC51455 62B
SC51456 64H
SC51457 64H
SC51458 61A
SC51459 64H
SC51460 64H
SC51461 64H
SC51462 64H
SC51463 64H
SC51464 64H
SC51465 67C
SC51466 64H
SC51467 64H
SC51468 64H
SC51469 67C
SC51470 64H

Class 105 Motor Brake Second. Built by Cravens. Two-car Units

E51471 40A
E51472 40A
SC51473 61A
SC51474 61A
SC51475 61A
SC51476 61A
SC51477 61A
SC51478 61A
SC51479 61A
SC51480 61A
SC51481 61A
SC51482 66C
SC51483 66C
SC51484 66C
SC51485 66C
SC51486 66C
SC51487 66C
SC51488 66C
SC51489 66C
SC51490 61A
SC51491 66C
SC51492 66C
SC51493 61A
SC51494 66C

Class 101 Motor Composite. Built by Metropolitan-Cammell. Two-car Units

E51495 56G
E51496 56G
E51497 56G
E51498 56G
E51499 56G
E51500 56G
E51501 56G
E51502 56G
E51503 56G
E51504 56G

Class 101 Motor Composite. Built by Metropolitan-Cammell. Three- or Four-car Units

E51505 52J
E51506 52J
E51507 52J
E51508 52J
E51509 52J
E51510 55H
E51511 52J
E51512 55H
E51513 52J
E51514 51A
SC51515 62B
SC51516 62B
SC51517 62B
SC51518 62B
SC51519 62B
SC51520 62B
SC51521 62B
SC51522 62B
SC51523 62B
SC51524 62B
SC51525 62B
SC51526 64H
SC51527 64H
SC51528 61A
SC51529 64H
SC51530 64H
SC51531 64H
SC51532 64H
SC51533 64H
SC51534 64H
SC51535 67C
SC51536 64H
SC51537 64H
SC51538 64H
SC51539 67C
SC51540 64H

Class 111 Motor Brake Second. Built by Metropolitan-Cammell. Three-car Units

E51541	55H
E51542	55H
E51543	55H
E51544	55H
E51545	55H
E51546	55H
E51547	55H

Class 111 Motor Brake Second. Built by Metropolitan-Cammell. Two-car Units

E51548	55H
E51549	55H
E51550	55H

Class 111 Motor Composite. Built by Metropolitan-Cammell. Three-car Units

E51551	55H
E51552	55H
E51553	55H
E51554	55H
E51555	55H
E51556	55H
E51557	55H

Class 111 Motor Composite. Built by Metropolitan-Cammell. Two-car Units

E51558	55H
E51559	55H
E51560	55H

Class 108 Motor Composite. Built by BR Derby Works. Two-car Units

M51561	6A
M51562	6A
M51563	6A
M51564	6A
M51565	6A
M51566	6A
M51567	6A
M51568	6A
M51569	6A
M51570	6A
M51571	6A
M51572	6A

Class 120 Motor Brake Composite. Built by BR Swindon Works. Three-car Cross-Country Units

W51573	84E
W51574	84E
W51575	84E
W51576	84E
W51577	84E
W51578	84E
W51579	84E
W51580	84E
W51581	84E
W51582	84E
W51583	84E
W51584	84E
W51585	84E
W51586	84E
W51587	84E
W51588	84E
W51589	84E
W51590	84E

Class 127 Motor Brake Second. Built by BR Derby Works. Four-car Suburban Units

M51591	14A
M51592	14A
M51593	14A
M51594	14A
M51595	14A
M51596	14A
M51597	14A
M51598	14A
M51599	14A
M51600	14A
M51601	14A
M51602	14A
M51603	14A
M51604	14A
M51605	14A
M51606	14A
M51607	14A
M51608	14A
M51609	14A
M51610	14A
M51611	14A
M51612	14A
M51613	14A
M51614	14A
M51615	14A
M51616	14A
M51617	14A
M51618	14A
M51619	14A
M51620	14A
M51621	14A
M51622	14A
M51623	14A
M51624	14A
M51625	14A
M51626	14A
M51627	14A
M51628	14A
M51629	14A
M51630	14A
M51631	14A
M51632	14A
M51633	14A
M51634	14A
M51635	14A
M51636	14A
M51637	14A
M51638	14A
M51639	14A
M51640	14A
M51641	14A
M51642	14A
M51643	14A
M51644	14A
M51645	14A
M51646	14A
M51647	14A
M51648	14A
M51649	14A
M51650	14A

Class 115 Motor Brake Second. Built by BR Derby Works. Four-car Suburban Units

M51651	18A
M51652	18A
M51653	14F
M51654	14F
M51655	14F
M51656	14F
M51657	14F
M51658	14F
M51659	18A
M51660	14A
M51661	14F

Two four-car Class 127 units form a St Pancras to Luton service not far from its destination in July 1962. The leading unit is No M51641/M59614/M59644/M51642 which was added to stock in November 1959. Withdrawal for this class commenced in 1976 with the last examples going in January 1984. *R. H. G. Simpson*

M51662 14A
M51663 18A
M51664 14F
M51665 18A
M51666 14A
M51667 14F
M51668 14F
M51669 14F
M51670 14F
M51671 14F
M51672 14F
M51673 14A
M51674 14A
M51675 14A
M51676 14F
M51677 18A
M51678 18A
M51679 14F
M51680 14F

Class 112 Motor Brake Second. Built by Cravens. Two-car Units

M51681 26A
M51682 26A
M51683 26A
M51684 26A
M51685 26A
M51686 26A
M51687 26A
M51688 26A
M51689 26A
M51690 26A
M51691 26A
M51692 26A
M51693 26A
M51694 26A
M51695 26A
M51696 26A
M51697 26A
M51698 26A
M51699 26A
M51700 26A
M51701 26A
M51702 26A
M51703 24A
M51704 24A
M51705 24A

Class 112 Motor Composite. Built by Cravens. Two-car Units

M51706 26A
M51707 26A
M51708 26A
M51709 26A
M51710 26A
M51711 26A
M51712 26A
M51713 26A
M51714 26A
M51715 26A
M51716 26A
M51717 26A
M51718 26A
M51719 26A
M51720 26A
M51721 26A
M51722 26A
M51723 24A
M51724 26A
M51725 26A
M51726 26A
M51727 26A
M51728 24A
M51729 26A
M51730 24A

Class 113 Motor Brake Second. Built by Cravens. Two-car Units

M51731 24A
M51732 24A
M51733 24A
M51734 24A
M51735 24A
M51736 24A
M51737 24A
M51738 24A
M51739 24A
M51740 24A
M51741 24A
M51742 24A
M51743 24A
M51744 24A
M51745 24A
M51746 24A
M51747 24A
M51748 24A
M51749 24A
M51750 24A
M51751 24A
M51752 24A
M51753 24A
M51754 24A
M51755 24A

Class 113 Motor Composite. Built by Cravens. Two-car Units

M51756 24A
M51757 24A
M51758 24A
M51759 24A
M51760 24A
M51761 24A
M51762 24A
M51763 24A
M51764 24A
M51765 24A
M51766 24A
M51767 24A
M51768 24A
M51769 24A
M51770 24A
M51771 24A
M51772 24A
M51773 24A
M51774 24A
M51775 24A
M51776 24A
M51777 24A
M51778 24A
M51779 24A
M51780 24A

Class 120 Motor Brake Composite. Built by BR Swindon Works. Three-car Cross-Country Units

SC51781 62B
SC51782 61A
SC51783 62B
SC51784 62B
SC51785 61A
SC51786 62B
SC51787 62B

Class 120 Motor Second Built by BR Swindon Works. Three-car Cross-Country Units

SC51788 62B
SC51789 61A
SC51790 62B
SC51791 62B
SC51792 61A
SC51793 62B
SC51794 62B

Class 101 Motor Brake Second. Built by Metropolitan-Cammell. Three-car Units

SC51795 64H
SC51796 64H
SC51797 64H
SC51798 64H
SC51799 64H
SC51800 64H
SC51801 64H

Class 101 Motor Composite. Built by Metropolitan-Cammell. Three-car Units

SC51802 64H
SC51803 64H
SC51804 64H
SC51805 64H
SC51806 64H
SC51807 64H
SC51808 64H

Class 110 Motor Composite. Built by Birmingham RC&W Co. Three-car Units

E51809 56G
E51810 56G
E51811 51A
E51812 51A
E51813 56G
E51814 51A
E51815 56G
E51816 56G
E51817 56G
E51818 56G
E51819 56G
E51820 56G
E51821 56G
E51822 56G
E51823 56G
E51824 56G
E51825 56G
E51826 56G
E51827 56G
E51828 56G

Class 110 Motor Brake Composite. Built by Birmingham RC&W Co. Three-car Units

E51829 56G
E51830 56G
E51831 51A
E51832 51A
E51833 56G
E51834 51A
E51835 56G
E51836 56G
E51837 56G
E51838 56G
E51839 56G
E51840 56G
E51841 56G
E51842 56G
E51843 56G
E51844 56G
E51845 56G
E51846 56G
E51847 56G
E51848 56G

Class 115 Motor Brake Second. Built by BR Derby Works. Four-car Suburban Units

M51849 8H
M51850 8H
M51851 8H
M51852 8H
M51853 8H
M51854 8H
M51855 8H
M51856 8H
M51857 8H
M51858 8H
M51859 8H
M51860 8H
M51861 14F
M51862 14F
M51863 18A
M51864 18A
M51865 14F
M51866 14F
M51867 14F
M51868 14F
M51869 14F
M51870 14F
M51871 14F
M51872 14F
M51873 14F
M51874 14F
M51875 14F
M51876 14F
M51877 14F
M51878 14F
M51879 14F
M51880 14F
M51881 14F
M51882 14F
M51883 8H
M51884 8H
M51885 14F
M51886 14F
M51887 14F
M51888 14F
M51889 14F
M51890 14F
M51891 14F
M51892 14F
M51893 14F
M51894 14F
M51895 14F
M51896 14F
M51897 14F
M51898 14F
M51899 14F
M51900 14F

Class 108 Motor Brake Second. Built by BR Derby Works. Two-car Units

M51901 9E
M51902 9E
M51903 9E
M51904 9E
M51905 9E
M51906 9E
M51907 9E
M51908 9E
M51909 8H
M51910 8H
M51911 8H
M51912 8H
M51913 8H
M51914 8H
M51915 8H
M51916 8H
M51917 8H
M51918 8H
M51919 8H
M51920 8H
M51921 8H
M51922 8H
M51923 8H
M51924 8H
M51925 8H
M51926 8H
M51927 8H
M51928 8H
M51929 8H
M51930 8H

M51931	8H
M51932	26A
M51933	26A
M51934	26A
M51935	26A
M51936	26A
M51937	24F
M51938	26A
M51939	24F
M51940	24F
M51941	26A
M51942	26A
M51943	26A
M51944	26A
M51945	24F
M51946	26A
M51947	26A
M51948	26A
M51949	24F
M51950	26A

Class 124 Motor Composite Built by BR Swindon Works. Six-car Trans-Pennine Units

E51951	55H
E51952	55H
E51953	55H
E51954	55H
E51955	55H
E51956	55H
E51957	55H
E51958	55H
E51959	55H
E51960	55H
E51961	55H
E51962	55H
E51963	55H
E51964	55H
E51965	55H
E51966	55H
E51967	55H

Class 124 Motor Brake Second. Built by BR Swindon Works. Six-car Trans-Pennine Units

E51968	55H
E51969	55H
E51970	55H
E51971	55H
E51972	55H
E51973	55H
E51974	55H
E51975	55H
E51976	55H
E51977	55H
E51978	55H
E51979	55H
E51980	55H
E51981	55H
E51982	55H
E51983	55H
E51984	55H

Class 107 Motor Brake Second. Built by BR Derby Works. Three-car Units

SC51985	66C
SC51986	66C
SC51987	66C
SC51988	66C
SC51989	66C
SC51990	66C
SC51991	66C
SC51992	66C
SC51993	66C
SC51994	66C
SC51995	66C
SC51996	66C
SC51997	66C
SC51998	66C
SC51999	64H
SC52000	62B
SC52001	64H
SC52002	62B
SC52003	66C
SC52004	66C
SC52005	66C
SC52006	66C
SC52007	66C
SC52008	66C
SC52009	66C
SC52010	66C

Class 107 Motor Composite. Built by BR Derby Works. Three-car Units

SC52011	66C
SC52012	66C
SC52013	66C
SC52014	66C
SC52015	66C
SC52016	66C
SC52017	66C
SC52018	66C
SC52019	66C
SC52020	66C
SC52021	66C
SC52022	66C
SC52023	66C
SC52024	66C
SC52025	64H
SC52026	62B
SC52027	64H
SC52028	62B
SC52029	66C
SC52030	66C
SC52031	66C
SC52032	66C
SC52033	66C
SC52034	66C
SC52035	66C
SC52036	66C

Class 108 Motor Composite. Built by BR Derby Works. Two-car Units

M52037	8H
M52038	8H
M52039	8H
M52040	8H
M52041	8H
M52042	8H
M52043	8H
M52044	8H
M52045	8H
M52046	8H
M52047	26A
M52048	26A
M52049	26A
M52050	26A
M52051	26A
M52052	24F
M52053	26A
M52054	24F
M52055	24F
M52056	26A
M52057	26A
M52058	26A
M52059	26A
M52060	24F
M52061	26A
M52062	26A
M52063	26A
M52064	24F
M52065	26A

Class 110 Motor Brake Composite. Built by Birmingham RC&W Co. Three-car Units

M52066	26A
M52067	26A
M52068	26A
M52069	26A
M52070	26A
M52071	26A
M52072	26A
M52073	26A
M52074	26A
M52075	26A

Class 110 Motor Brake Second. Built by Birmingham RC&W Co. Three-car Units

M52076	26A
M52077	26A
M52078	26A
M52079	26A
M52080	26A
M52081	26A
M52082	26A
M52083	26A
M52084	26A
M52085	26A

Class 122 Motor Brake Second. Built by Gloucester RC&W Co. Single Units

W55000	83D
W55001	83D
W55002	84E
W55003	84E
W55004	84E
W55005	84E
W55006	84E
W55007	84E
W55008	84E
W55009	84E
W55010	84E
W55011	83D
W55012	84E
W55013	83D
W55014	82B
W55015	83D
W55016	83D
W55017	83D
W55018	84E
W55019	83D

Class 121 Motor Brake Second. Built by Pressed Steel Co Ltd. Single Units

W55020	81C
W55021	81C
W55022	81C
W55023	81C
W55024	81C
W55025	81C
W55026	81D
W55027	81C
W55028	81C
W55029	81C
W55030	81D
W55031	81D
W55032	82B
W55033	82B
W55034	82B
W55035	81D

Class 128 Motor Parcels Vans. Built by Gloucester RC&W Co. Single Units

M55987	14A
M55988	26A
M55989	14A
M55990	14A
W55991	81C
W55992	81C
W55993	84E
W55994	84E
W55995	84E
W55996	84E

Class 129 Motor Parcels Vans Built by Cravens. Single Units

M55997	12B
M55998	21F
M55999	5D

Class 114 Driving Trailer Composite. Built by BR Derby Works. Two-car Units

E56000	40A
E56001	40A
E56002	40A
E56003	40A
E56004	40A
E56005	40A
E56006	40A
E56007	40A
E56008	40A
E56009	40A
E56010	40A
E56011	40A
E56012	40A
E56013	40A
E56014	41A
E56015	41A
E56016	41A
E56017	41A
E56018	41A
E56019	41A
E56020	41A
E56021	41A
E56022	41A
E56023	41A
E56024	41A
E56025	40A
E56026	41A
E56027	41A
E56028	41A
E56029	41A
E56030	41A
E56031	41A
E56032	40A
E56033	41A
E56034	41A
E56035	41A
E56036	41A
E56037	41A
E56038	40A
E56039	40A
E56040	40A
E56041	40A
E56042	40A
E56043	40A
E56044	40A
E56045	40A
E56046	40A
E56047	40A
E56048	40A
E56049	40A

Class 101 Driving Trailer Composite. Built by Metropolitan-Cammell. Two-car Units

E56050	52J
E56051	52J

Class 122 single-unit DMU No W55000 is at Swindon Works outside the stock shed in May 1958 when just delivered. Alongside is 2-8-0 No 2800 which had been withdrawn that month. No W55000 lasted until January 1994 when it was withdrawn but that was not the end of the story, for it is now in preservation at the South Devon Railway at Buckfastleigh. *R. H. G. Simpson*

Class 128 parcels car No W55992 is near Old Oak Common , London, on a working from Southall to Paddington in April 1962. New in February 1960, withdrawal came in November 1990. *R. H. G. Simpson*

E56052	51A
E56053	51A
E56054	51A
E56055	51A
E56056	52J
E56057	51A
E56058	51A
E56059	52J
E56060	51A
E56061	51A
E56062	52J
E56063	51A
E56064	52J
E56065	52J
E56066	51A
E56067	51A
E56068	52J
E56069	52J
E56070	52J
E56071	52J
E56072	52J
E56073	51A
E56074	52J
E56075	52J
E56076	52J
E56077	52J
E56078	52J
E56079	52J
E56080	52J
E56081	52J
E56082	52J
E56083	50C
E56084	52J
E56085	52J
E56086	51A
E56087	51A
E56088	51A
E56089	52J

Class 111 Driving Trailer Composite. Built by Metropolitan-Cammell. Two-car Units

M56090	24F
M56091	9D
M56092	9D
M56093	24F

Class 100 Driving Trailer Composite. Built by Gloucester RC&W Co. Two-car Units

SC56094	64H
SC56095	64H
SC56096	64H

SC56097	64H
SC56098	66C
SC56099	66C
SC56100	64H
SC56101	64H
SC56102	64H
M56103	21F
M56104	21F
M56105	21F
M56106	21F
M56107	21F
M56108	21F
M56109	21F
M56110	21F
M56111	21F
M56112	21F
M56113	21F

Class 105 Driving Trailer Composite. Built by Cravens. Two-car Units

E56114	50C
E56115	50C
E56116	50C
E56117	50C
E56118	50C
E56119	50C
E56120	50C
E56121	50C
E56122	50C
E56123	50C
E56124	50C
E56125	50C
E56126	50C
E56127	50C
E56128	50C
E56129	50C
E56130	50C
E56131	50C
E56132	50C
E56133	50C
E56134	50C
E56135	50C
E56136	50C
E56137	50C
E56138	50C
E56139	50C
E56140	50C
E56141	50C
E56142	50C
E56143	50C
E56144	50C
M56145	18A
M56146	18A
M56147	18A
M56148	18A
M56149	18A

Class 103 Driving Trailer Composite. Built by Park Royal Vehicles. Two-car Units

M56150	21F
M56151	21F
M56152	21F
M56153	21F
M56154	21F
M56155	21F
M56156	21F
M56157	21F
M56158	21F
M56159	21F
M56160	21F
M56161	21F
M56162	21F
M56163	21F
M56164	21F
M56165	21F
M56166	1C
M56167	1C
M56168	1C
M56169	1C

Class 109 Driving Trailer Composite. Built by D. Wickham & Co Ltd. Two-car Units

E56171	31A
E56172	31A
E56173	31A

Class 104 Driving Trailer Composite. Built by Birmingham RC&W Co. Two-car Units

M56175	18A
M56176	18A
M56177	21F
M56178	21F
M56179	5B
M56180	5B
M56181	5B
M56182	21F
M56183	21F
M56184	21F
E56185	55H
E56186	50C
E56187	51A
E56188	52J
E56189	51A

Class 108 Driving Trailer Composite. Built by BR Derby Works. Two-car Units

E56190	55F
E56191	55F
E56192	55F
E56193	55F
E56194	55F
E56195	55F
E56196	55F
E56197	55F
E56198	55F
E56199	55F
E56200	55F
E56201	55F
E56202	55F
E56203	55F
E56204	55F
E56205	55F
E56206	55F
E56207	55F
E56208	55F
E56209	55F
E56210	55F
M56211	6A
M56212	6A
M56213	6A
M56214	8H
M56215	8H

Class 101 Driving Trailer Composite. Built by Metropolitan-Cammell. Two-car Units

E56218	52J
E56219	52J
E56220	50C

Class 108 Driving Trailer Composite. Built by BR Derby Works. Two-car Units

M56221	1E
M56222	1E
M56223	1E
M56224	1E
M56225	1E
M56226	1E
M56227	1E
M56228	1E
M56229	1E
M56230	9E
M56231	9E
M56232	9E
M56233	9E
M56234	9H
M56235	9E
M56236	9E
M56237	9E
M56238	9E
M56239	9E
M56240	9E
M56241	9E
M56242	9H
M56243	9E
M56244	9E
M56245	9D
M56246	9D
M56247	24F
M56248	6A
M56249	6A
M56250	6A
M56251	6A
M56252	18A
M56253	6A
M56254	6A
M56255	6A
M56256	8H
M56257	8H
M56258	8H
M56259	8H
M56260	8H
M56261	6A
M56262	18A
M56263	18A
M56264	18A
M56265	5D
M56266	18A
M56267	18A
M56268	6A
M56269	18A
M56270	6A
M56271	24F
M56272	6A
M56273	6A
M56274	6A
M56275	6A
M56276	6A
M56277	8H
M56278	8H
M56279	6A

Class 121 Driving Trailer Second. Built by Pressed Steel Co Ltd. Two-car Units

W56280	81C
W56281	81C
W56282	81C
W56283	81C
W56284	81C
W56285	81C
W56286	81C
W56287	81C
W56288	81C
W56289	81C

Class 122 Driving Trailer Second. For use with Single-car Units. Built by Gloucester RC&W Co.

W56291	84E
W56292	81C
W56293	83D
W56294	81C
W56295	84E
W56296	84E
W56297	81C
W56298	83D
W56299	84E

Class 100 Driving Trailer Composite. Built by Gloucester RC&W Co. Two-car Units

SC56300	64H
SC56301	64H
SC56302	64H
SC56303	64H
SC56304	64H
SC56305	66C
SC56306	66C
SC56307	64H
SC56308	64H
SC56309	64H
SC56310	64H
SC56311	66C
SC56312	64H
SC56313	64H
SC56314	64H
SC56315	64H
SC56316	64H
SC56317	64H
SC56318	66C
SC56319	64H

Class 101 Driving Trailer Composite. Built by Metropolitan-Cammell. Two-car Units

M56332	21E
M56333	21E
M56334	21E
M56335	21E
M56336	21E
M56337	21E
M56338	21E
M56339	21E
M56340	21E
M56341	21E
M56342	21E
M56343	21E
M56344	21E
M56345	21E
M56346	21E
M56347	21F
M56348	21F
M56349	21F
M56350	21F
M56351	24E
M56352	24E
M56353	24E
M56354	26A
M56355	26A
M56356	24E
M56357	24E
M56358	24E
M56359	24E
M56360	26A
M56361	24F
E56362	55H
E56363	55H
E56364	55F
E56365	55H
E56366	50C
E56367	50C
E56368	55F
E56369	55F
E56370	55F
E56371	55H
E56372	55H
E56373	50C
E56374	50C
E56375	52J
E56376	55H
E56377	51A
E56378	52J
E56379	52J
E56380	55H
E56381	55H
SC56382	64H
SC56383	62B
SC56384	66C

Class 122 Trailer Second No W56295 is attached to a 'W55xxx' single-car unit and a three-car Cross-Country set at Birmingham Moor Street, waiting to leave on the 5.15pm to Henley-in-Arden on Thursday 12 April 1962. No W56295 was new in July 1958 and was withdrawn in November 1982. *M. Mensing*

SC56385 66C
SC56386 66C
SC56387 66C
SC56388 66C
SC56389 64H
SC56390 66C
SC56391 66C
SC56392 66C
SC56393 66C
SC56394 66C
SC56395 66C
SC56396 62B
SC56397 62B
SC56398 62B
SC56399 62B
SC56400 62B
SC56401 62B
SC56402 62B
SC56403 62B
SC56404 62B
SC56405 62B
SC56406 64H
SC56407 62B
SC56408 62B
SC56409 66C
SC56410 62B
SC56411 62B

Class 105 Driving Trailer Composite. Built by Cravens. Two-car Units

E56412 34G
E56413 34G
E56414 34G
E56415 34G
E56416 34G
E56417 34G
E56418 34G
E56419 34G
E56420 34G
E56421 34G
E56422 34G
E56423 34G
E56424 34G
E56425 34G
E56426 34G
E56427 40A
E56428 40A
E56429 34G
E56430 34G
E56431 34G
E56432 31A
E56433 31A
E56434 31A
E56435 31A
E56436 31A
E56437 31A
E56438 31A
E56439 31A
E56440 31A
E56441 31A
E56442 31A
E56443 31A
E56444 31A
E56445 31A
E56446 31A
E56447 34G
E56448 34G
E56449 34G
E56450 34G
E56451 34G
E56452 34G
E56453 34G
E56454 34G
E56455 34G
E56456 40A
E56457 40A
E56458 34G
E56459 40A
E56460 40A
E56461 40A
SC56462 61A
SC56463 61A
SC56464 61A
SC56465 61A
SC56466 61A
SC56467 61A
SC56468 61A
SC56469 61A
SC56470 61A
SC56471 66C
SC56472 66C
SC56473 66C
SC56474 66C
SC56475 66C
SC56476 66C
SC56477 66C
SC56478 66C
SC56479 61A
SC56480 66C
SC56481 66C
SC56482 61A
SC56483 66C

Class 108 Driving Trailer Composite. Built by BR Derby Works. Two-car Units

M56484 9E
M56485 9E
M56486 9E
M56487 9E
M56488 9E
M56489 9E
M56490 9E
M56491 9E
M56492 8H
M56493 8H
M56494 8H
M56495 8H
M56496 8H
M56497 8H
M56498 8H
M56499 8H
M56500 8H
M56501 8H
M56502 8H
M56503 8H
M56504 8H

Class 116 Trailer Composite. Built by BR Derby Works. Three-car Suburban Units

W59000 84E
W59001 84E
W59002 84E
W59003 84E
W59004 84E
W59005 84E

W59006	84E
W59007	84E
W59008	84E
W59009	84E
W59010	84E
W59011	84E
W59012	84E
W59013	84E
W59014	84E
W59015	84E
W59016	84E
W59017	84E
W59018	84E
W59019	84E
W59020	84E
W59021	84E
W59022	84E
W59023	84E
W59024	84E
W59025	84E
W59026	84E
W59027	84E
W59028	84E
W59029	CAT
W59030	CAT
W59031	CAT

Class 116 Trailer Second. Built by BR Derby Works. Three-car Suburban Units

W59032	CAT
W59033	CAT
W59034	CAT
W59035	CAT
W59036	CAT
W59037	CAT
W59038	CAT
W59039	CAT
W59040	CAT
W59041	CAT

Class 101 Trailer Second. Built by Metropolitan-Cammell. Four-car Units

E59042	52J
E59043	52J
E59044	52J
E59045	52J
E59046	52J
E59047	52J
E59048	55H

Class 101 Trailer Brake Second. Built by Metropolitan-Cammell. Four-car Units

E59049	52J
E59050	52J
E59051	52J
E59052	52J
E59053	52J
E59054	52J
E59055	55H

Class 101 Trailer Second. Built by Metropolitan-Cammell. Four-car Units

E59060	51A
E59061	51A
E59062	55H
E59063	51A
E59064	51A
E59065	51A
E59066	51A
E59067	51A
E59068	51A
E59069	50C
E59070	51A
E59071	51A
E59072	51A

Class 101 Trailer Brake Second. Built by Metropolitan-Cammell. Four-car Units

E59073	51A
E59074	51A
E59075	55H
E59076	51A
E59077	51A
E59078	51A
E59079	51A
E59080	51A
E59081	51A
E59082	50C
E59083	51A
E59084	51A
E59085	51A

Class 101 Trailer Second. Built by Metropolitan-Cammell. Four-car Units

E59086	55H
E59087	55H
E59088	52J
E59089	55H
E59090	55H
E59091	55H

Class 101 Trailer Brake Second. Built by Metropolitan-Cammell. Four-car Units

E59092	55H
E59093	55H
E59094	52J
E59095	55H
E59096	55H
E59097	55H

Class 126 Trailer Buffet First. Built by BR Swindon Works. Three- or Six-car Inter-City Units

SC59098	64H
SC59099	64H

Class 101 Trailer Second. Built by Metropolitan-Cammell. Three-car Units

E59100	55H
E59101	55H
E59102	55H
E59103	56G
E59104	56G
E59105	56G
E59106	56G
E59107	56G
E59108	56G
E59109	56G

Class 101 Trailer Brake Second. Built by Metropolitan-Cammell. Four-car Units

E59112	51A
E59113	51A

Class 101 Trailer Composite. Built by Metropolitan-Cammell. Three-car Units

M59114	21E
M59115	21E
M59116	21E
M59117	21E
M59118	21E
M59119	21E
M59120	21E
M59121	21E
M59122	21E
M59123	21E
M59124	21E
M59125	21E
M59126	21E
M59127	21E
M59128	21E
M59129	21E
M59130	18A
M59131	21E

Class 104 Trailer Composite. Built by Birmingham RC&W Co. Three-car Units

M59132	9D
M59133	9D
M59134	9D
M59135	9D
M59136	9D
M59137	9D
M59138	9D
M59139	9D
M59140	9D
M59141	9D
M59142	9D
M59143	9D
M59144	9D
M59145	9D
M59146	9D
M59147	5A
M59148	5A
M59149	18A
M59150	5D
M59151	5D
M59152	5D
M59153	5D
M59154	5D
M59155	5D
M59156	5D
M59157	5D
M59158	5D
M59159	5D
M59160	5D
M59161	5D
M59162	5D
M59163	5D
M59164	5D
M59165	5D
M59166	5D
M59167	5D
M59168	5D
M59169	5D
M59170	9D
M59171	9D
M59172	9D
M59173	5B
M59174	5B
M59175	5B
M59176	5B
M59177	5B
M59178	5B
M59179	5B
M59180	5B
M59181	5B
M59182	5B
M59183	18A
M59184	18A
M59185	18A
M59186	18A
M59187	18A

Class 104 Trailer Second. Built by Birmingham RC&W Co. Four-car Units

E59188	55H
E59189	55H
E59190	55H
E59191	55H
E59192	55H
E59193	55H
E59194	55H
E59195	55H
E59196	50C
E59197	50C
E59198	55H
E59199	50C
E59200	50C
E59201	55H
E59202	52J
E59203	55H
E59204	50C
E59205	50C
E59206	50C
E59207	50C
E59208	50C

Class 104 Trailer Brake Second. Built by Birmingham RC&W Co. Four-car Units

E59209	55H
E59210	55H
E59211	55H
E59212	55H
E59213	55H
E59214	55H
E59215	55H
E59216	55H
E59217	50C
E59218	50C
E59219	55H
E59220	50C
E59221	50C
E59222	55H
E59223	52J
E59224	55H
E59225	50C
E59226	50C
E59227	50C
E59228	50C
E59229	50C

Class 104 Trailer Second. Built by Birmingham RC&W Co. Four-car Units

E59230	55H
E59231	50C
E59232	50C
E59233	55H
E59234	51A

Class 104 Trailer Brake Second. Built by Birmingham RC&W Co. Four-car Units

E59240	55H
E59241	50C
E59242	50C
E59243	55H
E59244	51A

Class 108 Trailer Brake Second. Built by BR Derby Works. Four-car Units

E59245	52J
E59246	50C
E59247	50C
E59248	52J
E59249	52J
E59250	52J

Class 120 Trailer Buffet Second. Built by BR Swindon Works. Cross-Country Three-car Units

W59255	84E
W59256	84E

W59257	88A
W59258	84E
W59259	84E
W59260	88A
W59261	88A
W59262	88A
W59263	88A
W59264	88A
W59265	88A
W59266	88A
W59267	84E
W59268	88A
W59269	84E
W59270	88A
W59271	88A
W59272	84E
W59273	88A
W59274	88A
W59275	88A
W59276	88A
W59277	88A
W59278	88A
W59279	88A
W59280	88A
W59281	84E
W59282	88A
W59283	88A
W59284	88A
W59285	88A
W59286	88A
W59287	84E
W59288	88A
W59289	84E
W59290	84E
W59291	88A
W59292	88A
W59293	88A
W59294	88A
W59295	82B
W59296	82B
W59297	82B
W59298	82B
W59299	82B
W59300	82B
W59301	82B

Class 101 Trailer Second. Built by Metropolitan-Cammell. Three- or Four-car Units

E59302	51A
E59303	51A
E59304	51A
E59305	51A
E59306	51A

Class 105 Trailer Second or Trailer Composite. Built by Cravens. Three-car Units

M59307	18A
M59308	18A
M59309	18A
M59310	18A
M59311	18A
M59312	18A
M59313	18A
M59314	18A
M59315	18A
M59316	18A
M59317	18A
M59318	18A
M59319	18A
M59320	18A
M59321	18A
M59322	18A
M59323	18A
M59324	18A
M59325	18A

Class 116 Trailer Composite. Built by BR Derby Works. Three-car Suburban Units

W59326	CAT
W59327	CAT
W59328	CAT
W59329	CAT
W59330	CAT
W59331	CAT
W59332	CAT
W59333	CAT
W59334	CAT
W59335	CAT
W59336	CAT
W59337	CAT
W59338	CAT
W59339	84E
W59340	CAT
W59341	84E
W59342	CAT
W59343	CAT
W59344	CAT
W59345	CAT
W59346	CAT
W59347	CAT
W59348	CAT
W59349	CAT
W59350	CAT
W59351	CAT
W59352	CAT
W59353	CAT
W59354	CAT
W59355	CAT
W59356	CAT
W59357	CAT
W59358	CAT
W59359	CAT
W59360	CAT
W59361	CAT
W59362	CAT
W59363	CAT
W59364	CAT
W59365	CAT
W59366	CAT
W59367	CAT
W59368	CAT
W59369	CAT
W59370	CAT
W59371	CAT
W59372	CAT
W59373	CAT
W59374	CAT
W59375	CAT
W59376	CAT

Class 108 Trailer Second. Built by BR Derby Works. Three- or Four-car Units

E59380	52J
E59381	50C
E59382	50C
E59383	52J
E59384	52J
E59385	52J
E59386	51A
E59387	52J
E59388	51A
E59389	51A
E59390	51A

Class 126 Trailer First. Built by BR Swindon Works. Six-car Inter-City Units

SC59391	67C
SC59392	67C
SC59393	67C
SC59394	67C
SC59395	67C
SC59396	67C
SC59397	67C
SC59398	67C
SC59399	67C
SC59400	67C

Class 126 Trailer Composite. Built by BR Swindon Works. Six-car Inter-City Units

SC59402	67C
SC59403	67C
SC59404	67C
SC59405	67C
SC59406	67C
SC59407	67C
SC59408	67C
SC59409	67C
SC59410	67C
SC59411	67C
SC59412	67C

Class 119 Trailer Buffet Second. Built by Gloucester RC&W Co. Three-car Cross-Country Units

W59413	88A
W59414	88A
W59415	88A
W59416	88A
W59417	88A
W59418	88A
W59419	82B
W59420	82B
W59421	82B
W59422	82B
W59423	82B
W59424	82B
W59425	82B
W59426	82B
W59427	82B
W59428	82B
W59429	82B
W59430	84E
W59431	84E
W59432	88A
W59433	88A
W59434	88A
W59435	84E
W59436	88A
W59437	88A

Class 116 Trailer Composite. Built by BR Derby Works. Three-car Suburban Units

W59438	82B
W59439	82B
W59440	82B
W59441	82B
W59442	CAT
W59443	82B
W59444	82B
W59445	82B
W59446	82B
W59447	82B
W59448	82B

Class 125 Trailer Second. Built by BR Derby Works. Three-car Suburban Units

E59449	30A
E59450	30A
E59451	30A
E59452	30A
E59453	30A
E59454	30A
E59455	30A
E59456	30A
E59457	30A
E59458	30A
E59459	30A
E59460	30A
E59461	30A
E59462	30A
E59463	30A
E59464	30A
E59465	30A
E59466	30A
E59467	30A
E59468	30A

Class 118 Trailer Composite. Built by Birmingham RC&W Co. Three-car Suburban Units

W59469	83D
W59470	83D
W59471	83D
W59472	83D
W59473	83D
W59474	83D
W59475	83D
W59476	83D
W59477	83D
W59478	81C
W59479	81D
W59480	81D
W59481	81D
W59482	81D
W59483	81D

Class 117 Trailer Composite. Built by Pressed Steel Co. Three-car Suburban Units

W59484	81D
W59485	81D
W59486	81C
W59487	81D
W59488	81D
W59489	81D
W59490	81D
W59491	81C
W59492	81C
W59493	81C
W59494	81C
W59495	81D
W59496	81D
W59497	81D
W59498	81C
W59499	81C
W59500	81C
W59501	81C
W59502	81C
W59503	81D
W59504	81D
W59505	81D
W59506	81D
W59507	81D
W59508	81C
W59509	81C
W59510	81D
W59511	81C
W59512	81C
W59513	81C
W59514	81D
W59515	81D
W59516	81C
W59517	81C
W59518	81C
W59519	81D
W59520	81D
W59521	81D
W59522	81D

Class 101 Trailer Composite. Built by Metropolitan-Cammell. Four-car Units

E59523	52J
E59524	55H
E59525	55H
E59526	52J
E59527	52J
E59528	55H
E59529	55H
E59530	52J
E59531	52J
E59532	55H
E59533	55H
E59534	55H
E59535	52J
E59536	55H
E59537	55H
E59538	55H
E59539	52J
E59540	52J
E59541	51A
E59542	51A

Class 101 Trailer Composite. Built by Metropolitan-Cammell. Three-car Units

SC59543	62B
SC59544	62B
SC59545	62B
SC59546	62B
SC59547	62B
SC59548	62B
SC59549	62B
SC59550	62B
SC59551	62B
SC59552	62B
SC59553	62B
SC59554	64H
SC59555	64H
SC59556	61A
SC59557	64H
SC59558	64H
SC59559	64H
SC59560	64H
SC59561	64H
SC59562	64H
SC59563	67C
SC59564	64H
SC59565	64H
SC59566	64H
SC59567	67C
SC59568	64H

Class 101 Trailer Second. Built by Metropolitan-Cammell. Three-car Units

E59569	55H
E59570	55H
E59571	55H
E59572	55H

Class 111 Trailer Buffet Second. Built by Metropolitan-Cammell. Four-car Units

E59573	52J
E59574	52J
E59575	52J
E59576	52J
E59577	52J
E59578	52J

Class 120 Trailer Second. Built by BR Swindon Works. Cross-Country Three-car Units

W59579	84E
W59580	84E
W59581	84E
W59582	84E
W59583	84E
W59584	84E
W59585	84E
W59586	84E
W59587	84E
W59588	84E

Class 127 Trailer Second. Built by BR Derby Works. Four-car Suburban Units

M59589	14A
M59590	14A
M59591	14A
M59592	14A
M59593	14A
M59594	14A
M59595	14A
M59596	14A
M59597	14A
M59598	14A
M59599	14A
M59600	14A
M59601	14A
M59602	14A
M59603	14A
M59604	14A
M59605	14A
M59606	14A
M59607	14A
M59608	14A
M59609	14A
M59610	14A
M59611	14A
M59612	14A
M59613	14A
M59614	14A
M59615	14A
M59616	14A
M59617	14A
M59618	14A
M59619	14A
M59620	14A
M59621	14A
M59622	14A
M59623	14A
M59624	14A
M59625	14A
M59626	14A
M59627	14A
M59628	14A
M59629	14A
M59630	14A
M59631	14A
M59632	14A
M59633	14A
M59634	14A
M59635	14A
M59636	14A
M59637	14A
M59638	14A
M59639	14A
M59640	14A
M59641	14A
M59642	14A
M59643	14A
M59644	14A
M59645	14A
M59646	14A
M59647	14A
M59648	14A

Class 115 Trailer Second. Built by BR Derby Works. Four-car Suburban Units

M59649	18A
M59650	14F
M59651	14F
M59652	14F
M59653	18A
M59654	14A
M59655	14F
M59656	14A
M59657	14F
M59658	14F
M59659	14F
M59660	14A
M59661	14A
M59662	18A
M59663	14F

Class 115 Trailer Composite. Built by BR Derby Works. Four-car Suburban Units

M59664	18A
M59665	14F
M59666	14F
M59667	14F
M59668	18A
M59669	14A
M59670	14F
M59671	14A
M59672	14F
M59673	14F
M59674	14F
M59675	14A
M59676	14A
M59677	18A
M59678	14F

Class 120 Trailer Buffet Second. Built by BR Swindon Works. Three-car Cross-Country Units

SC59679	62B
SC59680	62B
SC59681	62B
SC59682	62B
SC59683	61A
SC59684	61A
SC59685	62B

Class 101 Trailer Composite. Built by Metropolitan-Cammell. Three-car Units

SC59686	64H
SC59687	64H
SC59688	64H
SC59689	64H
SC59690	64H
SC59691	64H
SC59692	64H

Class 110 Trailer Second. Built by Birmingham RC &W Co. Three-car Units

E59693	56G
E59694	56G
E59695	51A
E59696	51A
E59697	56G
E59698	51A
E59699	56G
E59700	56G
E59701	56G
E59702	56G
E59703	56G
E59704	56G
E59705	56G
E59706	56G
E59707	56G
E59708	56G
E59709	56G
E59710	56G
E59711	56G
E59712	56G

Class 115 Trailer Second. Built by BR Derby Works. Four-car Suburban Units

M59713	8H
M59714	8H
M59715	8H
M59716	8H
M59717	8H
M59718	8H

Class 115 Trailer Composite. Built by BR Derby Works. Four-car Suburban Units

M59719	8H
M59720	8H
M59721	8H
M59722	8H
M59723	8H
M59724	8H

Class 115 Trailer Second. Built by BR Derby Works. Four-car Suburban Units

M59725	14F
M59726	18A
M59727	14F
M59728	14F
M59729	14F
M59730	14F
M59731	14F
M59732	14F
M59733	14F
M59734	14F
M59735	14F
M59736	8H
M59737	14F
M59738	14F
M59739	14F
M59740	14F
M59741	14F
M59742	14F
M59743	14F
M59744	14F

Class 115 Trailer Composite. Built by BR Derby Works. Four-car Suburban Units

M59745	14F
M59746	18A
M59747	14F
M59748	14F
M59749	14F
M59750	14F
M59751	14F
M59752	14F
M59753	14F
M59754	14F
M59755	14F
M59756	8H
M59757	14F
M59758	14F
M59759	14F
M59760	14F
M59761	14F
M59762	14F
M59763	14F
M59764	14F

Class 124 Trailer Second. Built by BR Swindon Works. Six-car Trans-Pennine Units

E59765	55H
E59766	55H
E59767	55H
E59768	55H
E59769	55H

E59770	55H
E59771	55H
E59772	55H
E59773	55H

Class 124 Trailer Buffet First. Built by BR Swindon Works. Six-car Trans-Pennine Units

E59774	55H
E59775	55H
E59776	55H
E59777	55H
E59778	55H
E59779	55H
E59780	55H
E59781	55H

Class 107 Trailer Second. Built by BR Derby Works. Three-car Units

SC59782	66C
SC59783	66C
SC59784	66C
SC59785	66C
SC59786	66C
SC59787	66C
SC59788	66C
SC59789	66C
SC59790	66C
SC59791	66C
SC59792	66C
SC59793	66C
SC59794	66C
SC59795	66C
SC59796	66C
SC59797	62B
SC59798	66C
SC59799	62B
SC59800	64H
SC59801	66C
SC59802	66C
SC59803	66C
SC59804	66C
SC59805	66C
SC59806	66C
SC59807	66C

Class 110 Trailer Second. Built by Birmingham RC&W Co. Three-car Units

M59808	26A
M59809	26A
M59810	26A
M59811	26A
M59812	26A
M59813	26A
M59814	26A
M59815	26A
M59816	26A
M59817	26A

Class 251 Midland Pullman Motor Brake First. Built by Metropolitan-Cammell. Six-car Units

M60090	14A
M60091	14A
M60092	14A
M60093	14A

Class 251 Western Pullman Motor Brake Second. Built by Metropolitan-Cammell. Eight-car Units.

W60094	82B
W60095	82B
W60096	82B
W60097	82B
W60098	82B
W60099	82B

Class 251 Western Pullman Motor Parlour Second Built by Metropolitan-Cammell. Eight-car Units

W60644	82B
W60645	82B
W60646	82B
W60647	82B
W60648	82B
W60649	82B

Class 251 Midland Pullman Motor Kitchen First. Built by Metropolitan-Cammell. Six-car Units

M60730	14A
M60731	14A
M60732	14A
M60733	14A

Class 251 Western Pullman Trailer Kitchen First. Built by Metropolitan-Cammell. Eight-car Units

W60734	82B
W60735	82B
W60736	82B
W60737	82B
W60738	82B
W60739	82B

Class 251 Midland Pullman Trailer Parlour First. Built by Metropolitan-Cammell. Six-car Units

M60740	14A
M60741	14A
M60742	14A
M60743	14A

Class 251 Western Pullman Trailer Parlour First. Built by Metropolitan-Cammell. Eight-car Units

W60744	82B
W60745	82B
W60746	82B
W60747	82B
W60748	82B
W60749	82B

Derby Lightweight Motor Brake Second. Built by BR Derby Works. Two-car Units

E79000	56G
E79001	56G
E79002	56G
E79003	56G
E79004	56G
E79005	56G
E79006	56G
E79007	56G

Derby Lightweight Motor Brake Second. Built by BR Derby Works. Two-car Units

M79008	12B
M79009	12B
M79010	9H
M79011	12B
M79012	12B
M79013	12B
M79014	12B
M79015	12F
M79016	12F
M79017	12F
M79018	12F
M79019	12F
M79020	12F
E79021	31A
E79022	31A
E79023	31A
E79024	31A
E79025	31A
E79026	31A
E79027	31A
E79028	31A
E79029	32A
E79030	31A
E79031	31A
E79032	31A
E79033	32A
E79034	32A
E79035	32A
E79036	32A
E79037	32A
E79038	32A
E79039	32A
E79040	32A
E79041	31A
E79043	32A
E79044	32A
E79045	32A
E79046	32A

Metropolitan-Cammell Motor Brake Second. Two-car Units

E79047	32A
E79048	32A
E79049	32A
E79050	32A
E79051	32A
E79052	32A
E79053	32A
E79054	32A
E79055	32A
E79056	32A
E79057	32A
E79058	32A
E79059	32A
E79060	32A
E79061	32A
E79062	32A
E79063	32A
E79064	32A
E79065	32A
E79066	32A
E79067	32A
E79068	32A
E79069	30A
E79070	30A
E79071	30A
E79072	30A
E79073	30A
E79074	30A
E79075	30A
M79076	26A
M79077	26A
M79078	26A
M79079	26A
M79080	26A
M79081	26A
M79082	26A

BR Swindon Works-built Motor Brake Second. Three- or Six-car Inter-City Units

SC79083	64H
SC79084	64H
SC79085	67C
SC79086	67C
SC79087	64H
SC79088	64H
SC79089	64H
SC79090	64H
SC79091	64H
SC79092	64H
SC79093	64H
SC79094	64H
SC79095	64H
SC79096	64H
SC79097	64H
SC79098	64H
SC79099	64H
SC79100	64H
SC79101	64H
SC79102	64H
SC79103	64H
SC79104	64H
SC79105	64H
SC79106	64H
SC79107	64H
SC79108	64H
SC79109	64H
SC79110	64H
SC79111	64H

Derby Lightweight Motor Brake Second. Built by BR Derby Works. Two-car Units

M79118	12B
M79119	12B
M79120	12B
M79121	9H
M79122	9H
M79123	9H
M79124	9H
M79125	9H
M79126	9H
M79127	9H
M79128	9H
M79129	9H
M79130	9H
M79131	9H
M79132	9H
M79133	6G
M79134	6G
M79135	6G
M79136	6G
E79137	52J
E79138	52J
E79139	52J
E79140	52J
M79141	9H
M79142	26A
M79143	9H
M79144	9H
M79145	9H
M79146	9H
M79147	8H
M79148	9H
M79149	9H

Derby Lightweight Motor Second. Built by BR Derby Works. Four-car Units

E79150	52J
E79151	52J
E79152	52J
E79153	52J
E79154	52J

BR Swindon Works-built Motor Second. Six-car Inter-City Units

SC79155	64H
SC79156	64H
SC79157	64H

British United Traction four-wheel three-car units are in store at Watford in 1960. Built in 1955, although officially withdrawn in February 1959, they remained in stock until cut up at Derby Carriage & Wagon Works in November 1963. *Pictorail*

SC79158 64H
SC79159 64H
SC79160 64H
SC79161 64H
SC79162 64H
SC79163 64H
SC79164 64H
SC79165 64H
SC79166 64H
SC79167 64H
SC79168 64H

Derby Lightweight Motor Brake Second. Built by BR Derby Works. Two-car Units

M79169 9H
M79171 9H
M79172 9H
M79173 9H
M79174 9H
M79175 9H
M79176 9H
M79177 9H
M79178 9H
M79179 9H
M79180 9H
M79181 9H

Derby Lightweight Motor Brake Second. Built by BR Derby Works. Two-car Units

M79184 6G
M79185 6G
M79186 6G
M79187 6G
M79188 6G

Derby Lightweight Motor Composite. Built by BR Derby Works. Two-car Units

M79189 6G
M79190 6G
M79191 6G
M79192 6G
M79193 6G

Derby Lightweight Driving Trailer Composite. Built by BR Derby Works. Two-car Units

E79250 32A
E79251 32A
E79252 31A
E79253 32A
E79254 32A
E79255 32A
E79256 32A
E79257 31A
E79258 32A
E79259 32A
E79260 32A
E79261 32A
E79262 31A

Metropolitan-Cammell Driving Trailer Second. Two-car Units

E79263 32A
E79264 32A
E79265 32A
E79266 32A
E79267 32A
E79268 32A
E79269 32A
E79270 32A
E79271 32A
E79272 30A
E79273 32A
E79274 32A
E79275 32A
E79276 32A
E79277 32A
E79278 32A
E79279 32A
E79280 32A
E79281 32A
E79282 32A
E79283 32A
E79284 32A
E79285 30A
E79286 30A
E79287 30A
E79288 30A
E79289 30A
E79290 30A
E79291 30A

Derby Lightweight Trailer Brake Second. Built by BR Derby Works. Four-car Units

E79325 52J
E79326 52J
E79327 52J
E79328 52J
E79329 52J

Derby Lightweight Trailer Second. Built by BR Derby Works. Four-car Units

E79400 52J
E79401 52J
E79402 52J
E79403 52J
E79404 52J

BR Swindon Works-built Trailer Buffet First. Three- or Six-car Inter-City Units

SC79440 67C
SC79441 67C
SC79442 64H
SC79443 64H
SC79444 64H
SC79445 64H
SC79446 64H
SC79447 64H

BR Swindon Works-built Trailer First. Three- or Six-car Inter-City Units

SC79470 64H
SC79471 64H
SC79472 64H
SC79473 64H
SC79474 64H
SC79475 64H
SC79476 64H
SC79477 64H
SC79478 64H
SC79479 64H
SC79480 64H
SC79481 64H
SC79482 64H

Derby Lightweight Motor Composite. Built by BR Derby Works. Two-car Units

E79500 56G
E79501 56G
E79502 56G
E79503 56G
E79504 56G
E79505 56G
E79506 56G
E79507 56G

Derby Lightweight Motor Composite. Built by BR Derby Works. Four-car Units

E79508 52J
E79509 52J
E79510 52J
E79511 52J
E79512 52J

Derby Lightweight Driving Trailer Composite. Built by BR Derby Works. Two car Units

M79600 12B
M79601 12B
M79602 9H
M79603 12B
M79604 12B
M79605 12B
M79606 12B
M79607 12F
M79608 12F
M79609 12F
M79610 12F
M79611 12F
M79612 12F
E79613 32A
E79614 31A
E79615 31A
E79616 31A
E79617 31A
E79618 32A
E79619 31A
E79620 31A
E79621 32A
E79622 31A
E79623 31A
E79624 31A
E79625 32A

Metropolitan-Cammell Driving Trailer Composite. Two-car Units

M79626 26A
M79627 26A
M79628 26A
M79629 26A
M79630 26A
M79631 26A
M79632 26A

Derby Lightweight Driving Trailer Composite. Built by BR Derby Works. Two-car Units

M79639 12B
M79640 12B
M79641 12B
M79642 9H
M79643 9H
M79644 9H
M79645 9H

M79646 9H
M79647 9H
M79648 9H
M79649 9H
M79650 9H
M79651 9H
M79652 9H
M79653 9H
M79654 6G
M79655 6G
M79656 6G
M79657 6G
E79658 52J
E79659 52J
E79660 52J
E79661 52J
M79662 9H
M79663 9H
M79664 9H
M79665 9H
M79666 9H
M79667 8H
M79668 9H
M79669 9H
M79670 9H
M79671 9H
M79672 9H
M79673 9H
M79674 9H
M79675 9H
M79676 9H
M79677 9H
M79678 9H
M79679 9H
M79680 9H
M79681 9H
M79682 9H
M79683 9H
M79684 26A

British United Traction Motor Second. Four-wheel Three-car Units

M79740 1C

British United Traction Trailer Second. Four-wheel Three-car Units

M79741 1C

British United Traction Motor Brake Second. Four-wheel Three-car Units

M79742 1C
M79743 1C
M79744 1C

British United Traction Motor Second. Four-wheel Three-car Units

M79745 1C

British United Traction Trailer Second. Four-wheel Three-car Units

M79746 1C
M79747 1C

British United Traction Motor Second. Four-wheel Three-car Units

M79748 1C

British United Traction Trailer Second. Four-wheel Three-car Units

M79749 1C

British United Traction Motor Brake Second. Four-wheel Three-car Units

M79750 1C

BR Derby Works-built Motor Brake Second. Single Units

M79900 1E
M79901 1E

Bristol/ECW-built Four-wheel Railbus

SC79958 66C
SC79959 66C

Waggon & Maschinenbau-built Four-wheel Railbus

E79960 31A
E79961 31A
E79962 31A
E79963 31A
E79964 31A

D. Wickham & Co-built Four-wheel Railbus

SC79965 64H
SC79966 63A
SC79967 63A
SC79968 64H
SC79969 60B

Park Royal Vehicles-built Four-wheel Railbus

SC79970 60B
SC79971 65A
SC79972 63A
SC79973 60B
SC79974 64H

AC Cars-Built Four-wheel Railbus

W79975 82C
W79976 82C
W79977 82C
W79978 82C
SC79979 67B

Battery Electric Railcar Built by Derby/Cowlairs Works Motor Brake Second. Two-car Units

SC79998 61A

Battery Electric Railcar Built by Derby/Cowlairs Works Driving Trailer Composite. Two-car Units

SC79999 61A

Ex-GWR Railcars. Single Units

W20W 85A
W21W 81C
W22W 85A
W23W 82B
W24W 82B
W25W 81C
W26W 85A
W29W 81D
W30W 81C
W31W 81C
W32W 85A
W33W 81D
W38W 81D

SOUTHERN REGION DIESEL MULTIPLE-UNITS ALL BUILT AT BR EASTLEIGH WORKS

Class 201 Hastings Units

1001 73F
1002 73F
1003 73F
1004 73F
1005 73F
1006 73F
1007 73F

Class 202 Hastings Units

1011 73F
1012 73F
1013 73F
1014 73F
1015 73F
1016 73F
1017 73F
1018 73F
1019 73F

Class 203 Hastings Units

1031 73F
1032 73F
1033 73F
1034 73F
1035 73F
1036 73F
1037 73F

Class 205 Hampshire Units

1101 71A
1102 71A
1103 71A
1104 71A
1105 71A
1106 71A
1107 71A
1108 71A
1109 71A
1110 71A
1111 71A
1112 71A
1113 71A
1114 71A
1115 71A
1116 71A
1117 71A
1118 71A
1119 71A
1120 71A
1121 71A
1122 71A
1123 71A
1124 71A
1125 71A
1126 71A

Wickham four-wheel railbus No SC79967 is at Crieff on Tuesday 19 May 1959 after arrival from Gleneagles. New in January 1959, it was withdrawn in October 1966 and scrapped at Cowlairs works. *G. W. Sharpe*

AC Cars four-wheel railbus No W79976 is at Swindon shed on Sunday 9 April 1961 having a rest from its usual duties on the Tetbury to Kemble branch. New in September 1958, it was withdrawn in February 1968 and is now preserved at the Colne Valley Railway in Essex. *H. D. Ramsey/Initial Photographics*

Ex-GWR railcar No W29W is at Sutton Bridge Junction Shrewsbury taking instructions from the signalman in July 1960. This unit dated from January 1941 and was withdrawn in August 1962. All the remaining ex-GWR single-unit railcars had been withdrawn by the end of 1962. *G. W. Sharpe*

British Railways Service Locomotives Allocations at 1 January 1962

Service No	BR No	Locomotive Type	Allocation
7	68166	Y3 Class Sentinel 0-4-0T	Boston Sleeper Depot
10	68911	J50 Class 0-6-0T	Doncaster Works
11	68914	J50 Class 0-6-0T	Doncaster Works
20		Ruston & Hornsby 0-4-0 Diesel	Reading Signal Works
32	68370	J66 Class 0-6-0T	Stratford Works London
33	68129	Y4 Class 0-4-0T	Stratford Works London
39	68131	Y1 Class Sentinel 0-4-0T	Norwich Engineer's Department
40	68173	Y3 Class Sentinel 0-4-0T	Lowestoft Engineer's Department
41	68177	Y3 Class Sentinel 0-4-0T	Lowestoft Engineer's Department
44	68498	J69 Class 0-6-0T	Stratford Works London
45	68543	J69 Class 0-6-0T	Stratford Works London
52	11104	Drewry 0-6-0 Diesel Shunter	West Hartlepool Permanent Way Depot
56		Ruston & Hornsby 0-6-0 Diesel	Hull Engineer's Depot
81		Ruston & Hornsby 0-4-0 Diesel	Cambridge Engineer's Department
82		Ruston & Hornsby 0-4-0 Diesel	Dinsdale Yard
83		Ruston & Hornsby 0-4-0 Diesel	Low Fell Yard
84		Ruston & Hornsby 0-4-0 Diesel	York Engineer's Yard
85		Ruston & Hornsby 0-4-0 Diesel	Crofton Permanent Way Depot
86		Ruston & Hornsby 0-4-0 Diesel	West Hartlepool Sleeper Depot
87		Ruston & Hornsby 0-4-0 Diesel	Geneva Yard, Darlington
88	D2612	Class 05 Hunslet 0-6-0 Diesel	Faverdale Works Darlington
91		Gardner 0-6-0 Diesel Shunter	Cambridge Engineer's Department
92		Gardner 0-6-0 Diesel Shunter	Cambridge Engineer's Department
11305		Aspinall Rebuilt 0-6-0ST	Horwich Works
11324		Aspinall Rebuilt 0-6-0ST	Horwich Works
11368		Aspinall Rebuilt 0-6-0ST	Horwich Works
DS274		LSWR/Dick Kerr Electric Bo-Bo	Durnsford Road Power Station
DS275		LSWR/Siemens Electric Bo	Waterloo & City Line
DS680		A1 Class 0-6-0T	Lancing Carriage Works
DS681		A1X Class 0-6-0T	Lancing Carriage Works
DS682	30238	G6 Class 0-6-0T	Meldon Quarry
DS1169		Ruston & Hornsby 0-4-0 Diesel	Broad Clyst Sleeper Depot
DS1173		Drewry 0-6-0 Diesel Shunter	Hither Green Engineer's Depot London
ED1		Fowler 0-4-0 Diesel Shunter	Beeston Creosote Works
ED2		Fowler 0-4-0 Diesel Shunter	Ditton Creosote Works
ED3		Fowler 0-4-0 Diesel Shunter	Lenton Permanent Way Depot
ED4		Fowler 0-4-0 Diesel Shunter	Northampton Engineers
ED5		Fowler 0-4-0 Diesel Shunter	Castleton Permanent Way Depot
ED6		Fowler 0-4-0 Diesel Shunter	Castleton Permanent Way Depot
ED7		Fowler 0-4-0 Diesel Shunter	Fazakerley Yard
PWM650		Ruston & Hornsby 0-6-0 Diesel	Didcot
PWM651		Ruston & Hornsby 0-6-0 Diesel	Cardiff Radyr
PWM652		Ruston & Hornsby 0-6-0 Diesel	Taunton
PWM653		Ruston & Hornsby 0-6-0 Diesel	Theale
PWM654		Ruston & Hornsby 0-6-0 Diesel	Hookagate, Shrewsbury
ZM32		Ruston & Hornsby 0-4-0 Diesel	Horwich Works 18in Gauge System

British Railways Narrow Gauge Locomotive Allocations at 1 January

No	Gauge	Locomotive Type	Allocation
7	1ft 11½in	Davies and Metcalfe 2-6-2T	Vale of Rheidol Railway Aberystwyth
8	1ft 11½in	Davies and Metcalfe 2-6-2T	Vale of Rheidol Railway Aberystwyth
9	1ft 11½in	Davies and Metcalfe 2-6-2T	Vale of Rheidol Railway Aberystwyth
823	2ft 6in	Beyer Peacock 0-6-0T	Welshpool & Llanfair Railway

Vale of Rheidol 2-6-2T No 9 *Prince of Wales* awaiting departure from the old station at Aberystwyth in August 1960. According to official records this was a rebuild of the original locomotive, No 1213, and entered service in 1924. In practise, however, it was a totally new locomotive. *P. H. Groom*

Welshpool and Llanfair 0-6-0T No 823 in store inside Oswestry works in 1962. Dating from 1902 it had been rebuilt with a new boiler under GWR ownership in 1930, along with sister engine 822. Freight working ceased on the W&LR in 1956, and the line closed. Both No 822 and 823 were placed in store, with No 822 being withdrawn in August 1961 and No 823 in July 1962. Both were held for preservation and can now be seen once again working over the re-opened line. *R. H. G. Simpson*

British Railways Locomotives Withdrawn During 1962

Withdrawal dates are either for the actual date withdrawn, the week ending (w/e) or the month

No	Month Withdrawn	Last Allocation
823	July	Oswestry
1003	22 October	Plymouth Laira
1004	September	Penzance
1007	5 October	Didcot
1015	13 November	Didcot
1017	19 December	Shrewsbury
1018	September	Didcot
1022	5 October	Shrewsbury
1026	September	Shrewsbury
1029	5 December	Swindon
1363	20 November	Plymouth Laira
1365	20 November	Swindon
1426	3 April	Gloucester Horton Road
1434	4 July	Exeter
1435	5 January	Oxford
1438	9 November	Oswestry
1462	1 September	Exeter
1468	15 March	Oxford
1470	1 October	Exeter
1473	10 August	Gloucester Barnwood
1505	May	Old Oak Common
1508	September	Cardiff Canton
1605	February	Gloucester Horton Road
1609	July	Llanelly
1618	May	Wrexham Croes Newydd
1624	February	St Blazey
1626	August	Gloucester Horton Road
1633	30 October	Llanelly
1642	January	Gloucester Horton Road
1645	30 October	Neath
1646	29 December	Perth
1649	29 December	Helmsdale
1653	5 December	Newport Ebbw Junction
2200	September	Westbury
2209	August	Newport Ebbw Junction
2212	5 December	Reading
2216	January	Carmarthen
2223	May	Templecombe
2229	September	Bristol Barrow Road
2230	January	Didcot
2234	May	Worcester
2239	May	Machynlleth
2240	June	Newport Ebbw Junction
2250	August	Swindon
2255	May	Machynlleth
2256	September	Hereford
2271	September	Machynlleth
2276	September	Machynlleth
2292	June	Severn Tunnel Junction
2294	September	Machynlleth
2295	July	Hereford
2834	5 November	Didcot
2849	August	Newport Ebbw Junction
2853	May	Reading
2855	12 December	Banbury
2860	April	Severn Tunnel Junction
2883	19 November	Westbury
3207	5 December	Worcester
3211	September	Newport Ebbw Junction
3404	July	Cardiff Radyr
3407	5 October	Cardiff Radyr
3408	September	Cardiff Radyr
3602	February	Shrewsbury
3606	18 December	Bristol Barrow Road
3611	August	Neath
3614	March	Westbury
3623	September	Bristol St Philips Marsh
3624	May	Neyland
3630	September	Wrexham Croes Newydd
3632	13 November	Bristol St Philips Marsh
3636	February	Newport Ebbw Junction
3637	22 October	Goodwick
3640	May	Pontypool Road
3641	August	Swansea East Dock
3645	May	Swindon
3655	18 December	Aberdare
3656	February	Llantrisant
3663	18 December	Barry
3666	12 December	Old Oak Common
3674	19 December	Newport Pill
3684	May	Swindon
3688	September	Duffryn Yard
3694	September	Newport Ebbw Junction
3697	May	Didcot
3703	May	Pontypool Road
3713	February	Llanelly
3718	May	Duffryn Yard
3722	May	Newport Ebbw Junction
3723	April	Reading
3726	January	Newport Ebbw Junction
3732	May	Wellington
3741	September	Neath
3743	May	Neath
3750	September	Old Oak Common
3755	22 October	Cardiff East Dock
3760	September	Wrexham Croes Newydd
3769	30 October	Shrewsbury
3773	23 October	Bristol St Philips Marsh
3774	May	Neath
3780	18 December	Swindon
3783	September	Abercynon
3785	July	Swansea East Dock
3827	13 November	Newport Ebbw Junction
4037	September	Exeter
4077	August	Bristol St Philips Marsh
4078	July	Llanelly
4085	May	Old Oak Common
4086	April	Reading
4094	March	Carmarthen
4095	12 December	Reading
4099	September	Llanelly
4102	September	Bristol St Philips Marsh

4106	September	Gloucester Horton Road
4112	August	Banbury
4116	September	Gloucester Horton Road
4118	September	Llantrisant
4126	January	Birmingham Tyseley
4129	September	Kidderminster
4145	18 December	Severn Tunnel Junction
4146	August	Severn Tunnel Junction
4152	September	Severn Tunnel Junction
4163	30 October	Gloucester Horton Road
4218	5 October	Tondu
4230	September	Llanelly
4235	August	Newport Ebbw Junction
4236	September	Aberdare
4246	13 November	Tondu
4250	September	Duffryn Yard
4266	August	Newport Ebbw Junction
4267	23 October	Llantrisant
4269	19 November	Tondu
4270	September	Cardiff East Dock
4274	June	Tondu
4276	13 November	Newport Pill
4289	5 October	Aberdare
4291	September	Aberbeeg
4293	August	Newport Ebbw Junction
4557	September	Neyland
4558	July	Neyland
4561	May	Plymouth Laira
4566	April	Plymouth Laira
4567	September	Plymouth Laira
4588	July	Plymouth Laira
4601	17 November	London Nine Elms
4605	23 October	Wellington
4625	May	Wolverhampton Oxley
4632	January	Merthyr
4641	May	Kidderminster
4647	23 October	Westbury
4656	8 December	Yeovil Town
4685	May	Aberbeeg
4700	23 October	Southall
4702	June	Southall
4708	22 October	Old Oak Common
4906	September	Wolverhampton Oxley
4909	September	Swindon
4912	August	Wolverhampton Oxley
4913	September	Hereford
4917	September	Westbury
4921	September	Reading
4925	August	Southall
4931	July	Cardiff Canton
4934	September	Taunton
4937	September	Pontypool Road
4938	30 December	Llanelly
4941	22 October	Westbury
4944	September	Southall
4947	September	Bristol St Philips Marsh
4948	September	Swindon
4952	September	Cardiff Canton
4957	March	Reading
4960	September	Bristol St Philips Marsh
4961	5 November	Westbury
4963	June	Worcester
4965	March	Didcot
4967	September	Neath
4968	July	Bristol St Philips Marsh
4969	September	Southall
4971	August	Cardiff Canton
4973	July	Cardiff Canton
4974	April	Gloucester Horton Road
4977	May	Cardiff Canton
4982	May	Plymouth Laira
4984	September	Cardiff Canton
4986	May	Southall
4987	April	Southall
4990	April	Hereford
4995	June	Southall
4999	September	Bristol St Philips Marsh
5003	August	Newton Abbot
5004	April	Neath
5006	April	Carmarthen
5007	September	Gloucester Horton Road
5008	September	Old Oak Common
5011	September	Old Oak Common
5012	April	Oxford
5013	July	Neath
5016	September	Llanelly
5017	September	Gloucester Horton Road
5019	September	Stafford Road
5020	20 November	Llanelly
5021	September	Cardiff Canton
5024	May	Newton Abbot
5027	20 November	Llanelly
5030	September	Carmarthen
5032	September	Old Oak Common
5033	September	Oxford
5034	September	Old Oak Common
5035	May	Swindon
5036	September	Old Oak Common
5044	April	Cardiff Canton
5045	September	Stafford Road
5046	September	Stafford Road
5047	September	Stafford Road
5048	August	Llanelly
5052	September	Bristol St Philips Marsh
5053	July	Cardiff Canton
5059	June	Shrewsbury
5061	September	Cardiff Canton
5062	August	Llanelly
5064	September	Gloucester Horton Road
5066	September	Old Oak Common
5067	July	Reading
5068	September	Oxford
5069	February	Plymouth Laira
5072	30 October	Stafford Road
5075	September	Bristol St Philips Marsh
5077	July	Llanelly
5078	20 November	Neath
5082	July	Old Oak Common
5084	July	Old Oak Common
5088	September	Stafford Road
5090	May	Old Oak Common
5094	September	Bristol St Philips Marsh
5095	August	Shrewsbury
5151	August	Kidderminster
5167	January	Banbury
5173	August	Gloucester Horton Road
5180	July	Westbury
5181	August	Severn Tunnel Junction
5182	May	Gloucester Horton Road
5183	May	Stafford Road

5187	May	Stourbridge Junction
5188	July	Newport Ebbw Junction
5190	September	Exeter
5193	June	Severn Tunnel Junction
5204	19 November	Neath
5212	May	Severn Tunnel Junction
5219	6 December	Llanelly
5258	19 December	Aberdare
5326	March	Bristol St Philips Marsh
5357	September	Llanelly
5358	July	Machynlleth
5376	June	Bristol St Philips Marsh
5385	July	Llanelly
5399	September	Wrexham Croes Newydd
5412	April	Exeter
5421	September	Oswestry
5520	September	Neyland
5521	April	Plymouth Laira
5525	September	Newton Abbot
5526	June	Westbury
5532	July	Plymouth Laira
5537	August	Penzance
5539	April	St Blazey
5541	July	Plymouth Laira
5544	September	Plymouth Laira
5547	February	Swindon
5549	January	Neyland
5550	September	Neyland
5560	April	Exeter
5562	September	Penzance
5572	April	Plymouth Laira
5600	July	Treherbert
5604	13 November	Llanelly
5617	September	Abercynon
5630	5 December	Abercynon
5631	September	Swansea East Dock
5636	May	Merthyr
5639	May	Barry
5642	September	Aberdare
5646	September	Treherbert
5652	September	Merthyr
5657	July	Abercynon
5661	July	Merthyr
5663	August	Cardiff Radyr
5664	August	Barry
5682	May	Abercynon
5695	18 December	Treherbert
5698	September	Aberdare
5720	January	Neath
5728	May	Duffryn Yard
5744	April	Westbury
5746	September	Didcot
5758	May	Newport Pill
5761	May	Neath
5766	May	Slough
5773	September	Neath
5774	5 October	Wrexham Croes Newydd
5778	July	Neath
5779	May	Bristol St Philips Marsh
5783	March	Swansea East Dock
5789	May	Pontypool Road
5793	April	Newton Abbot
5798	September	Taunton
5902	13 November	Bristol St Philips Marsh
5906	May	Reading
5909	July	Cardiff Canton
5910	September	Wolverhampton Oxley
5911	September	Cardiff Canton
5912	18 December	Banbury
5913	May	Exeter
5916	July	Wolverhampton Oxley
5917	September	Southall
5918	September	Oxford
5920	January	Westbury
5921	January	Westbury
5925	22 October	Southall
5926	September	Banbury
5928	May	Goodwick
5930	September	Worcester
5931	September	Old Oak Common
5935	May	Cardiff Canton
5940	September	Bristol St Philips Marsh
5941	July	Bristol St Philips Marsh
5946	July	Goodwick
5947	July	Banbury
5953	22 October	Bristol St Philips Marsh
5959	September	Birmingham Tyseley
5960	September	Oxford
5964	September	Westbury
5965	July	Birmingham Tyseley
5966	September	Oxford
5968	September	Gloucester Horton Road
5969	August	Carmarthen
5973	September	Reading
5980	September	Gloucester Horton Road
5981	September	Neath
5982	September	Reading
5989	July	Neath
5996	August	Wolverhampton Oxley
5997	July	Swindon
5999	September	Westbury
6000	4 December	Old Oak Common
6001	4 September	Stafford Road
6002	7 September	Stafford Road
6003	25 June	Cardiff Canton
6004	19 June	Cardiff Canton
6005	20 November	Old Oak Common
6006	15 February	Stafford Road
6007	7 September	Stafford Road
6008	19 June	Stafford Road
6009	7 September	Old Oak Common
6010	22 June	Cardiff Canton
6011	18 December	Old Oak Common
6012	7 September	Stafford Road
6013	12 June	Stafford Road
6014	7 September	Stafford Road
6015	7 September	Stafford Road
6016	9 September	Stafford Road
6017	23 July	Stafford Road
6018	18 December	Old Oak Common
6019	7 September	Stafford Road
6020	24 July	Stafford Road
6021	7 September	Old Oak Common
6022	7 September	Stafford Road
6023	19 June	Cardiff Canton
6024	19 June	Cardiff Canton
6025	18 December	Old Oak Common
6026	7 September	Old Oak Common
6027	21 September	Stafford Road
6028	20 November	Old Oak Common

6029	24 July	Old Oak Common
6101	March	Birmingham Tyseley
6109	August	Didcot
6120	April	Didcot
6123	April	Oxford
6127	March	Slough
6146	September	Taunton
6152	January	Slough
6153	January	Reading
6157	May	Taunton
6162	March	Southall
6166	January	Newton Abbot
6168	March	Old Oak Common
6301	22 October	Wrexham Croes Newydd
6302	March	Didcot
6310	July	Llanelly
6312	September	Bristol St Philips Marsh
6316	July	Llanelly
6324	April	Reading
6330	September	Gloucester Horton Road
6336	April	Machynlleth
6339	July	Wrexham Croes Newydd
6340	July	Taunton
6342	September	Shrewsbury
6348	February	Hereford
6362	September	Severn Tunnel Junction
6366	September	Cardiff Canton
6374	August	Shrewsbury
6376	May	Bristol Barrow Road
6386	September	Severn Tunnel Junction
6387	June	Worcester
6388	September	Kidderminster
6390	May	Taunton
6391	September	Reading
6408	February	Tondu
6410	13 November	Slough
6418	26 November	Stourbridge Junction
6422	September	Stafford Road
6429	March	Wellington
6436	September	Tondu
6438	13 November	Plymouth Laira
6600	August	Llantrisant
6601	5 November	Tondu
6616	September	Neath
6617	September	Wrexham Croes Newydd
6629	22 October	Merthyr
6630	September	Cardiff Canton
6640	September	Wolverhampton Oxley
6641	September	Neath
6645	August	Wolverhampton Oxley
6647	September	Cardiff Radyr
6669	5 December	Cardiff Radyr
6687	May	Aberdare
6738	1 October	Swansea East Dock
6739	June	Newport Pill
6749	30 October	Swansea East Dock
6754	18 December	Swansea East Dock
6755	June	Swansea East Dock
6757	12 December	Swansea East Dock
6758	June	Newport Pill
6767	12 December	Swansea East Dock
6770	30 October	Swansea East Dock
6778	May	Swansea East Dock
6865	May	Bristol St Philips Marsh
7016	26 November	Cardiff East Dock
7224	6 December	Llanelly
7241	26 November	Barry
7300	September	Shrewsbury
7301	September	Bristol St Philips Marsh
7302	August	Pontypool Road
7305	September	Taunton
7309	September	Shrewsbury
7311	September	Exeter
7313	July	Wrexham Croes Newydd
7316	September	Exeter
7321	September	Llanelly
7323	August	Bristol St Philips Marsh
7324	22 October	Didcot
7328	April	Severn Tunnel Junction
7330	September	Shrewsbury
7331	September	Reading
7334	April	Carmarthen
7336	September	Shrewsbury
7338	August	Bristol St Philips Marsh
7341	September	Wrexham Croes Newydd
7402	July	Carmarthen
7406	March	Machynlleth
7408	August	Carmarthen
7422	March	Carmarthen
7425	June	Carmarthen
7428	5 October	Machynlleth
7434	22 October	Oswestry
7440	30 October	Wrexham Croes Newydd
7713	August	Taunton
7718	April	Llanelly
7720	May	Aberdare
7721	July	Newport Pill
7724	September	Pontypool Road
7729	July	Bristol St Philips Marsh
7732	22 October	Tondu
7736	May	Newport Ebbw Junction
7739	4 November	Neath
7744	September	Abercynon
7749	31 December	Bristol St Philips Marsh
7753	April	Tondu
7755	May	Aberbeeg
7762	May	Stoubridge Junction
7764	May	Barry
7765	July	Llanelly
7783	September	Bristol St Philips Marsh
7784	March	Westbury
7785	May	Llanelly
7786	May	Neath
7788	July	Stourbridge Junction
7790	5 November	Bristol St Philips Marsh
7796	February	Pontypool Road
7799	May	Neath
8100	4 October	Leamington Spa
8107	May	Worcester
8407	5 October	Duffryn Yard
8416	5 October	Duffryn Yard
8422	July	Southall
8428	5 October	Wolverhampton Oxley
8435	February	Old Oak Common
8438	5 October	Cardiff Radyr
8439	5 October	Neath
8440	July	Aberbeeg
8445	September	Cardiff East Dock
8449	September	Shrewsbury
8453	5 October	Tondu

8467	February	Llanelly
8470	January	Cardiff Radyr
8477	July	Llanelly
8482	September	Duffryn Yard
8483	February	Swansea East Dock
8489	February	Aberbeeg
8490	5 October	Duffryn Yard
8494	January	Didcot
8499	June	Aberbeeg
8700	February	Birmingham Tyseley
8709	September	Pontypool Road
8711	March	Swindon
8713	March	Birmingham Tyseley
8715	April	Neath
8719	May	St Blazey
8724	July	Duffryn Yard
8725	22 October	Bristol Barrow Road
8727	April	Wrexham Croes Newydd
8729	5 December	Gloucester Horton Road
8730	July	Abercynon
8731	July	Southall
8733	February	St Blazey
8734	March	Wrexham Croes Newydd
8735	January	Abercynon
8736	March	Llanelly
8737	12 December	Neath
8741	May	Bristol St Philips Marsh
8742	September	St Blazey
8744	5 October	Westbury
8746	19 December	Duffryn Yard
8748	September	Tondu
8750	May	Swansea East Dock
8751	18 December	Newport Ebbw Junction
8753	February	Southall
8756	22 October	Old Oak Common
8757	September	Old Oak Common
8760	January	Neath
8761	May	Old Oak Common
8763	August	Old Oak Common
8764	May	Barry
8765	September	Old Oak Common
8770	12 December	Southall
8771	July	Old Oak Common
8773	22 October	Old Oak Common
8776	18 December	Barry
8779	February	Swindon
8780	July	Cardiff Radyr
8781	13 November	Newport Ebbw Junction
8784	April	Neath
8788	May	Neath
8790	May	Bristol St Philips Marsh
8792	February	Stourbridge Junction
8797	April	Stourbridge Junction
8799	1 December	Weymouth
9407	July	Old Oak Common
9409	May	Southall
9410	July	Old Oak Common
9416	January	Swansea East Dock
9421	February	Slough
9424	29 November	Newport Ebbw Junction
9433	July	Penzance
9448	July	Neath
9451	July	Tondu
9454	January	Duffryn Yard
9460	February	Aberbeeg
9465	February	Llanelly
9467	May	Plymouth Laira
9469	March	Old Oak Common
9476	June	Swindon
9478	July	Neath
9486	July	Worcester
9487	July	Exeter
9497	May	Exeter
9604	12 December	Swindon
9627	July	Neath
9643	May	Merthyr
9702	May	Old Oak Common
9709	May	Old Oak Common
9712	September	Aberdare
9717	18 December	Hereford
9718	May	Taunton
9719	July	Stourbridge Junction
9721	June	Swindon
9722	July	Slough
9723	July	Abercynon
9725	12 December	Old Oak Common
9727	9 November	Barry
9728	May	Abercynon
9738	January	Tondu
9740	February	Swindon
9741	August	Wellington
9750	May	Neath
9756	1 December	Weymouth
9757	August	Taunton
9758	May	Old Oak Common
9759	22 October	Swansea East Dock
9761	22 October	Swansea East Dock
9775	5 November	Barry
9783	May	Neath
9785	September	Duffryn Yard
9797	September	Pontypool Road
30028	29 September	Eastleigh
30033	22 December	Salisbury
30045	8 December	Exmouth Junction
30049	2 June	Guildford
30050	27 January	Bournemouth
30051	29 September	London Nine Elms
30061	20 October	Southampton Docks
30062	1 December	Southampton Docks
30063	2 June	Southampton Docks
30065	6 October	Southampton Docks
30066	30 December	Southampton Docks
30070	6 October	Southampton Docks
30125	30 December	Exmouth Junction
30131	1 December	Yeovil Town
30132	27 October	Guildford
30193	3 April	Plymouth Friary
30199	23 December	Eastleigh
30200	11 August	Plymouth Friary
30225	23 December	Eastleigh
30245	17 November	London Nine Elms
30306	21 April	Eastleigh
30309	23 December	Salisbury
30315	23 December	Salisbury
30316	23 December	Eastleigh
30321	8 September	Plymouth Friary
30325	23 December	Guildford
30326	10 February	Guildford
30339	19 May	Feltham
30346	17 November	Feltham

30350	24 March	Guildford
30368	23 December	Basingstoke
30375	8 September	Plymouth Friary
30377	18 August	Eastleigh
30378	30 December	Bournemouth
30451	16 June	Salisbury
30494	8 December	Feltham
30495	15 December	Feltham
30502	15 December	Feltham
30504	17 November	Feltham
30505	17 November	Feltham
30516	17 November	Feltham
30517	29 December	Feltham
30518	17 November	Feltham
30519	17 November	Feltham
30520	17 November	Feltham
30534	22 December	London Stewarts Lane
30537	8 December	London Stewarts Lane
30540	24 November	Three Bridges
30585	29 December	Wadebridge
30586	29 December	Wadebridge
30587	29 December	Wadebridge
30689	17 November	Exmouth Junction
30690	23 December	Guildford
30692	3 February	Salisbury
30695	23 December	Eastleigh
30697	17 November	Exmouth Junction
30698	19 May	Guildford
30700	17 November	Exmouth Junction
30765	29 September	Basingstoke
30770	24 November	Basingstoke
30773	10 February	Eastleigh
30781	12 May	Bournemouth
30782	15 September	Bournemouth
30788	10 February	Eastleigh
30793	1 September	Basingstoke
30795	4 August	Basingstoke
30796	3 March	Salisbury
30798	16 June	Salisbury
30804	17 February	Eastleigh
30826	1 December	Salisbury
30850	18 August	Eastleigh
30852	17 February	Eastleigh
30853	3 March	Eastleigh
30856	22 September	Eastleigh
30857	22 September	Eastleigh
30860	11 August	Eastleigh
30861	6 October	Eastleigh
30862	6 October	Eastleigh
30863	10 February	Eastleigh
30864	27 January	Eastleigh
30900	10 February	Brighton
30901	22 December	Brighton
30902	30 December	London Nine Elms
30903	30 December	London Nine Elms
30906	23 December	Brighton
30909	17 February	Guildford
30911	30 December	Brighton
30912	1 December	London Nine Elms
30913	27 January	London Nine Elms
30915	23 December	Brighton
30916	30 December	Brighton
30917	24 November	Brighton
30921	30 December	London Nine Elms
30923	30 December	Brighton
30924	13 January	Redhill
30925	30 December	Basingstoke
30926	30 December	Basingstoke
30927	20 January	London Nine Elms
30928	17 November	Brighton
30929	8 December	Brighton
30930	30 December	Brighton
30934	30 December	Basingstoke
30935	23 December	London Nine Elms
30936	23 December	London Nine Elms
30937	8 December	London Nine Elms
30950	20 October	Exmouth Junction
30951	24 November	Exmouth Junction
30952	24 November	Exmouth Junction
30953	15 December	Exmouth Junction
30954	8 December	Exmouth Junction
30955	15 December	Exmouth Junction
30956	22 December	Exmouth Junction
30957	17 November	Exmouth Junction
31112	5 May	Ashford
31218	5 May	Ashford
31267	30 June	London Stewarts Lane
31268	5 May	Ashford
31278	6 October	Tunbridge Wells West
31293	5 May	London Bricklayers Arms
31305	17 November	London Stewarts Lane
31308	23 December	Tunbridge Wells West
31317	24 February	London Stewarts Lane
31324	28 July	Three Bridges
31409	17 November	Exmouth Junction
31414	24 November	Guildford
31510	30 June	London Stewarts Lane
31521	19 May	Tunbridge Wells West
31530	24 March	Three Bridges
31533	15 September	Tunbridge Wells West
31542	17 November	London Stewarts Lane
31584	17 February	London Stewarts Lane
31588	23 June	London Stewarts Lane
31610	30 December	Guildford
31630	17 November	Guildford
31686	5 May	Ashford
31689	31 March	London Bricklayers Arms
31690	23 June	London Stewarts Lane
31717	24 February	London Bricklayers Arms
31719	19 May	London Bricklayers Arms
31721	31 March	Ashford
31722	5 May	Ashford
31723	3 February	Guildford
31724	5 May	Ashford
31786	10 February	London Nine Elms
31822	17 November	London Stewarts Lane
31876	17 November	London Stewarts Lane
31877	17 November	London Stewarts Lane
31878	17 November	London Stewarts Lane
31879	17 November	London Stewarts Lane
31880	17 November	London Stewarts Lane
31892	24 November	Three Bridges
31893	30 December	Three Bridges
31894	30 December	Three Bridges
31895	23 December	Brighton
31896	30 December	Brighton
31897	17 November	London Stewarts Lane
31898	30 December	Brighton
31899	30 December	London Norwood Junction
31900	30 December	London Norwood Junction

31902	17 November	London Norwood Junction
31903	30 December	London Norwood Junction
31904	24 November	London Norwood Junction
31905	30 December	London Norwood Junction
31906	22 December	London Norwood Junction
31907	30 December	London Norwood Junction
31908	30 December	London Norwood Junction
31909	22 December	London Norwood Junction
32101	15 September	Southampton Docks
32103	6 October	Southampton Docks
32105	22 September	Southampton Docks
32106	6 October	Southampton Docks
32337	8 December	Brighton
32338	30 December	Brighton
32339	10 November	Brighton
32340	23 December	Brighton
32341	30 December	Brighton
32342	30 December	Brighton
32343	23 December	Brighton
32344	24 November	Brighton
32345	29 December	Three Bridges
32346	24 November	Three Bridges
32347	22 December	Three Bridges
32348	10 November	Three Bridges
32349	24 November	Three Bridges
32350	24 November	Three Bridges
32351	24 November	Three Bridges
32352	24 November	Three Bridges
32353	30 December	Three Bridges
32408	23 December	Eastleigh
32416	10 February	Feltham
32417	23 December	Brighton
32418	23 December	Brighton
32470	23 June	Brighton
32472	3 June	London Nine Elms
32473	27 October	London Nine Elms
32487	23 December	London Nine Elms
32500	27 January	London Nine Elms
32509	31 March	Brighton
32510	29 September	Eastleigh
32523	10 February	Three Bridges
32525	3 February	Three Bridges
32535	10 February	Three Bridges
32557	23 December	London Nine Elms
32580	7 April	Brighton
32581	7 April	Brighton
W25	30 December	Ryde
40006	w/e 13 October	London Willesden
40009	w/e 19 May	Heaton Mersey
40022	w/e 15 December	London Cricklewood
40024	w/e 3 March	London Kentish Town
40026	w/e 1 December	London Kentish Town
40031	w/e 1 December	London Kentish Town
40063	w/e 8 September	Newton Heath
40072	w/e 1 September	Lower Darwen
40073	w/e 18 August	Kirkby-in-Ashfield
40078	w/e 1 December	Bangor
40080	w/e 8 September	London Willesden
40082	27 February	Normanton
40083	w/e 1 December	Llandudno Junction
40085	w/e 7 July	Chester
40086	w/e 24 November	Llandudno Junction
40087	w/e 24 November	Nuneaton
40088	w/e 21 July	Kirkby-in-Ashfield
40089	w/e 4 August	Kirkby-in-Ashfield
40090	w/e 21 July	Southport
40093	w/e 27 January	Llandudno Junction
40098	w/e 17 November	Llandudno Junction
40099	w/e 13 October	Lower Darwen
40100	w/e 18 August	London Kentish Town
40104	w/e 15 September	Nuneaton
40105	w/e 21 July	Heaton Mersey
40106	w/e 24 November	Llandudno Junction
40109	w/e 21 July	Blackpool
40110	w/e 5 May	London Willesden
40112	19 November	Leeds Copley Hill
40113	w/e 21 July	Heaton Mersey
40114	19 November	Leeds Copley Hill
40116	w/e 24 November	Bangor
40117	19 November	Scarborough
40119	w/e 18 August	London Kentish Town
40120	w/e 13 October	Lower Darwen
40122	w/e 23 June	Llandudno Junction
40128	w/e 21 July	London Willesden
40135	w/e 24 November	Nuneaton
40137	w/e 17 November	Llandudno Junction
40138	w/e 22 September	Llandudno Junction
40145	w/e 22 September	Southport
40146	w/e 4 August	Kirkby-in-Ashfield
40147	19 November	Wakefield
40148	23 August	Royston
40150	29 December	Perth
40151	29 December	Hurlford
40152	8 January	Dumfries
40153	29 December	Glasgow Dawsholm
40154	8 January	Glasgow Dawsholm
40157	w/e 1 December	London Willesden
40158	8 January	Glasgow Dawsholm
40159	29 December	Glasgow Dawsholm
40164	w/e 13 October	Lower Darwen
40170	8 January	Dumfries
40173	w/e 21 July	Bangor
40174	w/e 9 June	Blackpool
40176	29 December	Glasgow Dawsholm
40177	29 December	Glasgow Dawsholm
40179	27 February	Normanton
40180	w/e 20 January	Birmingham Aston
40181	30 March	Normanton
40185	w/e 24 February	Llandudno Junction
40186	29 December	Motherwell
40187	29 December	Motherwell
40188	29 December	Glasgow Dawsholm
40189	29 December	Glasgow Dawsholm
40190	19 November	Darlington
40191	w/e 22 September	Southport
40193	23 August	Royston
40196	w/e 29 December	Southport
40197	w/e 21 July	Southport
40198	w/e 21 July	Southport
40200	29 December	Glasgow Dawsholm
40201	w/e 21 July	London Willesden
40202	w/e 15 September	Llandudno Junction
40203	w/e 21 July	London Kentish Town
40205	w/e 24 November	Bangor
40206	w/e 17 February	Carnforth
40207	w/e 10 February	Nuneaton
40453	w/e 22 September	Manchester Patricroft
40537	w/e 1 September	Templecombe
40540	w/e 10 February	Gloucester Barnwood
40563	w/e 19 May	Templecombe

40564	w/e 10 February	Templecombe
40634	w/e 19 May	Templecombe
40638	21 May	Stranraer
40646	w/e 12 May	Bescot
40657	w/e 20 October	Watford
40664	16 July	Stranraer
40665	11 June	Hurlford
40670	17 December	Dumfries
40672	w/e 20 October	Watford
40681	w/e 4 August	Manchester Patricroft
40694	w/e 17 November	Bescot
40696	w/e 26 May	Bath Green Park
40697	w/e 10 February	Bath Green Park
40700	w/e 1 September	Bath Green Park
41235	w/e 17 November	Llandudno Junction
41236	w/e 3 November	Llandudno Junction
41246	16 September	Canklow
41247	17 November	Malton
41252	23 November	Leeds Neville Hill
41254	24 November	Leeds Farnley Junction
41255	19 June	Leeds Farnley Junction
41256	19 June	Leeds Farnley Junction
41257	19 June	Bradford Manningham
41258	27 September	Leeds Farnley Junction
41259	19 June	Leeds Neville Hill
41263	12 December	Bradford Low Moor
41265	10 December	Malton
41266	17 November	Bradford Manningham
41267	23 November	Leeds Holbeck
41269	w/e 8 December	Liverpool Bank Hall
41271	w/e 3 November	Leicester Midland
41277	w/e 1 December	Southport
41278	w/e 17 November	Llandudno Junction
41280	w/e 8 December	Leicester Midland
41288	w/e 3 November	Warrington Dallam
41702	w/e 30 June	Manchester Gorton
41769	28 February	Staveley Barrow Hill
41900	w/e 17 March	Leamington Spa
41981	18 June	Tilbury
42088	w/e 3 November	Manchester Gorton
42094	16 November	Sowerby Bridge
42097	w/e 8 December	Watford
42111	w/e 8 December	Manchester Trafford Park
42117	w/e 29 December	London Willesden
42122	29 December	Ayr
42130	29 December	Beattock
42144	29 December	Glasgow Polmadie
42146	w/e 3 November	Derby
42162	29 December	Carstairs
42164	29 December	Motherwell
42172	29 December	Edinburgh Dalry Road
42173	29 December	Carstairs
42175	29 December	Greenock Ladyburn
42191	29 December	Ardrossan
42193	29 December	Ardrossan
42203	21 December	Stranraer
42205	29 December	Beattock
42207	w/e 8 December	Bolton
42211	w/e 8 December	Bangor
42215	29 December	Beattock
42219	18 June	Shoeburyness
42223	18 June	Shoeburyness
42227	w/e 20 October	Bletchley
42237	w/e 8 December	Rowsley
42248	w/e 15 December	Manchester Gorton
42254	18 June	Tilbury
42255	18 June	Tilbury
42257	18 June	Tilbury
42258	29 December	Greenock Ladyburn
42268	29 December	Glasgow Polmadie
42272	29 December	Edinburgh Dalry Road
42276	29 December	Glasgow Polmadie
42290	w/e 29 September	Southport
42298	w/e 17 November	Lostock Hall
42303	w/e 27 October	Wigan Springs Branch
42304	w/e 8 September	Carlisle Kingmoor
42305	w/e 1 September	Swansea East Dock
42306	w/e 29 December	Buxton
42314	w/e 29 December	Buxton
42315	w/e 29 December	Carnforth
42318	w/e 8 September	Barrow
42320	w/e 17 November	Carlisle Kingmoor
42323	w/e 23 June	Stoke-on-Trent
42324	14 November	Bradford Low Moor
42331	w/e 1 September	Leicester Midland
42336	w/e 20 October	London Kentish Town
42340	w/e 9 June	Barrow
42342	w/e 2 June	London Kentish Town
42347	w/e 15 September	Barrow
42351	w/e 25 August	Birkenhead
42352	w/e 28 April	Leicester Midland
42358	w/e 27 October	Stoke-on-Trent
42362	w/e 2 June	Stoke-on-Trent
42367	w/e 25 August	London Willesden
42370	w/e 30 June	Buxton
42371	w/e 28 April	Buxton
42372	w/e 29 December	Stockport Edgeley
42375	w/e 24 February	Uttoxeter
42376	w/e 17 November	Barrow
42385	w/e 8 September	Swansea East Dock
42387	w/e 31 March	Swansea East Dock
42388	2 November	Swansea East Dock
42393	w/e 26 May	Carlisle Upperby
42396	w/e 7 July	Tebay
42402	w/e 13 October	Barrow
42403	w/e 29 December	Tebay
42407	12 November	Mirfield
42412	3 January	Huddersfield
42415	w/e 29 December	Tebay
42420	w/e 19 May	Barrow
42422	w/e 22 December	Birmingham Saltley
42429	w/e 29 September	Manchester Gorton
42433	w/e 12 May	Lostock Hall
42443	w/e 17 November	Stoke-on-Trent
42448	w/e 6 January	Manchester Trafford Park
42452	w/e 10 March	Nottingham Midland
42454	w/e 8 December	Stoke-on-Trent
42457	w/e 17 November	Carnforth
42470	w/e 29 September	London Willesden
42472	w/e 3 November	Manchester Gorton
42473	w/e 3 November	Wigan L&Y
42476	w/e 29 September	Lostock Hall
42483	w/e 29 September	Lower Darwen
42500	18 June	Shoeburyness
42501	18 June	Shoeburyness
42502	18 June	Shoeburyness
42503	18 June	Shoeburyness
42504	18 June	Shoeburyness
42505	18 June	Shoeburyness
42508	18 June	Shoeburyness

42509	18 June	Shoeburyness
42511	18 June	Shoeburyness
42513	18 June	Shoeburyness
42514	11 April	Shoeburyness
42515	18 June	Shoeburyness
42516	18 June	Shoeburyness
42517	18 June	Shoeburyness
42518	18 June	Shoeburyness
42519	18 June	Shoeburyness
42520	18 June	Shoeburyness
42522	18 June	Shoeburyness
42523	18 June	Shoeburyness
42525	18 June	Shoeburyness
42526	18 June	Shoeburyness
42527	18 June	Shoeburyness
42528	18 June	Shoeburyness
42529	18 June	Shoeburyness
42530	18 June	Shoeburyness
42532	18 June	Shoeburyness
42533	18 June	Shoeburyness
42535	18 June	Shoeburyness
42536	18 June	Shoeburyness
42537	w/e 22 September	Southport
42538	18 June	Shoeburyness
42540	w/e 3 November	Walton-on-the-Hill
42541	w/e 15 December	Rugby
42544	w/e 1 December	Stafford
42553	12 November	Darlington
42568	w/e 15 December	Rowsley
42575	w/e 13 October	Crewe North
42576	18 June	Shoeburyness
42578	w/e 13 October	Manchester Longsight
42579	18 June	Shoeburyness
42580	w/e 17 November	Liverpool Speke Junction
42585	w/e 1 December	London Willesden
42591	w/e 29 September	Barrow
42593	18 June	Shoeburyness
42596	w/e 11 August	Manchester Trafford Park
42599	w/e 29 September	Liverpool Edge Hill
42600	w/e 17 November	Stoke-on-Trent
42615	w/e 29 September	London Willesden
42621	w/e 3 November	Wigan L&Y
42624	w/e 17 November	Wigan L&Y
42638	w/e 8 December	Blackpool
42641	w/e 29 September	Wigan L&Y
42642	w/e 29 September	Wigan L&Y
42646	w/e 29 September	Manchester Agecroft
42653	w/e 29 September	Bolton
42658	w/e 29 September	Birkenhead
42661	w/e 29 September	Lostock Hall
42666	w/e 29 September	Barrow
42671	w/e 8 December	Stockport Edgeley
42672	18 June	Shoeburyness
42674	w/e 17 November	Stoke-on-Trent
42677	18 June	Shoeburyness
42678	18 June	Shoeburyness
42679	18 June	Shoeburyness
42684	18 June	Shoeburyness
42685	w/e 29 September	Rowsley
42687	18 June	Shoeburyness
42692	29 December	Greenock Ladyburn
42713	30 November	Leeds Farnley Junction
42714	w/e 29 September	Newton Heath
42720	w/e 29 December	Carlisle Canal
42724	w/e 18 August	Manchester Agecroft
42726	w/e 27 October	Newton Heath
42742	30 July	Ardrossan
42743	29 December	Hurlford
42744	29 December	Hurlford
42745	29 December	Ayr
42749	30 July	Stranraer
42752	w/e 29 December	Carlisle Canal
42764	w/e 20 Jan	Birmingham Saltley
42766	30 November	Leeds Farnley Junction
42773	w/e 24 November	Birkenhead
42775	w/e 6 October	Manchester Gorton
42779	w/e 19 May	Lancaster Green Ayre
42781	w/e 1 December	Chester
42784	w/e 22 December	Birmingham Saltley
42786	w/e 3 November	Birkenhead
42797	w/e 10 March	Birkenhead
42804	w/e 29 December	Birkenhead
42807	29 December	Ayr
42808	29 December	Ayr
42809	29 December	Ayr
42811	w/e 14 July	Nuneaton
42818	w/e 5 May	Burton-on-Trent
42822	w/e 2 June	Burton-on-Trent
42824	w/e 7 July	Burton-on-Trent
42825	w/e 30 June	Burton-on-Trent
42829	w/e 30 June	Burton-on-Trent
42830	w/e 10 November	Carlisle Kingmoor
42833	w/e 29 December	Lancaster Green Ayre
42834	w/e 29 December	Carlisle Kingmoor
42835	w/e 29 December	Carlisle Canal
42836	w/e 29 December	Carlisle Canal
42837	w/e 29 December	Carlisle Kingmoor
42847	w/e 30 June	Manchester Gorton
42850	30 July	Glasgow Polmadie
42857	w/e 15 December	Manchester Gorton
42862	30 November	Wakefield
42866	18 October	Leeds Farnley Junction
42868	w/e 9 June	Manchester Agecroft
42874	w/e 6 October	Manchester Gorton
42875	w/e 29 December	Carlisle Kingmoor
42876	w/e 29 December	Stoke-on-Trent
42877	w/e 29 December	Birkenhead
42881	w/e 17 November	Carlisle Kingmoor
42882	w/e 29 December	Carlisle Kingmoor
42883	w/e 29 December	Carlisle Kingmoor
42884	w/e 29 December	Carlisle Kingmoor
42887	w/e 29 September	Stoke-on-Trent
42889	w/e 5 May	Stoke-on-Trent
42891	w/e 20 October	Stoke-on-Trent
42899	w/e 29 December	Carlisle Kingmoor
42903	w/e 18 August	Birmingham Saltley
42906	w/e 29 December	Carlisle Kingmoor
42915	29 December	Dumfries
42918	29 December	Dumfries
42927	30 July	Ayr
42929	w/e 4 August	Stoke-on-Trent
42939	w/e 23 June	Nuneaton
43213	w/e 19 May	Buxton
43216	w/e 1 September	Templecombe
43240	w/e 29 September	Warrington Dallam
43242	w/e 4 August	Birmingham Saltley
43254	w/e 18 August	Derby
43257	w/e 29 September	Warrington Dallam
43261	w/e 8 December	Manchester Gorton
43263	w/e 2 June	Birmingham Saltley

43282	w/e 13 October	Warrington Dallam
43389	w/e 4 August	Birmingham Saltley
43400	w/e 10 March	Manchester Gorton
43410	w/e 24 March	Warrington Dallam
43428	w/e 8 December	Bedford
43435	w/e 21 April	Birmingham Saltley
43436	w/e 30 June	Rose Grove
43446	17 April	Royston
43449	w/e 8 September	Bedford
43464	w/e 31 March	Crewe South
43496	w/e 4 August	Rowsley
43499	w/e 4 August	Manchester Gorton
43510	w/e 12 May	Derby
43514	w/e 13 October	Buxton
43565	w/e 23 June	Bedford
43583	w/e 4 August	Birmingham Saltley
43585	w/e 22 September	Hellifield
43586	2 August	Bradford Manningham
43593	17 November	Gloucester Barnwood
43599	w/e 29 December	Birmingham Saltley
43608	w/e 4 August	Burton-on-Trent
43615	w/e 13 October	Warrington Dallam
43618	w/e 24 March	Rhyl
43621	w/e 21 April	Derby
43645	17 November	Gloucester Barnwood
43657	w/e 13 October	Warrington Dallam
43668	w/e 4 August	Birmingham Saltley
43679	w/e 27 January	Derby
43680	w/e 4 August	Birmingham Saltley
43682	w/e 1 September	Templecombe
43687	w/e 4 August	Birmingham Saltley
43709	w/e 4 August	Burton-on-Trent
43714	18 January	Normanton
43721	w/e 17 March	Manchester Gorton
43734	w/e 22 September	Rose Grove
43754	17 November	Gloucester Barnwood
43756	w/e 22 September	Hellifield
43760	w/e 31 March	Buxton
43763	w/e 10 March	Manchester Gorton
43766	w/e 4 August	Bedford
43789	w/e 9 June	Manchester Gorton
43793	w/e 10 March	Manchester Gorton
43808	w/e 8 September	Bedford
43822	w/e 11 August	Buxton
43825	w/e 7 April	Rowsley
43844	24 May	Staveley Barrow Hill
43848	11 June	Motherwell
43849	12 March	Motherwell
43859	w/e 3 March	London Kentish Town
43869	21 June	Staveley Barrow Hill
43876	w/e 8 December	Coalville
43899	1 October	Hurlford
43902	w/e 2 June	Carlisle Kingmoor
43914	7 September	Royston
43932	w/e 1 September	Manchester Gorton
43933	w/e 17 November	Kirkby-in-Ashfield
43938	w/e 7 April	Birmingham Saltley
43985	w/e 31 March	Birmingham Saltley
43996	12 March	Ardrossan
44001	26 March	Glasgow Corkerhill
44004	w/e 22 December	Birmingham Saltley
44008	w/e 25 August	Carlisle Kingmoor
44011	1 October	Glasgow Polmadie
44016	w/e 21 July	Carnforth
44020	w/e 1 September	Wellingborough
44036	21 June	Staveley Barrow Hill
44062	16 August	Wakefield
44070	26 June	Staveley Barrow Hill
44087	27 February	Royston
44104	24 May	Staveley Barrow Hill
44122	w/e 1 September	Hasland
44128	29 December	Staveley Barrow Hill
44129	27 September	Staveley Barrow Hill
44138	w/e 14 July	Derby
44143	w/e 13 October	Birmingham Saltley
44154	w/e 7 April	Westhouses
44158	w/e 14 July	Leicester Midland
44159	1 October	Hurlford
44166	w/e 27 January	Coalville
44187	w/e 21 July	Birmingham Saltley
44189	29 December	Hurlford
44193	1 October	Motherwell
44194	29 December	Glasgow St Rollox
44196	8 January	Motherwell
44198	29 December	Hurlford
44199	29 December	Glasgow St Rollox
44216	28 August	Bradford Manningham
44224	w/e 3 February	Toton
44228	w/e 29 December	Bedford
44234	1 October	Grangemouth
44245	17 May	Canklow
44251	1 October	Glasgow Polmadie
44253	1 October	Perth
44254	1 October	Perth
44255	29 December	Fort William
44256	30 April	Glasgow Polmadie
44257	1 October	Perth
44258	21 May	Inverness
44267	24 May	Staveley Barrow Hill
44273	16 September	March
44281	29 December	Hurlford
44283	29 December	Hurlford
44307	w/e 6 October	Stoke-on-Trent
44312	1 October	Hurlford
44314	16 July	Perth
44318	1 October	Glasgow Polmadie
44320	1 October	Grangemouth
44322	29 December	Hurlford
44323	1 October	Glasgow Corkerhill
44325	1 October	Hurlford
44328	29 December	Perth
44329	16 July	Ayr
44330	1 October	Glasgow Corkerhill
44331	29 December	Hurlford
44338	16 August	Normanton
44340	3 December	Leeds Holbeck
44368	15 August	Leeds Stourton
44388	w/e 29 December	Toton
44393	5 November	Leeds Holbeck
44397	w/e 31 March	Bletchley
44404	2 December	Staveley Barrow Hill
44407	w/e 1 September	Heaton Mersey
44417	27 November	Bath Green Park
44435	w/e 13 October	Burton-on-Trent
44482	2 May	Staveley Barrow Hill
44487	w/e 7 April	Barrow
44491	8 October	Leeds Holbeck
44508	w/e 18 August	Buxton
44509	16 September	March
44518	29 August	Staveley Barrow Hill

44521	16 September	March
44537	8 October	Leeds Holbeck
44550	2 March	Royston
44553	w/e 27 October	Warrington Dallam
44557	w/e 15 September	Carlisle Kingmoor
44561	3 April	Bath Green Park
44573	24 May	Staveley Barrow Hill
44576	17 May	Canklow
44579	w/e 3 November	Skipton
44594	8 October	Leeds Holbeck
44606	23 March	Staveley Barrow Hill
45030	29 December	Edinburgh Dalry Road
45036	29 December	Edinburgh Dalry Road
45085	29 December	Motherwell
45086	29 December	Edinburgh Dalry Road
45098	29 December	Glasgow Polmadie
45119	29 December	Glasgow St Rollox
45125	29 December	Grangemouth
45151	29 December	Motherwell
45152	29 December	Motherwell
45157	29 December	Glasgow St Rollox
45159	29 December	Glasgow St Rollox
45165	29 December	Motherwell
45169	29 December	Dumfries
45174	29 December	Carstairs
45179	29 December	Motherwell
45265	w/e 19 May	Birmingham Saltley
45266	29 December	Hurlford
45355	29 December	Edinburgh Dalry Road
45452	29 December	Carstairs
45453	29 December	Dumfries
45458	29 December	Glasgow Polmadie
45504	w/e 17 March	Bristol Barrow Road
45505	w/e 2 June	Lancaster Green Ayre
45506	w/e 17 March	Bristol Barrow Road
45507	w/e 20 October	Lancaster Green Ayre
45510	w/e 9 June	Lancaster Green Ayre
45513	w/e 15 Sept	Liverpool Edge Hill
45515	w/e 9 June	Newton Heath
45517	w/e 9 June	Liverpool Bank Hall
45518	w/e 20 October	Lancaster Green Ayre
45519	w/e 17 March	Bristol Barrow Road
45520	w/e 19 May	Liverpool Edge Hill
45524	w/e 15 Sept	Liverpool Edge Hill
45533	w/e 15 Sept	Liverpool Edge Hill
45536	29 December	Sheffield Darnall
45537	w/e 9 June	Nuneaton
45538	w/e 22 September	Nuneaton
45541	w/e 9 June	Nuneaton
45542	w/e 9 June	Nuneaton
45543	w/e 17 November	Carnforth
45546	w/e 9 June	Warrington Dallam
45547	w/e 15 Sept	Liverpool Edge Hill
45548	w/e 9 June	Nuneaton
45549	w/e 16 June	Warrington Dallam
45550	w/e 1 December	Carnforth
45551	w/e 16 June	Liverpool Edge Hill
45559	w/e 2 October	Blackpool
45566	12 November	Leeds Holbeck
45570	29 December	Sheffield Darnall
45576	29 December	Sheffield Darnall
45582	w/e 8 December	Carnforth
45587	w/e 15 December	Carnforth
45594	29 December	Sheffield Darnall
45603	w/e 8 December	Nuneaton
45607	w/e 1 December	Manchester Agecroft
45615	w/e 8 December	Burton-on-Trent
45621	29 December	Glasgow Corkerhill
45628	w/e 8 December	London Kentish Town
45636	w/e 8 December	Burton-on-Trent
45651	w/e 24 November	Shrewsbury
45656	29 December	Sheffield Darnall
45662	w/e 24 November	Shrewsbury
45665	29 December	Glasgow Corkerhill
45673	29 December	Glasgow Corkerhill
45677	29 December	Glasgow Corkerhill
45678	w/e 8 December	Stockport Edgeley
45679	w/e 29 December	Newton Heath
45683	29 December	Sheffield Darnall
45686	w/e 17 November	Carnforth
45687	29 December	Glasgow Corkerhill
45688	w/e 15 December	Carlisle Kingmoor
45691	w/e 29 December	Blackpool
45692	29 December	Glasgow Corkerhill
45693	29 December	Glasgow Corkerhill
45707	29 December	Glasgow Corkerhill
45711	29 December	Glasgow Corkerhill
45713	w/e 20 October	Liverpool Bank Hall
45715	w/e 29 December	Liverpool Bank Hall
45718	w/e 20 October	Manchester Agecroft
45720	29 December	Glasgow Corkerhill
45722	w/e 1 December	Rugby
45724	w/e 3 November	Nuneaton
45725	29 December	Sheffield Darnall
45727	29 December	Glasgow Corkerhill
45728	w/e 20 October	Manchester Agecroft
45729	w/e 20 October	Manchester Agecroft
45731	w/e 20 October	Blackpool
46100	w/e 13 October	Nottingham Midland
46102	29 December	Glasgow Corkerhill
46103	19 December	Leeds Holbeck
46104	29 December	Glasgow Corkerhill
46105	29 December	Glasgow Polmadie
46106	w/e 8 December	Carlisle Upperby
46107	29 December	Glasgow Polmadie
46109	27 December	Leeds Holbeck
46113	17 December	Leeds Holbeck
46117	26 November	Leeds Holbeck
46121	29 December	Glasgow Polmadie
46123	w/e 3 November	Carlisle Upperby
46124	w/e 29 December	Carlisle Kingmoor
46127	w/e 8 December	Carlisle Upperby
46130	17 December	Leeds Holbeck
46131	w/e 3 November	Llandudno Junction
46134	w/e 1 December	Carlisle Upperby
46135	24 December	Leeds Holbeck
46137	w/e 3 November	Carlisle Upperby
46139	w/e 13 October	Newton Heath
46145	6 December	Leeds Holbeck
46146	w/e 1 December	London Willesden
46147	w/e 1 December	London Willesden
46151	29 December	Sheffield Darnall
46153	w/e 22 December	Annesley
46154	w/e 1 December	London Willesden
46159	w/e 1 December	London Willesden
46161	26 November	Leeds Holbeck
46164	29 December	Sheffield Darnall
46170	w/e 1 December	Llandudno Junction
46200	w/e 17 November	Carlisle Kingmoor
46201	w/e 20 October	Carlisle Upperby

46203	w/e 20 October	Carlisle Kingmoor	47474	w/e 1 September	Stafford
46206	w/e 3 November	London Camden	47475	w/e 24 February	Stafford
46208	w/e 20 October	Liverpool Edge Hill	47479	w/e 4 August	Nuneaton
46209	w/e 29 September	London Camden	47483	w/e 3 March	Lancaster Green Ayre
46227	29 December	Glasgow Polmadie	47488	w/e 1 December	Liverpool Edge Hill
46231	29 December	Glasgow Polmadie	47491	w/e 15 December	Manchester Patricroft
46232	29 December	Glasgow Polmadie	47497	w/e 22 September	Birkenhead
46408	26 October	Malton	47504	w/e 21 April	Chester
46415	31 October	Goole	47514	w/e 19 May	Carnforth
46453	16 April	Leeds Holbeck	47516	w/e 10 Feb	Crewe South
46466	30 August	March	47522	w/e 4 August	Workington
46469	30 August	March	47526	w/e 1 December	Crewe South
46471	18 October	Tweedmouth	47536	11 June	Motherwell
46476	29 January	Tweedmouth	47542	w/e 27 May	Templecombe
46477	17 December	Darlington	47545	2 August	Staveley Barrow Hill
46478	30 April	Goole	47546	w/e 7 July	Newton Heath
46481	14 December	Malton	47548	15 August	Canklow
46493	18 October	Leeds Holbeck	47552	12 November	Templecombe
46494	12 September	March	47554	w/e 25 August	Manchester Gorton
47163	29 December	Greenock Ladyburn	47555	18 June	Tilbury
47168	1 October	Greenock Ladyburn	47556	10 December	York
47213	w/e 3 March	London Kentish Town	47562	w/e 1 December	Rose Grove
47217	w/e 18 August	Newton Heath	47572	w/e 19 May	Lostock Hall
47224	w/e 28 April	Manchester Agecroft	47574	w/e 15 December	Manchester Agecroft
47235	w/e 13 October	Walton-on-the-Hill	47588	w/e 13 October	Stafford
47259	w/e 24 March	Liverpool Aintree	47593	w/e 1 September	Workington
47261	w/e 30 June	London Kentish Town	47601	w/e 17 March	Crewe South
47269	w/e 8 September	Carlisle Upperby	47604	w/e 4 August	Workington
47270	w/e 8 September	Wigan Springs Branch	47608	w/e 1 December	Crewe South
47275	w/e 17 March	Bath Green Park	47610	w/e 4 August	Workington
47290	w/e 23 June	Workington	47621	w/e 12 May	Bury
47292	w/e 29 December	Carlisle Upperby	47630	2 August	Staveley Barrow Hill
47302	w/e 8 September	London Willesden	47633	w/e 8 September	Stoke-on-Trent
47304	w/e 23 June	London Willesden	47642	w/e 19 May	London Kentish Town
47310	w/e 7 April	Stafford	47644	w/e 24 November	Derby
47316	12 November	Templecombe	47678	w/e 20 January	Manchester Agecroft
47319	w/e 25 August	Lostock Hall	48009	w/e 22 December	Kirkby-in-Ashfield
47328	18 June	Tilbury	48773	29 December	Glasgow Polmadie
47332	w/e 5 May	Carlisle Kingmoor	48774	29 December	Glasgow Polmadie
47340	w/e 24 March	Carlisle Upperby	48775	29 December	Glasgow Polmadie
47342	w/e 12 May	Carlisle Upperby	48898	w/e 30 June	Buxton
47348	w/e 8 Sept	Wolverton Works	48930	w/e 8 December	Bescot
47351	18 June	Tilbury	48964	w/e 21 April	Bescot
47353	w/e 17 February	Liverpool Edge Hill	49002	w/e 15 Sept	Wigan Springs Branch
47356	w/e 1 September	Lancaster Green Ayre	49008	w/e 8 December	Wigan Springs Branch
47358	w/e 8 December	Carlisle Kingmoor	49025	w/e 15 Sept	Wigan Springs Branch
47366	w/e 28 April	Sutton Oak	49034	w/e 22 September	Manchester Patricroft
47376	w/e 29 December	Sutton Oak	49037	w/e 29 December	Liverpool Edge Hill
47381	w/e 22 September	Lancaster Green Ayre	49045	w/e 22 December	Bescot
47392	w/e 4 August	Sutton Oak	49049	w/e 1 December	Wigan Springs Branch
47402	w/e 29 December	Horwich Works	49070	w/e 17 November	Wolverhampton Bushbury
47404	w/e 24 February	Liverpool Edge Hill	49078	w/e 15 December	Bletchley
47414	w/e 5 May	Crewe South	49079	w/e 1 December	Bescot
47417	12 November	Gloucester Barnwood	49081	w/e 1 December	Bescot
47422	w/e 28 July	Gloucester Barnwood	49087	w/e 22 September	Manchester Patricroft
47424	23 May	Staveley Barrow Hill	49093	w/e 1 December	Bletchley
47425	w/e 19 May	Liverpool Aintree	49094	w/e 1 December	Bletchley
47426	15 August	Staveley Barrow Hill	49099	w/e 21 July	Wolverhampton Bushbury
47431	w/e 13 October	Crewe South	49104	w/e 1 December	Wigan Springs Branch
47433	w/e 8 Sept	London Cricklewood	49106	w/e 15 December	Bletchley
47455	23 May	Staveley Barrow Hill	49114	w/e 1 December	Liverpool Edge Hill
47457	w/e 18 August	Rowsley	49122	w/e 1 December	Wigan Springs Branch
47466	w/e 8 Sept	Westhouses	49125	w/e 15 Sept	Bescot
47470	w/e 23 June	Lancaster Green Ayre	49126	w/e 15 Sept	Bescot
47473	w/e 17 February	Carnforth	49129	w/e 1 December	Wigan Springs Branch

49130	w/e 1 December	Liverpool Edge Hill
49134	w/e 31 March	Manchester Patricroft
49139	w/e 15 Sept	Wigan Springs Branch
49141	w/e 21 July	Wigan Springs Branch
49142	w/e 22 December	Bescot
49144	w/e 10 November	Liverpool Edge Hill
49147	w/e 22 September	Manchester Patricroft
49154	w/e 1 December	Wigan Springs Branch
49155	w/e 26 May	Liverpool Edge Hill
49199	w/e 22 September	Manchester Patricroft
49216	w/e 24 November	Liverpool Edge Hill
49224	w/e 1 December	Liverpool Edge Hill
49240	w/e 15 Sept	Wolverhampton Bushbury
49246	w/e 13 January	Bletchley
49262	w/e 8 December	Buxton
49267	w/e 1 December	Wigan Springs Branch
49277	w/e 17 February	Nuneaton
49281	w/e 8 December	Buxton
49287	w/e 1 December	Bletchley
49293	w/e 1 December	Liverpool Edge Hill
49314	w/e 1 December	Wigan Springs Branch
49323	w/e 22 September	Manchester Patricroft
49328	w/e 1 December	Bescot
49335	w/e 29 September	Manchester Patricroft
49344	w/e 1 December	Wigan Springs Branch
49350	w/e 8 December	Buxton
49352	w/e 15 September	Liverpool Edge Hill
49373	w/e 8 December	Bescot
49375	w/e 8 December	Liverpool Edge Hill
49377	w/e 27 October	Liverpool Edge Hill
49381	w/e 1 December	Wigan Springs Branch
49382	w/e 22 September	Manchester Patricroft
49391	w/e 20 January	Buxton
49394	w/e 27 October	Liverpool Edge Hill
49402	w/e 1 December	Wigan Springs Branch
49403	w/e 2 June	Buxton
49404	w/e 28 April	Liverpool Edge Hill
49408	w/e 1 December	Wigan Springs Branch
49415	w/e 1 December	Liverpool Edge Hill
49416	w/e 1 September	Liverpool Edge Hill
49425	w/e 15 September	Buxton
49426	w/e 22 September	Manchester Patricroft
49428	w/e 8 December	Carnforth
49431	w/e 1 December	Wigan Springs Branch
49432	w/e 1 December	Liverpool Edge Hill
49434	w/e 20 October	Liverpool Edge Hill
49437	w/e 1 September	Liverpool Edge Hill
49438	w/e 1 December	Wigan Springs Branch
49439	w/e 8 December	Buxton
49440	w/e 24 March	Nuneaton
49447	w/e 1 December	Wigan Springs Branch
49449	w/e 8 December	Carnforth
49451	w/e 1 December	Wigan Springs Branch
49452	w/e 8 December	Bescot
49508	w/e 20 January	Manchester Agecroft
51204	w/e 8 September	Manchester Agecroft
51206	w/e 15 September	Manchester Agecroft
51207	w/e 17 March	Manchester Agecroft
51222	6 March	Goole
51241	18 January	Goole
51244	6 March	Goole
51408	w/e 17 February	Manchester Agecroft
51412	w/e 1 September	Crewe Works
51446	w/e 10 March	Crewe Works
52093	w/e 1 September	Crewe Works
52119	w/e 13 October	Rhyl
52121	8 December	Sowerby Bridge
52218	w/e 28 April	Crewe Works
52248	w/e 17 March	Lees, Oldham
52275	w/e 13 October	Lees, Oldham
52311	w/e 3 March	Liverpool Aintree
52312	w/e 1 September	Crewe Works
52345	w/e 22 September	Bolton
52413	8 December	Sowerby Bridge
52438	w/e 14 April	Rhyl
52441	w/e 1 September	Crewe Works
52456	w/e 13 October	Lees, Oldham
52461	12 November	Sowerby Bridge
52515	12 December	Sowerby Bridge
52523	w/e 22 September	Bolton
53803	w/e 10 February	Bath Green Park
53804	w/e 10 February	Bath Green Park
54463	17 December	Glasgow Polmadie
54465	1 October	Motherwell
54466	12 March	Aviemore
54482	12 March	Aviemore
54486	12 March	Perth
54495	12 March	Helmsdale
54500	12 March	Perth
54502	1 October	Dumfries
55173	4 January	Oban
55189	29 December	Carstairs
55204	29 December	Perth
55217	30 July	Oban
55225	8 January	Glasgow Corkerhill
55234	29 December	Beattock
55260	29 December	Perth
55269	26 March	Inverness
56029	29 December	Glasgow Kipps
56031	2 April	Motherwell
56039	8 October	Glasgow Dawsholm
56159	2 April	Glasgow Polmadie
56232	30 April	Ardrossan
56278	11 June	Motherwell
56282	2 April	Ardrossan
56302	29 December	Dumfries
56312	21 May	Dumfries
56313	8 January	Motherwell
56325	29 December	Motherwell
56336	29 December	Motherwell
56347	16 July	Perth
57237	8 October	Motherwell
57240	8 October	Glasgow St Rollox
57242	16 July	Hamilton
57249	16 July	Hurlford
57251	8 October	Glasgow St Rollox
57252	22 November	Stirling
57253	8 October	Glasgow St Rollox
57254	30 July	Ardrossan
57258	8 October	Glasgow St Rollox
57259	8 October	Glasgow Dawsholm
57265	16 July	Grangemouth
57266	13 December	Stranraer
57267	2 April	Motherwell
57274	30 April	Ardrossan
57275	2 April	Glasgow Polmadie
57284	8 October	Hurlford
57295	11 June	Hurlford
57299	22 October	Motherwell
57300	11 June	Hurlford

57311	17 September	Grangemouth
57314	12 March	Glasgow Dawsholm
57329	8 October	Dumfries
57331	24 September	Hurlford
57338	26 March	Grangemouth
57340	29 November	Stranraer
57341	16 July	Hurlford
57345	12 March	Perth
57347	26 March	Glasgow Polmadie
57357	26 March	Ardrossan
57359	26 March	Hurlford
57362	11 June	Dumfries
57365	21 May	Glasgow Polmadie
57369	8 October	Glasgow Polmadie
57370	26 March	Motherwell
57378	24 September	Dumfries
57383	30 July	Hurlford
57385	11 June	Carstairs
57386	21 May	Carstairs
57398	21 May	Motherwell
57417	8 October	Glasgow Polmadie
57445	6 August	Stranraer
57447	8 October	Hamilton
57550	29 December	Edinburgh Dalry Road
57555	15 November	Glasgow Polmadie
57562	21 May	Hurlford
57565	29 December	Edinburgh Dalry Road
57569	12 November	Ayr
57571	30 April	Glasgow Polmadie
57577	30 July	Hurlford
57587	16 July	Oban
57594	29 December	Ardrossan
57596	1 October	Ayr
57597	2 April	Glasgow Polmadie
57601	29 December	Dumfries
57602	29 December	Dumfries
57603	26 March	Glasgow Polmadie
57604	10 December	Carstairs
57608	17 December	Carstairs
57611	12 November	Ayr
57612	30 April	Grangemouth
57613	10 September	Carstairs
57614	1 October	Ayr
57615	5 November	Ayr
57617	1 October	Glasgow St Rollox
57618	26 March	Carstairs
57620	11 June	Glasgow Polmadie
57621	30 April	Dumfries
57622	16 July	Glasgow Polmadie
57626	5 March	Carstairs
57631	1 October	Glasgow St Rollox
57635	26 March	Oban
57642	16 July	Stirling
57643	1 October	Hurlford
57644	1 October	Ayr
57645	19 November	Edinburgh Dalry Road
57654	9 April	Edinburgh Dalry Road
57655	2 April	Carstairs
57658	29 December	Motherwell
57666	16 July	Motherwell
57667	16 July	Glasgow Polmadie
57671	30 July	Motherwell
57672	8 October	Glasgow Polmadie
57673	26 March	Ardrossan
57674	8 November	Glasgow Polmadie
57681	8 October	Motherwell
57682	21 May	Glasgow Polmadie
57684	8 November	Glasgow Polmadie
57686	26 March	Glasgow St Rollox
57691	16 July	Hurlford
58120	w/e 17 November	Barrow
58123	w/e 7 July	Bescot
58124	w/e 7 July	Bescot
58128	w/e 13 October	Toton
58138	w/e 22 December	Coalville
58160	w/e 1 September	Barrow
58166	w/e 24 March	Coalville
58177	w/e 29 September	Barrow
58185	w/e 7 July	Bescot
58214	w/e 10 February	Coalville
58218	w/e 7 July	Bescot
58228	w/e 24 March	Toton
60003	29 December	London Kings Cross
60014	29 December	London Kings Cross
60028	29 December	London Kings Cross
60030	29 December	London Kings Cross
60033	29 December	London Kings Cross
60049	29 December	Grantham
60059	17 December	London Kings Cross
60067	29 December	London Kings Cross
60068	27 August	Carlisle Canal
60069	1 October	Ardsley
60072	22 October	Heaton
60076	29 October	Heaton
60078	22 October	Heaton
60081	1 October	Leeds Neville Hill
60093	24 April	Carlisle Canal
60109	29 December	London Kings Cross
60111	29 December	Grantham
60113	19 November	Doncaster
60115	12 November	Leeds Copley Hill
60122	17 December	Doncaster
60123	1 October	Ardsley
60135	12 November	Ardsley
60137	29 October	Tweedmouth
60153	2 November	York
60511	12 November	Tweedmouth
60514	29 December	New England
60515	12 November	York
60516	12 November	York
60517	12 November	Tweedmouth
60518	12 November	York
60519	18 December	York
60521	12 November	Tweedmouth
60526	12 November	York
60529	29 December	Edinburgh St Margarets
60531	10 December	York
60534	29 December	Edinburgh St Margarets
60536	17 December	York
60537	29 December	Edinburgh St Margarets
60538	12 November	Tweedmouth
60539	12 November	Tweedmouth
60800	21 August	London Kings Cross
60801	1 October	Tweedmouth
60807	19 November	Heaton
60811	23 April	Heaton
60815	30 April	Leicester Great Central
60819	29 December	Edinburgh St Margarets
60820	20 June	New England
60821	29 December	New England

60823	26 March	Perth
60826	12 April	Doncaster
60827	29 December	Edinburgh St Margarets
60829	31 May	New England
60832	29 December	New England
60839	22 October	York
60840	29 December	Edinburgh St Margarets
60842	22 October	York
60845	23 September	New England
60848	16 July	York
60849	12 April	Doncaster
60850	26 February	Doncaster
60851	29 December	Aberdeen Ferryhill
60857	17 April	Doncaster
60860	22 October	Heaton
60863	23 April	Leicester Great Central
60866	29 December	New England
60867	1 May	New England
60873	29 December	Edinburgh St Margarets
60874	22 August	New England
60875	5 March	Doncaster
60878	22 October	York
60879	3 December	York
60888	29 December	Aberdeen Ferryhill
60890	30 April	Leicester Great Central
60893	23 September	New England
60894	29 December	Edinburgh St Margarets
60896	23 September	Doncaster
60907	28 May	York
60908	4 June	Doncaster
60909	8 June	Doncaster
60911	3 December	York
60914	23 September	New England
60915	26 November	Darlington
60917	13 April	Doncaster
60918	8 October	York
60920	29 December	Edinburgh St Margarets
60926	1 October	Tweedmouth
60927	3 December	Edinburgh St Margarets
60928	5 March	Doncaster
60930	23 September	Doncaster
60933	29 December	Edinburgh St Margarets
60934	22 October	Tweedmouth
60936	23 September	Doncaster
60937	29 December	Edinburgh St Margarets
60938	1 October	Doncaster
60943	23 September	Doncaster
60947	1 October	Tweedmouth
60949	26 November	Tweedmouth
60951	29 December	Edinburgh St Margarets
60953	28 May	Edinburgh St Margarets
60956	23 September	New England
60958	29 December	Edinburgh St Margarets
60960	26 February	Thornaby
60965	29 December	Edinburgh St Margarets
60971	29 December	Edinburgh St Margarets
60977	26 February	York
60978	19 November	Heaton
60979	1 October	Gateshead
60980	29 December	Edinburgh St Margarets
60983	23 September	Grantham
61000	5 March	Nottingham Colwick
61005	16 September	March
61009	16 September	Lincoln
61011	2 November	Manchester Gorton
61015	19 November	Wakefield
61020	26 November	York
61025	3 December	Alnmouth
61027	16 September	Sheffield Darnall
61028	8 October	Woodford Halse
61036	16 September	Doncaster
61043	9 July	March
61045	16 September	London Stratford
61046	24 April	Cambridge
61047	16 September	Sheffield Darnall
61048	16 September	London Stratford
61052	16 September	March
61054	16 September	March
61060	16 September	Lincoln
61063	26 March	Woodford Halse
61064	15 October	Carlisle Canal
61066	16 September	March
61067	29 December	Glasgow Parkhead
61077	14 May	Manchester Gorton
61078	8 October	Woodford Halse
61079	18 June	Immingham
61082	29 December	Immingham
61086	3 December	York
61091	10 September	New England
61096	16 September	March
61100	19 November	Leeds Copley Hill
61106	2 November	Woodford Halse
61108	29 December	Edinburgh St Margarets
61111	16 September	Sheffield Darnall
61112	29 December	Mexborough
61114	16 September	Immingham
61124	16 September	Doncaster
61128	29 December	Doncaster
61130	16 September	Immingham
61136	22 October	Woodford Halse
61137	28 May	Manchester Gorton
61139	16 September	Sheffield Darnall
61149	23 September	March
61150	16 September	Sheffield Darnall
61151	16 September	Sheffield Darnall
61154	16 September	Sheffield Darnall
61163	16 September	Nottingham Colwick
61164	10 September	Sheffield Darnall
61166	16 September	Sheffield Darnall
61170	9 July	Doncaster
61171	16 September	March
61182	16 September	March
61183	9 July	Sheffield Darnall
61184	29 December	Edinburgh St Margarets
61186	5 November	Woodford Halse
61187	3 September	Woodford Halse
61192	8 October	Woodford Halse
61193	16 September	Doncaster
61200	29 December	London Kings Cross
61201	1 January	Manchester Agecroft
61202	16 September	Lincoln
61203	23 July	March
61206	3 September	Woodford Halse
61209	16 September	Nottingham Colwick
61211	5 November	Retford
61217	21 March	Carlisle Canal
61222	18 January	Carlisle Canal
61226	16 September	London Stratford
61228	16 September	Sheffield Darnall
61230	19 November	Bradford Low Moor

61231	30 July	Retford	61816	31 May	Sheffield Darnall
61234	13 August	Sheffield Darnall	61817	16 September	March
61235	16 September	Immingham	61818	5 March	Hull Dairycoates
61236	16 September	March	61819	17 December	Hull Dairycoates
61239	27 August	Manchester Gorton	61820	4 November	Lincoln
61241	3 December	Heaton	61821	16 September	Immingham
61246	29 December	Edinburgh St Margarets	61822	4 November	Lincoln
61247	12 June	Nottingham Colwick	61825	16 September	New England
61253	16 September	London Stratford	61826	16 September	Nottingham Colwick
61254	16 September	March	61827	16 September	Nottingham Colwick
61260	29 December	Edinburgh St Margarets	61829	28 February	Doncaster
61265	19 February	Leicester Great Central	61830	4 November	Doncaster
61266	16 September	Sheffield Darnall	61831	16 September	Nottingham Colwick
61267	10 December	West Hartlepool	61832	29 October	Woodford Halse
61271	30 July	Woodford Halse	61834	15 May	March
61280	16 September	March	61835	16 September	New England
61282	16 September	New England	61837	27 April	Nottingham Colwick
61283	16 September	London Stratford	61839	9 January	Doncaster
61284	16 September	Lincoln	61840	16 September	March
61286	16 September	March	61841	27 March	Woodford Halse
61287	16 September	March	61843	29 October	Woodford Halse
61290	21 March	Carlisle Canal	61845	16 September	Lincoln
61295	26 November	Ardsley	61846	17 December	Hull Dairycoates
61296	19 November	Wakefield	61847	10 December	Hull Dairycoates
61297	26 November	Ardsley	61848	16 September	Lincoln
61298	14 June	Manchester Gorton	61853	18 December	Ardsley
61301	16 September	London Stratford	61854	29 October	Hull Dairycoates
61311	16 September	London Stratford	61856	18 December	Ardsley
61316	29 December	Canklow	61857	3 December	Hull Dairycoates
61317	16 September	Immingham	61859	4 November	Lincoln
61332	29 December	Thornton Junction	61861	12 January	New England
61333	29 December	Glasgow Parkhead	61862	16 January	March
61335	16 September	London Stratford	61864	16 September	New England
61339	26 November	Leeds Copley Hill	61867	4 November	Doncaster
61352	22 October	Manchester Gorton	61868	10 May	Doncaster
61362	16 September	London Stratford	61869	3 December	Hull Dairycoates
61363	23 September	March	61870	12 July	Nottingham Colwick
61364	16 September	New England	61871	3 December	Hull Dairycoates
61366	17 December	Immingham	61872	3 December	Hull Dairycoates
61368	29 January	Woodford Halse	61873	8 May	Nottingham Colwick
61371	16 September	March	61875	10 December	Hull Dairycoates
61373	16 September	Sheffield Darnall	61877	24 July	Nottingham Colwick
61376	5 February	Leicester Great Central	61880	16 September	March
61377	16 September	Langwith Junction	61883	3 December	Hull Dairycoates
61379	6 August	Immingham	61884	23 July	Hull Dairycoates
61380	26 March	Woodford Halse	61886	16 September	March
61381	1 November	Manchester Gorton	61887	2 March	Doncaster
61391	10 September	New England	61889	4 November	Immingham
61395	1 October	Manchester Gorton	61890	16 September	March
61405	16 September	Lincoln	61893	17 December	Hull Dairycoates
61408	29 December	Immingham	61895	18 July	Doncaster
61417	3 September	York	61896	14 May	Nottingham Colwick
61439	20 August	York	61897	17 December	Hull Dairycoates
61742	15 May	New England	61899	18 December	Hull Dairycoates
61756	22 June	London Kings Cross	61905	4 November	Lincoln
61800	13 July	Doncaster	61906	17 December	Hull Dairycoates
61801	17 April	March	61907	16 September	Nottingham Colwick
61804	27 March	Woodford Halse	61908	19 January	Mexborough
61805	16 September	New England	61910	17 July	Woodford Halse
61807	4 November	Immingham	61912	16 September	London Kings Cross
61809	1 March	Woodford Halse	61913	12 February	Woodford Halse
61810	15 August	New England	61914	23 August	Nottingham Colwick
61811	4 November	Lincoln	61915	16 September	March
61812	16 September	Doncaster	61917	26 November	Ardsley
61813	9 April	Hull Dairycoates	61918	28 March	March

61922	7 May	Hull Dairycoates
61923	30 April	Hull Dairycoates
61926	10 April	Lincoln
61929	4 July	March
61930	17 December	Hull Dairycoates
61932	12 February	Hull Dairycoates
61934	26 November	Ardsley
61935	23 July	Hull Dairycoates
61939	4 November	Immingham
61940	4 May	Doncaster
61942	16 September	March
61943	16 September	Nottingham Colwick
61944	16 September	Nottingham Colwick
61945	26 February	Hull Dairycoates
61946	14 June	March
61947	1 August	Nottingham Colwick
61948	28 March	March
61949	10 April	Doncaster
61950	4 November	Doncaster
61951	4 November	Doncaster
61952	6 December	Hull Dairycoates
61953	14 March	Doncaster
61954	16 September	March
61956	16 September	Immingham
61957	16 September	Nottingham Colwick
61958	31 May	Mexborough
61960	16 September	Immingham
61962	18 December	Hull Dairycoates
61963	16 September	March
61965	3 December	Hull Dairycoates
61966	19 February	Nottingham Colwick
61969	17 December	Hull Dairycoates
61970	4 November	Doncaster
61972	16 September	Doncaster
61973	4 November	Doncaster
61974	2 July	Immingham
61976	4 January	Sheffield Darnall
61977	16 September	Nottingham Colwick
61980	17 December	Ardsley
61981	4 November	Doncaster
61982	16 September	Nottingham Colwick
61984	2 November	Ardsley
61985	21 December	Hull Dairycoates
61986	28 May	Hull Dairycoates
61987	19 March	Hull Dairycoates
61989	19 June	Staveley Great Central
62031	29 December	Fort William
62034	29 December	Fort William
62052	29 December	Fort William
62685	15 January	Edinburgh Haymarket
63460	3 December	Tyne Dock
63461	10 December	Tyne Dock
63462	3 December	Tyne Dock
63463	3 December	Tyne Dock
63464	3 December	Tyne Dock
63465	3 December	Tyne Dock
63466	3 December	Tyne Dock
63467	26 November	Tyne Dock
63468	26 November	Tyne Dock
63469	3 December	Tyne Dock
63470	3 December	Tyne Dock
63471	17 December	Tyne Dock
63472	3 December	Tyne Dock
63473	17 December	Tyne Dock
63474	17 December	Tyne Dock
63574	23 September	Sheffield Darnall
63575	2 November	Manchester Gorton
63578	17 November	Annesley
63579	21 November	Annesley
63584	8 August	Ardsley
63587	23 September	Nottingham Colwick
63588	8 August	Wakefield
63591	17 November	Annesley
63598	31 October	Manchester Gorton
63599	9 February	Sheffield Darnall
63600	31 October	Manchester Gorton
63602	29 December	Retford
63603	20 July	Manchester Gorton
63605	8 August	Ardsley
63609	23 September	Sheffield Darnall
63610	21 November	Annesley
63616	23 September	Nottingham Colwick
63617	12 December	Frodingham
63621	23 September	Sheffield Darnall
63623	9 February	Mexborough
63624	9 December	Sheffield Darnall
63631	11 September	Manchester Gorton
63633	8 August	Ardsley
63634	23 September	Immingham
63635	9 May	Langwith Junction
63637	9 December	Retford
63641	11 September	Manchester Gorton
63648	26 January	Mexborough
63655	29 December	Retford
63656	25 November	Staveley Great Central
63657	23 September	Nottingham Colwick
63658	9 December	Sheffield Darnall
63659	9 December	Mexborough
63664	23 September	Langwith Junction
63666	15 December	Frodingham
63676	21 November	Annesley
63677	2 March	Doncaster
63681	22 February	Manchester Gorton
63686	11 September	Manchester Gorton
63689	17 November	Annesley
63690	9 December	Frodingham
63693	26 November	Frodingham
63695	9 December	Sheffield Darnall
63698	9 December	Doncaster
63708	23 September	Immingham
63711	17 November	Annesley
63712	26 November	Tyne Dock
63713	10 August	Manchester Gorton
63718	29 December	Retford
63721	2 November	Manchester Gorton
63724	8 August	Ardsley
63735	29 December	Staveley Great Central
63737	9 December	Sheffield Darnall
63740	17 November	Annesley
63743	8 June	Manchester Gorton
63748	26 November	Frodingham
63752	17 November	Annesley
63755	26 November	Tyne Dock
63758	24 May	Immingham
63759	23 September	Immingham
63760	26 November	Tyne Dock
63762	16 March	Staveley Great Central
63766	26 August	Manchester Gorton
63767	2 November	Manchester Gorton
63771	26 November	Retford

63775	22 March	Manchester Gorton
63776	29 December	Langwith Junction
63777	26 October	Annesley
63779	13 April	Retford
63783	9 December	Sheffield Darnall
63787	8 June	Staveley Great Central
63789	17 November	Annesley
63792	26 October	Annesley
63794	2 November	Manchester Gorton
63796	26 October	Annesley
63798	24 May	Retford
63805	2 November	Manchester Gorton
63806	21 November	Annesley
63808	17 November	Annesley
63817	17 November	Annesley
63821	29 December	Sheffield Darnall
63823	8 August	Ardsley
63832	29 December	Frodingham
63833	19 January	Langwith Junction
63837	29 December	Nottingham Colwick
63838	26 October	Annesley
63848	2 November	Manchester Gorton
63854	17 November	Annesley
63856	26 November	Tyne Dock
63857	8 August	Ardsley
63862	2 November	Manchester Gorton
63864	8 August	Ardsley
63865	17 November	Annesley
63867	17 November	Annesley
63869	17 November	Annesley
63870	26 January	Langwith Junction
63874	26 November	Tyne Dock
63881	9 December	Sheffield Darnall
63883	29 December	Mexborough
63885	8 August	Ardsley
63886	26 October	Annesley
63895	20 July	Manchester Gorton
63900	23 September	Nottingham Colwick
63901	17 November	Annesley
63911	9 December	Mexborough
63912	9 December	Langwith Junction
63917	5 June	Frodingham
63920	8 August	Wakefield
63922	5 November	Grantham
63923	29 December	Grantham
63929	9 July	Grantham
63930	29 December	Grantham
63933	29 December	Grantham
63934	16 July	Retford
63948	16 October	Grantham
63951	25 June	Retford
63955	7 May	Retford
63961	29 December	Retford
63965	10 October	Retford
63966	29 December	Retford
63967	26 November	Doncaster
63971	29 December	Retford
63979	10 September	Retford
63982	9 December	Grantham
64177	21 February	New England
64191	21 February	Boston
64203	19 June	Ardsley
64226	20 June	Leeds Copley Hill
64245	20 February	Retford
64253	14 May	New England
64277	20 June	Leeds Copley Hill
64284	25 July	Immingham
64292	20 July	Sheffield Darnall
64305	20 July	Immingham
64314	23 September	Langwith Junction
64318	15 August	Lincoln
64324	23 September	Retford
64329	24 August	Sheffield Darnall
64332	23 September	Retford
64333	9 August	Langwith Junction
64346	23 September	Lincoln
64354	21 October	Retford
64355	25 July	Immingham
64362	23 September	Lincoln
64373	23 September	Sheffield Darnall
64375	15 September	Manchester Gorton
64377	20 July	Mexborough
64379	23 September	Langwith Junction
64386	23 September	Lincoln
64393	26 June	Mexborough
64394	24 August	Sheffield Darnall
64395	31 January	Retford
64406	23 September	Mexborough
64419	10 August	Sheffield Darnall
64420	9 June	Manchester Gorton
64423	30 March	Frodingham
64437	9 June	Manchester Gorton
64442	23 September	Mexborough
64443	19 April	Sheffield Darnall
64445	24 August	Sheffield Darnall
64450	6 April	Retford
64470	26 February	Glasgow Kipps
64472	26 March	Glasgow Kipps
64478	20 August	Carlisle Canal
64480	3 September	Dunfermline
64491	29 December	Thornton Junction
64497	9 April	Bathgate
64499	22 October	Carlisle Canal
64507	11 January	Glasgow Kipps
64510	29 November	Edinburgh St Margarets
64514	26 February	Glasgow Parkhead
64519	9 April	Edinburgh St Margarets
64525	16 July	Dunfermline
64527	11 June	Edinburgh St Margarets
64533	11 January	Edinburgh St Margarets
64540	29 December	Glasgow Eastfield
64543	10 December	Dunfermline
64544	29 December	Glasgow Kipps
64545	25 June	Dunfermline
64553	8 March	Bathgate
64556	17 December	Dundee Tay Bridge
64566	9 April	Edinburgh St Margarets
64574	29 December	Glasgow Kipps
64578	21 May	Glasgow Eastfield
64581	29 December	Glasgow Eastfield
64590	14 May	Edinburgh St Margarets
64594	29 December	Edinburgh St Margarets
64598	6 September	Dundee Tay Bridge
64601	29 December	Edinburgh St Margarets
64604	27 August	Dunfermline
64607	13 August	Edinburgh St Margarets
64609	29 December	Glasgow Parkhead
64612	29 December	Edinburgh St Margarets
64615	29 December	Dundee Tay Bridge
64617	29 December	Dunfermline

64622	29 December	Glasgow Eastfield
64628	29 March	Glasgow Kipps
64630	6 September	Dunfermline
64631	29 December	Dundee Tay Bridge
64635	29 December	Thornton Junction
64637	27 August	Edinburgh St Margarets
64638	29 December	Glasgow Eastfield
64639	29 December	Glasgow Eastfield
64657	16 September	London Stratford
64664	16 September	London Stratford
64671	11 February	Norwich
64673	6 August	London Stratford
64687	16 September	March
64690	16 September	March
64691	16 September	March
64696	6 April	Cambridge
64699	16 September	March
64701	16 November	Sunderland
64703	29 March	Sunderland
64704	3 December	Sunderland
64705	29 March	Ardsley
64706	29 March	Sunderland
64709	23 November	Hull Dairycoates
64711	23 May	Tweedmouth
64713	18 April	Sunderland
64718	7 February	Manchester Gorton
64719	23 November	Ardsley
64727	15 October	Woodford Halse
64730	16 November	Thornaby
64739	31 October	Annesley
64740	11 September	Manchester Gorton
64742	20 July	Woodford Halse
64744	22 March	Manchester Gorton
64747	5 November	Woodford Halse
64749	12 November	Ardsley
64754	12 November	Ardsley
64756	3 December	Ardsley
64757	26 November	Thornaby
64758	16 November	Thornaby
64760	30 November	Ardsley
64786	29 December	Dundee Tay Bridge
64790	29 December	Thornton Junction
64791	26 November	Bradford Low Moor
64792	4 January	Thornton Junction
64794	13 August	Thornton Junction
64795	29 December	Dunfermline
64796	13 December	Ardsley
64798	11 September	Annesley
64801	26 November	Bradford Low Moor
64806	17 May	Sunderland
64809	26 January	Woodford Halse
64811	30 March	Ardsley
64812	3 December	Sunderland
64813	3 December	Tweedmouth
64814	23 November	Alnmouth
64817	29 March	Bradford Low Moor
64818	3 December	Ardsley
64819	12 September	Hull Dairycoates
64820	24 May	Ardsley
64821	16 November	Thornaby
64822	29 December	Dundee Tay Bridge
64833	26 November	Sunderland
64835	3 December	West Auckland
64836	25 April	Ardsley
64840	27 November	Ardsley
64842	18 April	Heaton
64843	29 March	Sunderland
64844	3 December	Tweedmouth
64846	16 November	Sunderland
64847	16 November	Sunderland
64848	3 December	West Auckland
64849	16 November	West Hartlepool
64850	3 December	Hull Dairycoates
64851	3 December	Sunderland
64852	3 December	Heaton
64853	3 December	Sunderland
64854	3 December	Sunderland
64855	20 August	Heaton
64856	15 October	Heaton
64857	3 December	Leeds Neville Hill
64858	29 March	Sunderland
64859	3 December	Ardsley
64860	3 December	Gateshead
64861	3 December	Leeds Neville Hill
64863	31 January	Leeds Neville Hill
64864	3 December	Heaton
64865	3 December	Gateshead
64866	24 September	Heaton
64867	24 February	Malton
64868	18 April	Alnmouth
64869	3 December	Alnmouth
64870	18 January	Thornaby
64871	15 October	Heaton
64872	26 November	Bradford Low Moor
64875	15 October	Woodford Halse
64877	22 October	Carlisle Canal
64879	13 November	Ardsley
64880	15 October	Manchester Gorton
64884	21 March	Carlisle Canal
64886	27 November	Ardsley
64888	22 October	Carlisle Canal
64895	22 October	Carlisle Canal
64897	3 December	Alnmouth
64899	22 October	Carlisle Canal
64903	13 April	Bradford Low Moor
64907	26 November	Bradford Low Moor
64910	23 November	Alnmouth
64911	12 November	Ardsley
64915	29 March	Heaton
64917	3 December	Alnmouth
64918	30 November	Ardsley
64919	3 December	Bradford Low Moor
64921	3 December	Heaton
64922	23 November	Leeds Neville Hill
64923	15 October	Heaton
64924	23 November	Alnmouth
64925	3 December	Tweedmouth
64926	15 October	Heaton
64927	3 December	Ardsley
64929	23 November	Alnmouth
64933	12 December	Leeds Neville Hill
64934	17 December	Leeds Neville Hill
64935	17 December	Leeds Neville Hill
64936	3 December	Gateshead
64938	16 November	Gateshead
64939	18 April	Heaton
64940	17 December	Hull Dairycoates
64941	3 December	Tweedmouth
64942	3 December	Heaton
64943	17 December	Hull Dairycoates

64944	12 December	Leeds Neville Hill
64945	15 October	Heaton
64946	29 December	Dunfermline
64947	23 May	Leeds Neville Hill
64949	22 August	Alnmouth
64950	29 December	Dundee Tay Bridge
64955	20 July	Woodford Halse
64963	29 January	Dunfermline
64969	30 November	Ardsley
64971	25 June	Hull Dairycoates
64975	29 December	Glasgow Dawsholm
64978	3 December	Gateshead
64979	5 January	West Auckland
64982	3 December	West Auckland
64986	29 December	Thornton Junction
65033	23 April	South Blyth
65210	8 October	Glasgow Kipps
65211	16 July	Glasgow Parkhead
65216	30 April	Glasgow Kipps
65217	8 October	Grangemouth
65218	8 October	Glasgow Eastfield
65228	29 December	Glasgow Eastfield
65230	8 October	Glasgow Parkhead
65237	5 November	Carlisle Canal
65241	8 October	Glasgow Kipps
65246	11 January	Glasgow Parkhead
65257	8 October	Grangemouth
65258	5 March	Edinburgh Haymarket
65260	8 October	Glasgow Kipps
65266	21 May	Glasgow Kipps
65268	1 November	Bathgate
65275	29 December	Grangemouth
65280	21 May	Polmont
65293	5 November	Carlisle Canal
65296	26 February	Glasgow Eastfield
65300	16 July	Fort William
65303	29 December	Glasgow St Rollox
65304	8 October	Stirling
65305	26 February	Bathgate
65306	16 July	Grangemouth
65310	16 July	Stirling
65312	5 November	Carlisle Canal
65313	30 July	Fort William
65315	30 April	Glasgow Eastfield
65316	19 December	Bathgate
65318	31 May	Bathgate
65320	30 April	Glasgow Parkhead
65321	5 November	Carlisle Canal
65330	18 June	Hawick
65334	8 October	Edinburgh St Margarets
65344	25 October	Edinburgh St Margarets
65361	16 September	London Stratford
65420	1 August	London Stratford
65445	1 August	London Stratford
65453	6 August	London Stratford
65457	11 February	Cambridge
65460	5 September	London Stratford
65462	16 September	London Stratford
65464	16 September	London Stratford
65465	16 September	London Stratford
65469	1 August	March
65476	5 September	London Stratford
65521	11 February	Norwich
65532	11 February	Cambridge
65541	16 September	March

65560	5 June	March
65567	6 August	March
65576	16 September	March
65577	11 February	March
65578	5 March	March
65581	25 April	Cambridge
65582	16 September	March
65583	11 February	Norwich
65586	17 April	March
65645	23 April	Gateshead
65663	5 April	Heaton
65670	4 June	Tyne Dock
65693	9 April	Tyne Dock
65695	4 June	Tyne Dock
65720	9 April	Thornaby
65726	18 June	Gateshead
65728	23 April	Gateshead
65731	18 June	West Auckland
65735	18 June	West Auckland
65743	4 June	Thornaby
65747	16 April	Thornaby
65751	8 January	Thornaby
65755	4 June	Thornaby
65756	4 June	Thornaby
65757	16 April	Thornaby
65761	18 June	Thornaby
65763	29 January	Thornaby
65768	4 June	Thornaby
65772	18 June	Thornaby
65773	18 June	Thornaby
65776	18 June	Thornaby
65786	16 April	North Blyth
65787	14 May	Sunderland
65797	27 November	North Blyth
65799	6 August	South Blyth
65800	10 September	South Blyth
65807	14 May	Percy Main
65818	30 July	Thornaby
65837	30 October	Percy Main
65839	22 January	Percy Main
65863	6 August	North Blyth
65867	6 June	North Blyth
65877	29 October	Percy Main
65923	29 December	Dunfermline
65928	29 December	Dunfermline
67600	29 December	Glasgow Eastfield
67601	22 January	Glasgow Eastfield
67602	7 May	Glasgow Eastfield
67603	2 April	Glasgow Eastfield
67604	29 December	Glasgow Eastfield
67605	29 December	Edinburgh St Margarets
67606	29 December	Edinburgh St Margarets
67607	29 December	Hurlford
67608	29 December	Glasgow Eastfield
67609	5 February	Glasgow Kipps
67611	29 December	Glasgow Parkhead
67613	25 January	Hurlford
67614	30 July	Glasgow Parkhead
67615	29 December	Edinburgh Haymarket
67616	29 December	Hurlford
67617	27 August	Edinburgh St Margarets
67618	29 December	Glasgow Kipps
67619	29 December	Glasgow Parkhead
67621	29 December	Glasgow Parkhead
67622	5 March	Glasgow Parkhead

67623	25 January	Hurlford	67756	29 March	Nottingham Colwick
67625	29 December	Glasgow Parkhead	67757	31 July	Grantham
67626	29 December	Glasgow Parkhead	67759	8 October	Bradford Low Moor
67629	7 May	Glasgow Parkhead	67761	14 November	Grantham
67630	29 December	Glasgow Parkhead	67763	30 November	Ardsley
67631	5 March	Glasgow Parkhead	67764	27 August	Bradford Low Moor
67632	29 December	Glasgow Parkhead	67765	29 November	Ardsley
67633	29 December	Hurlford	67766	10 December	Ardsley
67634	16 April	Blaydon	67767	29 December	Nottingham Colwick
67637	24 May	Heaton	67770	29 December	Nottingham Colwick
67639	22 October	Gateshead	67771	22 October	Woodford Halse
67641	22 October	Heaton	67773	29 December	Nottingham Colwick
67644	7 May	Glasgow Eastfield	67774	22 January	Grantham
67648	25 January	Hurlford	67776	29 December	Nottingham Colwick
67649	9 July	Edinburgh St Margarets	67777	21 December	Ardsley
67655	5 March	Glasgow Parkhead	67778	4 May	New England
67657	29 December	Edinburgh Haymarket	67779	29 December	Nottingham Colwick
67659	12 February	Edinburgh St Margarets	67780	29 December	Nottingham Colwick
67660	5 February	Edinburgh St Margarets	67781	8 October	Woodford Halse
67661	5 February	Hurlford	67783	19 December	Nottingham Colwick
67664	29 December	Hurlford	67784	8 November	Nottingham Colwick
67666	5 February	Edinburgh St Margarets	67785	29 December	Nottingham Colwick
67667	2 August	Hurlford	67786	29 December	Nottingham Colwick
67668	29 December	Edinburgh St Margarets	67787	29 December	Nottingham Colwick
67672	29 December	Dunfermline	67788	30 May	Nottingham Colwick
67673	1 October	Heaton	67789	8 October	Woodford Halse
67674	29 December	Edinburgh St Margarets	67791	27 November	Nottingham Colwick
67675	29 December	Glasgow Eastfield	67792	29 December	Nottingham Colwick
67676	30 July	Glasgow Parkhead	67793	21 September	Nottingham Colwick
67677	1 October	Hull Dairycoates	67795	3 May	New England
67679	25 January	Hurlford	67796	6 November	Grantham
67680	29 December	Glasgow Eastfield	67797	17 October	Nottingham Colwick
67685	10 December	Edinburgh Haymarket	67798	29 December	Nottingham Colwick
67687	29 December	Edinburgh Haymarket	67799	29 March	Nottingham Colwick
67688	29 December	Edinburgh Haymarket	67800	29 December	Nottingham Colwick
67689	29 December	Edinburgh Haymarket	68007	15 October	Darlington
67703	16 September	London Stratford	68009	31 July	Nottingham Colwick
67710	8 October	Woodford Halse	68017	26 November	Darlington
67715	28 February	Norwich	68018	2 August	Nottingham Colwick
67716	16 September	London Stratford	68030	2 April	Rowsley
67720	12 February	London Stratford	68034	22 October	Rowsley
67721	26 November	Bradford Low Moor	68044	29 October	West Hartlepool
67723	16 September	London Stratford	68048	8 October	Tyne Dock
67724	16 September	London Stratford	68052	18 June	Darlington
67727	11 January	Manchester Gorton	68055	16 July	West Hartlepool
67729	16 September	London Stratford	68056	15 October	West Hartlepool
67730	30 August	London Stratford	68057	18 June	West Hartlepool
67731	16 September	London Stratford	68058	29 October	West Hartlepool
67733	8 October	Woodford Halse	68063	1 January	Bidston
67734	16 September	London Stratford	68064	5 February	Manchester Gorton
67735	16 September	London Stratford	68065	22 December	Bidston
67737	30 August	London Stratford	68066	22 December	Bidston
67741	29 December	Nottingham Colwick	68069	23 September	Langwith Junction
67742	21 December	Ardsley	68074	17 October	Nottingham Colwick
67743	20 February	Nottingham Colwick	68075	29 December	Nottingham Colwick
67744	29 December	Nottingham Colwick	68077	29 December	Nottingham Colwick
67745	29 December	Nottingham Colwick	68095	29 December	Edinburgh St Margarets
67746	31 July	Nottingham Colwick	68101	8 October	Dunfermline
67747	9 July	Nottingham Colwick	68104	8 October	Glasgow Kipps
67749	29 December	Nottingham Colwick	68117	16 July	Glasgow Kipps
67751	29 March	Nottingham Colwick	68335	8 October	Glasgow Dawsholm
67752	23 March	Grantham	68336	28 May	Glasgow Dawsholm
67753	6 February	Nottingham Colwick	68342	12 February	Edinburgh St Margarets
67754	5 November	Bradford Low Moor	68345	29 December	Glasgow Kipps
67755	14 December	Ardsley	68346	8 October	Dunfermline

68350	16 July	Glasgow St Rollox	69138	1 October	Edinburgh St Margarets
68353	12 February	Thornton Junction	69150	1 October	Edinburgh St Margarets
68442	8 January	Glasgow Kipps	69155	8 September	Carlisle Canal
68445	8 October	Glasgow Kipps	69156	12 February	Bathgate
68448	8 October	Edinburgh St Margarets	69163	12 February	Glasgow Eastfield
68453	8 October	Edinburgh St Margarets	69178	29 December	Motherwell
68454	12 February	Edinburgh St Margarets	69181	12 February	Glasgow Eastfield
68458	18 January	Ayr	69188	1 October	Glasgow Eastfield
68470	8 October	Edinburgh St Margarets	69191	1 October	Glasgow Eastfield
68472	12 February	Edinburgh St Margarets	69196	1 October	Hamilton
68477	29 December	Edinburgh St Margarets	69204	16 July	Thornton Junction
68479	8 October	Glasgow Eastfield	69211	1 October	Edinburgh Haymarket
68481	12 February	Edinburgh Haymarket	69212	1 October	Glasgow Eastfield
68499	16 September	London Stratford	69216	12 February	Bathgate
68542	16 September	London Stratford	69218	1 October	Glasgow Eastfield
68549	11 February	London Stratford	69224	1 October	Edinburgh St Margarets
68556	16 September	London Stratford	69504	23 September	New England
68565	6 August	London Stratford	69512	24 July	New England
68566	5 September	London Stratford	69520	23 September	New England
68600	16 September	London Stratford	69523	16 September	New England
68609	16 September	London Stratford	69529	23 September	New England
68621	16 September	London Stratford	69535	16 September	New England
68626	3 May	London Stratford	69538	16 September	New England
68635	16 September	London Stratford	69546	23 September	New England
68695	2 April	Gateshead	69568	16 September	New England
68707	2 April	West Hartlepool	69575	16 September	New England
68709	26 February	Hamilton	69579	16 September	New England
68733	16 July	Hamilton	69583	16 September	New England
68750	17 December	Dumfries	69593	16 September	New England
68754	2 April	Darlington	69621	11 September	London Stratford
68900	22 January	Ardsley	69632	16 September	London Stratford
68910	26 November	Wakefield	69640	16 September	London Stratford
68917	10 September	Doncaster	69646	16 September	London Stratford
68926	13 February	Doncaster	69653	3 May	London Stratford
68928	10 September	Doncaster	69671	16 September	London Stratford
68939	29 October	Wakefield	69692	16 September	London Stratford
68961	10 September	Doncaster	69697	16 September	London Stratford
68963	13 February	Bradford Low Moor	69725	16 September	London Stratford
68964	1 October	Bradford Low Moor	71000	w/e 24 November	Crewe North
68971	10 September	Doncaster	72000	29 December	Glasgow Polmadie
68972	16 September	Doncaster	72001	29 December	Glasgow Polmadie
68976	10 September	Doncaster	72002	29 December	Glasgow Polmadie
68982	16 September	Doncaster	72003	29 December	Glasgow Polmadie
68983	24 April	Doncaster	72004	29 December	Glasgow Polmadie
68986	2 July	Doncaster	80103	29 August	Tilbury
68987	24 April	Doncaster	90021	12 November	Normanton
68989	11 July	Doncaster	90022	31 October	Thornaby
69002	1 October	Darlington	90023	5 September	Tilbury
69007	1 October	Thornaby	90028	29 December	Canklow
69010	1 October	Hull Dairycoates	90034	5 September	Tilbury
69013	22 January	Motherwell	90060	11 June	Glasgow Polmadie
69014	19 February	Edinburgh St Margarets	90087	25 October	Frodingham
69017	30 April	Thornaby	90093	27 August	Tilbury
69018	8 October	Darlington	90105	w/e 29 December	Newton Heath
69022	31 December	West Hartlepool	90106	16 September	New England
69026	30 April	Heaton	90128	5 November	Grangemouth
69027	22 October	Gateshead	90134	30 July	Glasgow St Rollox
69097	9 April	Gateshead	90137	w/e 22 December	Woodford Halse
69101	9 April	Gateshead	90150	16 September	Doncaster
69109	9 April	Gateshead	90163	w/e 29 December	Newton Heath
69126	12 February	Glasgow Dawsholm	90167	w/e 17 March	Cardiff Canton
69128	1 October	Edinburgh St Margarets	90174	12 November	Southall
69131	12 February	Glasgow Eastfield	90196	5 September	Tilbury
69135	1 October	Edinburgh St Margarets	90198	17 December	Ayr
69137	21 May	Polmont	90244	9 August	Tilbury

90247	12 November	Normanton
90253	29 December	New England
90256	27 August	Tilbury
90270	29 December	New England
90278	w/e 29 December	Liverpool Aintree
90286	15 August	Doncaster
90287	29 December	Nottingham Colwick
90288	16 September	Frodingham
90298	6 August	Tilbury
90303	29 December	Nottingham Colwick
90307	w/e 29 December	Manchester Agecroft
90308	12 November	Huddersfield
90320	16 July	Glasgow Polmadie
90355	12 November	Southall
90356	12 November	Southall
90376	w/e 29 December	Newton Heath
90387	2 August	Glasgow Polmadie
90391	30 August	Canklow
90414	29 December	Canklow
90425	29 December	Frodingham
90431	29 December	Langwith Junction
90436	11 June	Glasgow Dawsholm
90455	10 September	Aberdeen Ferryhill
90473	16 September	Nottingham Colwick
90494	16 September	Doncaster
90495	29 December	Mexborough
90505	11 June	Ardrossan
90508	29 December	Mexborough
90512	16 September	Frodingham
90513	16 July	Thornton Junction
90523	w/e 29 December	Newton Heath
90526	29 December	Mexborough
90532	w/e 1 December	Widnes
90549	17 December	Ayr
90550	16 September	Frodingham
90554	16 September	Nottingham Colwick
90559	29 December	Doncaster
90562	12 November	Leeds Farnley Junction
90565	12 November	Southall
90575	16 July	Dunfermline
90591	12 November	Royston
90594	16 September	Nottingham Colwick
90603	12 February	Thornaby
90607	6 November	Wakefield
90608	29 December	Mexborough
90616	11 June	Glasgow Polmadie
90630	12 November	Southall
90634	29 December	Nottingham Colwick
90637	12 November	Normanton
90638	w/e 22 December	Woodford Halse
90648	30 August	Frodingham
90653	5 September	Tilbury
90657	7 September	Langwith Junction
90666	12 November	Huddersfield
90690	10 September	Motherwell
90691	w/e 26 May	Banbury
90693	12 November	Southall
90701	w/e 1 December	Woodford Halse
90726	12 November	Leeds Farnley Junction
90732	16 September	Frodingham
90750	9 May	Motherwell
90751	29 December	Motherwell
90755	29 December	Grangemouth
90756	29 December	Motherwell
90757	29 December	Grangemouth
90758	29 December	Motherwell
90759	29 December	Grangemouth
90760	9 May	Motherwell
90761	29 November	Motherwell
90762	29 December	Motherwell
90763	29 December	Carlisle Kingmoor
90764	9 May	Motherwell
90765	17 December	Grangemouth
90766	29 December	Grangemouth
90767	29 December	Motherwell
90768	30 July	Carstairs
90769	29 December	Grangemouth
90770	29 December	Motherwell
90771	29 December	Motherwell
90772	29 December	Motherwell
90773	29 December	Grangemouth
90774	13 December	Grangemouth

SERVICE LOCOMOTIVES

DS680	June	Lancing Carriage Works
DS682	December	Meldon Quarry
Dept 32	September	Stratford Works
Dept 44	September	Stratford Works
Dept 45	September	Stratford Works

Diesel LOCOMOTIVES

ED1	19 June	Beeston Creosote Works
12001	w/e 3 February	Crewe South
15004	5 October	New England

NOTES: Nos 7739 and 7749 were transferred to LTE stock on withdrawal. Transferred to service stock were; 30061 as DS233, 30062 as DS234, 30066 as DS235, 68917 as Dept 12, 68928 as Dept 13, 68961 as Dept 14, 68971 as Dept 15 and 68976 as Dept 16. Due to the severity of the 1962/63 winter the following Scottish Region locomotives were reinstated as on loan to operating stock: In January 1963, 44198 (67B), 44283 (67B), 44322 (67B), 44331 (67B), 45125 (65F), 45159 (65B), 45169 (67E), 45174 (66E), 45179 (66B), 45452 (66E), 48773 (66A), 48774 (66A), 48775 (66A), 64612 (64A), 64615 (62B), 64617 (62C), 64631 (62B), 64635 (62C) and in February 64601 (62C). Their later withdrawal dates in 1963 were: 44198 20 May, 44283 27 July, 44322 27 July, 44331 20 May, 45125 13 May, 45159 22 April, 45169 13 May, 45174 13 May, 45179 13 May, 45452 13 May, 48773 20 June, 48774 20 June, 48775 20 June, 64601 22 April, 64612 24 June, 64615 22 April, 64617 11 February, 64631 6 May, 64635 22 April. All were withdrawn from the same sheds as they were reinstated to. 48773, 48774 and 48775 were again returned to operating stock on 9 November 1963 and transferred to the LMR, all initially to Carlisle Kingmoor. Their final withdrawal dates were: 48773 from Rose Grove week ending 10 August 1968, 48774 from Liverpool Speke Junction week ending 24 July 1965 and 48775 from Lostock Hall week ending 3 August 1968. No 48773 is preserved at the Severn Valley Railway.

British Railways Locomotives Added to Stock During 1962

Diesel Locomotives

NUMBER	MONTH TO TRAFFIC	FIRST ALLOCATION
Class 45 1Co-Co1 From Crewe Works		
D50	22 May	Derby
D51	5 June	Derby
D52	7 June	Derby
D53	25 June	Derby
D54	8 August	Derby
D55	10 September	Derby
D56	23 November	London Cricklewood
D58	30 January	Derby
D59	6 February	Derby
D60	15 February	Derby
D61	8 March	Derby
D62	15 March	Derby
D63	29 March	Derby
D64	9 April	Derby
D65	13 April	Derby
D66	17 April	Derby
D67	3 May	Derby
Class 46 1Co-Co1 From Derby Works		
D151	17 January	Derby
D152	1 February	Derby
D153	25 January	Derby
D154	16 February	Derby
D155	16 February	Derby
D156	23 February	Derby
D157	3 March	Derby
D158	15 March	Derby
D159	23 March	Derby
D160	31 March	Derby
D161	31 March	Derby
D162	9 April	Derby
D163*	18 April	Derby
D164	19 April	Derby
D165	4 May	Derby
D166	9 May	Gateshead
D167	31 May	Gateshead
D168	31 May	Gateshead
D169	7 June	Gateshead
D170	21 June	Gateshead
D171	6 July	Gateshead
D172	2 July	Gateshead
D173	13 July	Gateshead
D174	13 July	Gateshead
D175	3 August	Gateshead
D176	14 August	Gateshead
D177	24 August	Gateshead
D178	14 September	Gateshead
D179	21 September	Gateshead
D180	14 September	Gateshead
D181	22 September	Gateshead
D182	27 September	Gateshead
D183	4 October	Gateshead
D184	15 October	Gateshead
D185	16 October	Gateshead
D186	9 November	Gateshead
D187	23 November	Gateshead
D188	17 December	Gateshead
Class 40 1Co-Co1 From English Electric/Vulcan Foundry		
D372	3 January	Manchester Longsight
D373	5 January	London Camden
D374	17 January	London Camden
D375	31 January	London Camden
D376	5 February	London Camden
D377	9 February	London Camden
D378	16 February	London Camden
D379	21 February	London Camden
D380	5 March	London Camden
D381	12 March	London Camden
D382	14 March	London Camden
D383	21 March	London Camden
D384	29 March	London Camden
D385	28 March	York
D386	4 April	York
D387	11 April	York
D388	18 April	York
D389	2 May	York
D390	9 May	York
D391	16 May	York
D392	30 May	Gateshead
D393	7 June	Gateshead
D394	13 June	Gateshead
D395	27 June	Gateshead
D396	4 July	Gateshead
D397	18 July	Gateshead
D398	15 August	Gateshead
D399	5 September	Gateshead
Class 43 Diesel-Hydraulic B-B 'Warship' Class From North British Loco Co		
D859*	January	Plymouth Laira
D860*	January	Plymouth Laira
D861*	March	Plymouth Laira
D862*	March	Plymouth Laira
D863*	April	Plymouth Laira
D864*	May	Plymouth Laira
D865*	June	Plymouth Laira
Class 52 Diesel-Hydraulic C-C 'Western' Class From Swindon Works		
D1001*	February	Plymouth Laira
D1002*	March	Plymouth Laira
D1003*	April	Plymouth Laira
D1004*	May	Plymouth Laira
D1005*	June	Plymouth Laira

D1006*	June	Plymouth Laira
D1007*	August	Plymouth Laira
D1008*	September	Plymouth Laira
D1009*	September	London Old Oak Common
D1010*	October	London Old Oak Common
D1011*	October	London Old Oak Common
D1012*	November	Cardiff Canton
D1013*	December	Cardiff Canton
D1014*	December	Cardiff Canton

Class 52 Diesel-Hydraulic C-C 'Western' Class From Crewe Works

D1035*	July	Plymouth Laira
D1036*	August	Plymouth Laira
D1037*	August	Plymouth Laira
D1038*	September	Plymouth Laira
D1039*	September	Plymouth Laira
D1040*	September	London Old Oak Common
D1041*	October	London Old Oak Common
D1042*	October	London Old Oak Common
D1043*	October	London Old Oak Common
D1044*	November	Cardiff Canton
D1045*	November	Cardiff Canton
D1046*	December	Bristol Bath Road
D1048*	December	Cardiff Canton
D1049*	December	Cardiff Canton

Class 47 Co-Co From Brush Works

D1500	28 September	London Finsbury Park
D1501	13 November	London Finsbury Park
D1502	30 November	London Finsbury Park
D1503	31 December	London Finsbury Park

Class 03 0-6-0 Shunter From Swindon Works

D2178	January	Ashford
D2179	January	London Hither Green
D2180	February	London Hither Green
D2181	February	Swindon
D2182	March	Taunton
D2183	March	Taunton
D2184	April	Llanelly
D2185	May	Swansea Danygraig
D2186	May	Swindon

Class 04 0-6-0 Shunter From Drewry/R. Stephenson & Hawthorns

D2340	9 March	Darlington

Class 07 0-6-0 Shunter From Ruston & Hornsby

D2985	16 June	Southampton Docks
D2986	16 June	Southampton Docks
D2987	16 June	Southampton Docks
D2988	16 June	Southampton Docks
D2989	23 June	Southampton Docks
D2990	14 July	Southampton Docks
D2991	21 July	Southampton Docks
D2992	28 July	Southampton Docks
D2993	21 August	Southampton Docks
D2994	5 September	Southampton Docks
D2995	22 September	Southampton Docks
D2996	6 October	Southampton Docks
D2997	20 October	Southampton Docks
D2998	10 November	Southampton Docks

Class 10 0-6-0 Shunter From Darlington Works

D4081	11 January	Doncaster
D4082	17 January	Doncaster
D4083	26 January	London Finsbury Park
D4084	3 February	London Finsbury Park
D4085	8 February	London Finsbury Park
D4086	15 February	Boston
D4087	28 February	Immingham
D4088	2 March	Immingham
D4089	8 March	Doncaster
D4090	14 March	Manchester Gorton
D4091	25 April	Sheffield Darnall
D4092	2 May	Sheffield Darnall
D4093	19 May	Sheffield Darnall
D4094	5 June	Sheffield Darnall

Class 09 0-6-0 Shunter From Horwich Works

D4113	6 January	Manchester Longsight
D4114	27 January	Lostock Hall

Class 08 0-6-0 Shunter From Horwich Works

D4115	20 January	Lostock Hall
D4116	27 January	London Cricklewood
D4117	3 February	London Cricklewood
D4118	February	Swindon
D4119	February	Swindon
D4120	February	Swindon
D4121	March	Swindon
D4122	March	Swindon
D4123	March	Swindon
D4124	March	Swindon
D4125	April	Swindon
D4126	April	Newport Ebbw Junction
D4127	April	Newport Ebbw Junction
D4128	April	Newport Ebbw Junction
D4129	May	Exeter
D4130	May	Exeter
D4131	19 May	London Cricklewood
D4132	2 June	London Cricklewood
D4133	2 June	London Cricklewood
D4134	9 June	Bedford
D4135	23 June	Bedford
D4136	23 June	London Cricklewood
D4137	30 June	Burton-on-Trent
D4138	7 July	London Cricklewood
D4139	14 July	Carnforth
D4140	4 August	Carnforth
D4141	11 August	Carnforth
D4142	18 August	Carnforth
D4143	25 August	Crewe South
D4144	1 September	Nuneaton
D4145	15 September	Stockport Edgeley
D4146	22 September	Liverpool Speke Junction
D4147	29 September	Liverpool Speke Junction
D4148	13 October	Liverpool Speke Junction
D4149	20 October	Burton-on-Trent
D4150	27 October	Burton-on-Trent
D4151	27 October	Burton-on-Trent
D4152	3 November	Liverpool Speke Junction
D4153	17 November	Liverpool Speke Junction
D4154	15 December	Liverpool Edge Hill
D4155	15 December	Liverpool Edge Hill
D4156	22 December	Lancaster Green Ayre
D4157	29 December	Lancaster Green Ayre

Class 08 0-6-0 Shunter From Darlington Works

D4158	April	St Blazey
D4159	April	Plymouth Laira
D4160	April	Newton Abbot
D4161	April	Penzance
D4162	May	Exeter
D4163	May	Taunton
D4164	May	Taunton
D4165	May	Taunton
D4166	May	St Blazey
D4167	May	Plymouth Laira
D4168	May	Swindon
D4169	May	Bristol Bath Road
D4170	June	Newport Ebbw Junction
D4171	June	Newport Ebbw Junction
D4172	June	Newport Ebbw Junction
D4173	June	Newport Ebbw Junction
D4174	June	Newport Ebbw Junction
D4175	June	Newport Ebbw Junction
D4176	August	Newport Ebbw Junction
D4177	August	Newport Ebbw Junction
D4178	August	Newport Ebbw Junction
D4179	September	Newport Ebbw Junction
D4180	September	Newport Ebbw Junction
D4181	September	Newport Ebbw Junction
D4182	September	Newport Ebbw Junction
D4183	October	Newport Ebbw Junction
D4184	October	Newport Ebbw Junction
D4185	November	Newport Ebbw Junction
D4186	27 June	London Stratford
D4187	6 July	London Stratford
D4188	11 July	London Stratford
D4189	31 July	London Stratford
D4190	2 August	London Stratford
D4191	14 August	London Stratford
D4192	17 August	London Stratford

Class 25 Bo-Bo From Darlington Works

D5171	3 February	Thornaby
D5172	17 February	Thornaby
D5173	17 March	Thornaby
D5174	30 March	Thornaby
D5175	21 April	Thornaby

Class 27 Bo-Bo From Birmingham Railway Carriage & Wagon Company

D5366	4 January	Glasgow Eastfield
D5367	4 January	Glasgow Eastfield
D5368	11 January	Glasgow Eastfield
D5369	17 January	Glasgow Eastfield
D5370	17 January	Thornaby
D5371	19 January	Thornaby
D5372	24 January	Thornaby
D5373	31 January	Thornaby
D5374	7 February	Thornaby
D5375	14 February	Thornaby
D5376	21 February	Thornaby
D5377	28 February	Thornaby
D5378	7 March	Thornaby
D5379	31 March	London Cricklewood
D5380	7 April	London Cricklewood
D5381	7 April	London Cricklewood
D5382	21 April	London Cricklewood
D5383	28 April	London Cricklewood
D5384	5 May	London Cricklewood
D5385	12 May	London Cricklewood
D5386	19 May	London Cricklewood
D5387	26 May	London Cricklewood
D5388	2 June	London Cricklewood
D5389	2 June	London Cricklewood
D5390	9 June	London Cricklewood
D5391	9 June	London Cricklewood
D5392	16 June	London Cricklewood
D5393	16 June	London Cricklewood
D5394	23 June	London Cricklewood
D5395	23 June	London Cricklewood
D5396	30 June	London Cricklewood
D5397	11 August	London Cricklewood
D5398	7 July	London Cricklewood
D5399	7 July	London Cricklewood
D5400	14 July	London Cricklewood
D5401	14 July	London Cricklewood
D5402	14 July	London Cricklewood
D5403	21 July	London Cricklewood
D5404	21 July	London Cricklewood
D5405	28 July	London Cricklewood
D5406	4 August	London Cricklewood
D5407	4 August	London Cricklewood
D5408	18 August	London Cricklewood
D5409	11 August	London Cricklewood
D5410	1 September	London Cricklewood
D5411	8 September	London Cricklewood
D5412	8 September	London Cricklewood
D5413	15 September	London Cricklewood
D5414	22 September	London Cricklewood
D5415	6 October	London Cricklewood

Class 31 A1A-A1A From Brush Works

D5829	4 January	Sheffield Darnall
D5830	11 January	Sheffield Darnall
D5831	18 January	Sheffield Darnall
D5832	1 February	Sheffield Darnall
D5833	15 February	Sheffield Darnall
D5834	1 March	Sheffield Darnall
D5835	26 April	Sheffield Darnall
D5836	12 April	Sheffield Darnall
D5837	19 April	Sheffield Darnall
D5838	26 April	Sheffield Darnall
D5839	3 May	Sheffield Darnall
D5840	10 May	Sheffield Darnall
D5841	17 May	Sheffield Darnall
D5842	24 May	Sheffield Darnall
D5843	31 May	Sheffield Darnall
D5844	7 June	Sheffield Darnall
D5845	14 June	Sheffield Darnall
D5846	21 June	Sheffield Darnall
D5847	28 June	Sheffield Darnall
D5848	5 July	Sheffield Darnall
D5849	12 July	Sheffield Darnall
D5850	18 July	Sheffield Darnall
D5851	26 July	Sheffield Darnall
D5852	2 August	Sheffield Darnall
D5853	23 August	London Stratford
D5854	23 August	London Stratford
D5855	30 August	March
D5856	30 August	March

D5857	6 September	Sheffield Darnall
D5858	20 September	Sheffield Darnall
D5859	4 October	Sheffield Darnall
D5860	11 October	Sheffield Darnall
D5861	18 October	Sheffield Darnall
D5862	25 October	Sheffield Darnall

Class 22 Bo-Bo From North British Locomotive Company

D6337	March	Newton Abbot
D6338	March	Plymouth Laira
D6339	April	Plymouth Laira
D6340	April	Plymouth Laira
D6341	May	Plymouth Laira
D6342	May	Plymouth Laira
D6343	May	Plymouth Laira
D6344	May	Plymouth Laira
D6345	May	Plymouth Laira
D6346	June	Plymouth Laira
D6347	June	Bristol Bath Road
D6348	June	Plymouth Laira
D6349	June	Plymouth Laira
D6350	June	Plymouth Laira
D6351	June	Plymouth Laira
D6352	July	Plymouth Laira
D6353	July	Plymouth Laira
D6354	August	Plymouth Laira
D6355	August	Bristol Bath Road
D6356	September	Bristol Bath Road
D6357	November	Bristol Bath Road

Class 33 Bo-Bo From Birmingham Railway Carriage & Wagon Company

D6583	6 January	London Hither Green
D6584	13 January	London Hither Green
D6585	13 January	London Hither Green
D6586	2 February	London Hither Green
D6587	9 February	London Hither Green
D6588	16 February	London Hither Green
D6589	23 February	London Hither Green
D6590	23 February	London Hither Green
D6591	9 March	London Hither Green
D6592	16 March	London Hither Green
D6593	23 March	London Hither Green
D6594	30 March	London Hither Green
D6595	13 April	London Hither Green
D6596	27 April	London Hither Green
D6597	11 May	London Hither Green

Class 37 Co-Co From English Electric/Vulcan Foundry

D6732	9 March	Hull Dairycoates
D6733	20 March	Hull Dairycoates
D6734	26 March	Hull Dairycoates
D6735	17 April	Hull Dairycoates
D6736	25 April	Hull Dairycoates
D6737	4 May	Hull Dairycoates
D6738	11 May	Hull Dairycoates
D6739	18 May	Hull Dairycoates
D6740	1 June	Hull Dairycoates
D6741	7 June	Hull Dairycoates
D6742	15 June	Sheffield Darnall
D6743	22 June	Sheffield Darnall
D6744	29 June	Sheffield Darnall
D6745	6 July	Sheffield Darnall
D6746	13 July	Sheffield Darnall
D6747	20 July	Sheffield Darnall
D6748	10 August	Sheffield Darnall
D6749	17 August	Sheffield Darnall
D6750	24 August	Sheffield Darnall
D6751	31 August	Sheffield Darnall
D6752	6 September	Sheffield Darnall
D6753	14 September	Sheffield Darnall
D6754	19 September	Sheffield Darnall
D6755	21 September	Thornaby
D6756	28 September	Thornaby
D6757	5 October	Thornaby
D6758	10 October	Thornaby
D6759	12 October	Thornaby
D6760	19 October	Thornaby
D6761	24 October	Thornaby
D6762	26 October	Thornaby
D6763	2 November	Thornaby
D6764	7 November	Thornaby
D6765	14 November	Thornaby
D6766	16 November	Thornaby
D6767	21 November	Thornaby
D6768	23 November	Thornaby

Class 37 Co-Co From English Electric/R. Stephenson & Hawthorns

D6769	17 July	Thornaby
D6770	17 August	Thornaby
D6771	22 August	Thornaby
D6772	4 September	Thornaby
D6773	10 September	Thornaby
D6774	17 September	Thornaby
D6775	24 September	Thornaby
D6776	8 October	Thornaby
D6777	12 October	Thornaby
D6778	29 October	Thornaby
D6779	6 November	Hull Dairycoates
D6780	14 November	Hull Dairycoates
D6781	22 November	Hull Dairycoates
D6782	29 November	Hull Dairycoates
D6783	5 December	Hull Dairycoates
D6784	12 December	Gateshead
D6785	19 December	Gateshead
D6786	28 December	Gateshead
D6787	31 December	Gateshead

Class 37 Co-Co From English Electric/Vulcan Foundry

D6796	30 November	Sheffield Darnall
D6797	7 December	Sheffield Darnall
D6798	12 December	Sheffield Darnall
D6799	14 December	Sheffield Darnall
D6800	20 December	Sheffield Darnall
D6801	28 December	Sheffield Darnall

Class 35 B-B Diesel-Hydraulic From Beyer Peacock

D7016	January	Bristol Bath Road
D7017	January	Bristol Bath Road
D7018	January	Bristol Bath Road
D7019	February	Bristol Bath Road
D7020	February	Bristol Bath Road
D7021	February	Bristol Bath Road
D7022	February	Cardiff Canton
D7023	February	Bristol Bath Road
D7024	March	Cardiff Canton

D7025	March	Cardiff Canton
D7026	March	Bristol Bath Road
D7027	April	Bristol Bath Road
D7028	April	Cardiff Canton
D7029	April	Cardiff Canton
D7030	April	Cardiff Canton
D7031	April	Cardiff Canton
D7032	May	Cardiff Canton
D7033	May	Cardiff Canton
D7034	May	Cardiff Canton
D7035	June	Cardiff Canton
D7036	June	Cardiff Canton
D7037	June	Cardiff Canton
D7038	June	Cardiff Canton
D7039	June	Cardiff Canton
D7040	July	Bristol Bath Road
D7041	July	Bristol Bath Road
D7042	July	Bristol Bath Road
D7043	July	Bristol Bath Road
D7044	August	Bristol Bath Road
D7045	August	Bristol Bath Road
D7046	August	Bristol Bath Road
D7047	August	Bristol Bath Road
D7048	September	Bristol Bath Road
D7049	October	Bristol Bath Road
D7050	October	Bristol Bath Road
D7051	October	Bristol Bath Road
D7052	October	Bristol Bath Road
D7053	October	Bristol Bath Road
D7054	November	Bristol Bath Road
D7055	November	Bristol Bath Road
D7056	November	Cardiff Canton
D7057	November	Cardiff Canton
D7058	November	Cardiff Canton
D7059	November	Cardiff Canton
D7060	December	Cardiff Canton
D7061	December	Cardiff Canton
D7063	December	Cardiff Canton

Class 20 Bo-Bo From English Electric/R. Stephenson & Hawthorns

D8110	10 January	Glasgow Eastfield
D8111	18 January	Glasgow Eastfield
D8112	26 January	Glasgow Eastfield
D8113	1 February	Glasgow Eastfield
D8114	8 February	Glasgow Eastfield
D8115	8 February	Glasgow Eastfield
D8116	15 February	Glasgow Eastfield
D8117	23 February	Glasgow Polmadie
D8118	8 March	Glasgow Polmadie
D8119	8 March	Glasgow Polmadie
D8120	16 March	Glasgow Polmadie
D8121	16 March	Glasgow Polmadie
D8122	22 March	Glasgow Polmadie
D8123	29 March	Glasgow Polmadie
D8124	13 April	Glasgow Polmadie
D8125	25 April	Glasgow Polmadie
D8126	15 May	Glasgow Polmadie
D8127	16 July	Glasgow Polmadie

Class 17 Bo-Bo From Clayton

D8500	10 September	Glasgow Polmadie
D8501	10 October	Glasgow Polmadie
D8502	6 October	Glasgow Polmadie
D8503	10 October	Glasgow Polmadie
D8504	17 October	Glasgow Polmadie
D8505	17 October	Glasgow Polmadie
D8506	24 October	Glasgow Polmadie
D8507	30 October	Glasgow Polmadie
D8508	30 October	Glasgow Polmadie
D8509	13 November	Glasgow Polmadie
D8510	13 November	Glasgow Polmadie
D8511	22 November	Glasgow Polmadie
D8512	7 December	Glasgow Polmadie
D8513	7 December	Glasgow Polmadie

Class 55 Co-Co 'Deltic' From English Electric/Vulcan Foundry

D9020*	12 February	London Finsbury Park
D9021	2 May	Edinburgh Haymarket

Electric Locomotives

NUMBER	MONTH TO TRAFFIC	FIRST ALLOCATION

Class 81 Bo-Bo From BTH/Birmingham Railway Carriage & Wagon Company

E3023	3 February	AC Electric Lines

Class 82 Bo-Bo From Metropolitan Vickers/Beyer Peacock

E3053	20 January	AC Electric Lines
E3055	7 April	AC Electric Lines

Class 85 Bo-Bo From Doncaster Works

E3066	21 April	AC Electric Lines
E3067	13 January	AC Electric Lines
E3068	5 May	AC Electric Lines
E3069	10 May	AC Electric Lines
E3070	21 July	AC Electric Lines
E3071	27 October	AC Electric Lines
E3072	7 July	AC Electric Lines
E3074	8 December	AC Electric Lines
E3086	24 March	AC Electric Lines
E3087	27 October	AC Electric Lines

Class 83 Bo-Bo From English Electric/Vulcan Foundry

E3100	23 June	AC Electric Lines

Class 73 Bo-Bo From Eastleigh Works

E6001	1 February	London Stewarts Lane
E6002	11 March	London Stewarts Lane
E6003	27 April	London Stewarts Lane
E6004	6 July	London Stewarts Lane
E6005	30 July	London Stewarts Lane
E6006	15 November	London Stewarts Lane

NOTE: No D2340 was built in 1956 and was on loan to BR at West Hartlepool, numbered 2593, until taken into stock in 1962.